Physical and Chemical Methods of Separation

Eugene W. Berg, Ph.D.

Professor of Chemistry

Coates Chemical Laboratories

Louisiana State University

Baton Rouge, Louisiana

McGraw-Hill Book Company

New York   San Francisco · Toronto · London

physical and chemical methods of separation

Repl. acc. #303

Physical and Chemical Methods of Separation

6 7 8 9 10 11 12 - MAMM - 7 6 5 4 3 2

ISBN 07-004844

Dedicated to

Dr. Arthur Eugene Wood

Professor Emeritus of Chemistry

Mississippi College

Preface

This book has been written to serve as the textbook for a course in separation techniques to be taught at the advanced undergraduate and beginning graduate level in chemistry. It can serve also as an introductory work and guide to the literature for practicing chemists who are unfamiliar with some of the more recent innovations in the field of separations. And last, but not least, I hope that this book will stimulate others to offer a formal course in separation techniques which will supplement the present offerings of their department in advanced analytical chemistry.

The formal presentation of separation methods in the chemistry curricula at both the undergraduate and graduate levels has been a hit-or-miss affair for some time. Generally, individual methods have been discussed only in relation to some other problem. Some separation topics are considered in quantitative analysis, others in physical chemistry, still others in courses in inorganic or organic chemistry, but they are usually treated inadequately and are of little use to the student in formulating ideas as to their general applicability. The demands placed on separation technology by modern research are entirely too great for us to continue with this lackadaisical approach. The beginning researcher must be made aware of some of the most potent tools available to him, namely, modern separation techniques.

Probably much of the reluctance in offering an advanced course on separation methods is traceable to the absence of a textbook in the field. The task of surveying the literature and sorting out the desired information for a number of separation methods is an onerous one. There is a voluminous literature on separation methods which is scattered through a variety of sources, such as encyclopedias, monographs, and treatises on organic, analytical, and physical chemistry and biochemistry, not to mention the reviews and specific research articles appearing in the old and current chemical literature. I undertook the job of assimilating this mass of material so as to be able to present a concise and informative survey of separation techniques to my students.

My objective has been to prepare the advanced student to recognize the inherent limitations of a particular method and the type of system to which the method would be applicable. To this end, no attempt has been made to treat each topic exhaustively or to give a complete survey of the pertinent literature. The physical principles which govern the behavior of a given method and pinpoint the important system variables are cited with a minimum of mathematical detail. Only a cursory knowledge of physical chemistry and thermodynamics is required by the student. Experimental details are avoided by giving schematic diagrams of the needed equipment with brief descriptions of the technique. Only that experimental detail is given which is necessary for an understanding of the method. A few specific examples of separations achieved by each technique are briefly discussed to emphasize the potentials of the method. Standard references, monographs, and important general sources to special topics are tabulated in a selected bibliography at the end of each chapter. In addition, there are the many necessary references in the text to specific research papers and reviews.

A course in separation techniques based on the content of this book has been offered at Louisiana State University since 1952 as a complement to our advanced course in instrumental analysis and the usual undergraduate offerings in analytical chemistry. The results have been gratifying. A void in the students' training has been partially filled. Now the beginning graduate student who must embark simultaneously upon a career of research and advanced study can at least be aware of the potentialities of modern separation methods.

I am grateful to my friends and colleagues who have discussed the preparation of this book with me and encouraged me to complete the task. Their thoughts and suggestions have been invaluable in the preparation of the manuscript. Much credit for any acclaim accorded this text must go to Drs. Philip W. West and Buddhadev Sen for their fine contributions to the text material and to Dr. Gilbert H. Ayres who made a painstaking review of the entire manuscript. Special thanks must go to Dr. Hulen B. Williams, Dean A. R. Choppin, and Louisiana State University for providing an academic atmosphere conducive to scholarly work. I hope that their faith in me has been justified.

My deepest appreciation is extended to my wife for her constant encouragement, for typing rough copy and final manuscript, and for untold hours spent reading proof, while maintaining a pleasant home atmosphere. I shall never know how she accomplished it.

Eugene W. Berg

Contents

CHAPTER 1

INTRODUCTION

1.1. The Scope and Aims of Separation Methods. Analytical chemistry is the chemistry of the identification and separation of substances— the resolution of substances into their component parts and their subsequent determination. In relatively recent years the development of instrumental methods of analysis and newer techniques not involving instrumentation has sometimes unwittingly relegated the actual separations of substances to a minor position in analytical work. Rather than separate substances prior to a determination, one now resorts to masking of interfering substances through complexation; controlling conditions such as pH, electrode potentials, etc., so carefully as to eliminate the reaction of possible interferences; or measuring some specific physical property that is characteristic of the material being analyzed. Unfortunately, we have not yet become ingenious enough to do away with separations prior to many qualitative and quantitative analyses; try as we may, it is still necessary to remove interfering substances. Separations are always a must when we consider the purification and isolation of substances.

Modern research has imposed very exacting requirements on separation procedures. Consider only a few accomplishments: the reduction of impurities in germanium to 10^9 atoms per mole, the separation of the rare-earth metals and complex mixtures of amino acids, the isolation and identification of some 10 to 40 atoms of a transuranium element, the separation of the various isotopes of an element and the various isomers of a complicated compound, the isolation and determination of some 20 hydrocarbons from milligram-sized samples. These are fabulous accomplishments which emphasize the importance of separation techniques to modern technology. Other more challenging separation problems are constantly arising to take the place of those solved.

Adsorption, chromatography, ion exchange, flotation, extraction, dialysis, zone melting, etc., must become as familiar tools in the hands of the researcher as the more conventional techniques of precipitation,

1

fractional crystallization, and distillation.   Simple awareness of the many techniques employed in separations is not enough.   Several methods may be suitable for the resolution of a mixture, but only one method may be the best.   The objective researcher can no longer confine himself to the conventional procedures.   Indeed, the outstanding accomplishments of recent years have stressed the need for the successive application of different techniques that depend upon widely different chemical or physical properties of the sample molecules.

Ingenious combinations of techniques and processes and selections of methods most applicable for a given system require a thorough knowledge of the practical limitations inherent in each method.   The choice of separation tool is usually governed by the size of sample available, the simplicity and selectivity of the method, the degree of resolution required, and the general applicability of the procedure.   An objective researcher would not necessarily expect to solve a difficult separation problem by using only one technique.

1.2. Classification of Separation Methods.   It is virtually impossible to arrange such a variety of separation methods as are treated here in a completely logical order that will be satisfying to everyone.   Any classification of these methods by basic principles is likely to be a tenuous one, which can be somewhat misleading in the practical presentation of the material.

One possible approach, though, would be to group all the methods utilizing columns (distillation, solvent extraction, chromatography, ion exchange, and ion exclusion) in sequence.   In all these methods the height equivalent of a theoretical plate (HETP) is a fundamental tie with sample holdup, throughput, and separation efficiency.   Unfortunately, the HETP concept is not a practical means of relating all column operations; it does not provide a mechanistic picture of the phase-distribution process.

A second approach would be to group all the differential-migration methods (solvent extraction, chromatography, ion exchange, ion exclusion, dialysis, and zone melting) in sequence.   All differential-migration methods of achieving separations depend on the different components of a mixture migrating through some medium at their individual characteristic rates.   Inherent in this idea is the concept of a driving force to produce the migration, either selectively or nonselectively, and a retarding force which can act on the migrating particles either selectively or nonselectively.[1]   Driving forces can be any single force or combination of forces acting on a particle that cause it to migrate.   The following group of factors is usually effective as a unidirectional force within a system and causes the net migration of particles to proceed in a single general direction.   Other forces acting within the system may cause migrations to occur, but frequently they are of such a nature as to redistribute the particles rather than lead toward a unidirectional flow.

DRIVING FORCES*

Force	Particles affected
Mechanical	Microscopic to macroscopic
Gravity	Microscopic to macroscopic
Centrifugal	Colloid to macroscopic
Magnetic	Magnetic or charged ions
Electrostatic	Magnetic or charged colloids
Concentration gradients	Ions, molecules, colloids
Flow of liquids	Ions, molecules, colloids, microscopic, macroscopic
Flow of gases	Ions, molecules, colloids, microscopic, macroscopic

* From H. H. Strain, T. R. Sato, and J. Engelke, *Anal. Chem.*, **26**, 91 (1954).

Similarly, any force or combination of forces that tend to resist the migration of particles is designated as a resistive force. The common resistive forces are listed here.

RESISTIVE FORCES*

Force	Particles affected
Viscosity	Ions to macroscopic
Density	Molecules, colloids, macroscopic
Hydrostatic and density gradients	Molecules, colloids, macroscopic
Adsorption	Ions, molecules, colloids
Permeability	Ions, molecules, colloids, macroscopic

* From H. H. Strain, T. R. Sato, and J. Engelke, *Anal. Chem.*, **26**, 91 (1954).

No restriction is placed on the type of migration medium employed or the character of the migrating particles. Intrinsic differences in the migration media and the size, weight, charge, and ionic or nonionic character of the migrating particle only enhance the selectivity of the driving or resistive forces and lead to more selective separation procedures.

Although there are numerous and varied possibilities for combining driving and retarding forces with various migration media and solutes, there is much that is common to all differential-migration separations. The basic requirements for efficiency in diffusion processes are the same regardless of how the migration is produced. Sample resolutions will depend on the dimensions of the initial zone and the arrangement or position of the constituent particles, the difference in migration rates of individual components, and the distance traversed by the migrating particles. These fundamental concepts should be kept in mind when differential-migration separations are considered because system variables are usually altered in order to enhance or suppress one of the above factors.

Regardless of the great similarity among various differential-migration methods, sequences of methods based upon differential-migration rates are unrealistic because as the migration medium, driving forces, and resistive forces are changed in progressing from one method to the next, there is little physical resemblance among the separation techniques. For example, the principles of differential-migration separations can be applied easily to both chromatography and dialysis but the physical manner by which separations are achieved with the two techniques is totally unlike.

Classification and arrangement of methods by either the column principle or the differential-migration-rate principle leave precipitation, coprecipitation, adsorption, flotation, and biological methods unclassified.

In view of these expressed difficulties (and many not expressed) the author fully anticipates considerable criticism of the arrangement of topics in this book. I believe, though, that the arrangement is a logical one for showing the similarity between methods *and* underlying principles and that it is particularly effective for introducing the topic to a person with a broad chemical background. A brief justification for the arrangement decided upon follows.

Distillation introduces the column concept, the HETP, and the phase diagram. Extraction follows naturally as a distribution of solutes between two liquid phases as opposed to the gas-liquid distribution in distillation. Adsorption chromatography follows extraction and introduces the concept of solid-liquid distribution and the differential-migration concept. Partition chromatography is a pseudoextraction method, but the principles of operation are exactly the same as for adsorption chromatography, so it logically follows adsorption chromatography. Gas chromatography extends the chromatographic principle to a solid-gas distribution. However, lest the student lose sight of the fact that chromatography is a column operation which can be treated by the HETP concept, the theory of gas chromatography is developed on both the HETP and differential-migration concept.

Paper chromatography supplants the solid adsorbent used in adsorption chromatography with cellulose and is the most reasonable precursor in the series for electrochromatography and ring-oven methods, both of which employ cellulose sheets for the migration medium. The principles of zone melting are not greatly different from those used in the ring-oven method, and zone melting fits into the series well at this point.

Ion exchange comes as a somewhat abrupt change in the sequence because it introduces an entirely new mechanism for the establishment of equilibrium in column operations, but with the change in thought a new principle, dialysis, is introduced which acts as the connecting link in the discussion of ion exchange, ion exclusion, dialysis, and electrodialysis.

A real discontinuity appears in the sequence of methods with the introduction of precipitation, but again, as with ion exchange, a new sequence is established with a common underlying principle. Precipitation leads naturally into a discussion of coprecipitation and adsorption. Adsorption in turn leads to flotation methods. The features common to each of these methods are the phenomena which occur at solid-liquid interfaces. There is indeed a remarkable similarity among precipitation (the formation of crystals in solution), coprecipitation, adsorption, and flotation.

Biological methods are an entity which must stand alone.

Masking and complexation are considered last because they offer an alternate approach to the determination of substances without their prior separation.

A brief description of the various separation methods treated in this text is given in the following paragraphs to familiarize the reader with the fundamental principles and general analytical importance of each method. The more detailed description of each method is then presented in the text.

1.3. Distillation. In its simplest case distillation is the volatilization of a liquid by the application of heat and the subsequent condensation of the vapor back to the liquid state. Every liquid has a tendency to vaporize and reach an equilibrium characterized by vaporization and condensation proceeding at equal rates. The pressure of the vapor above the liquid at equilibrium is characteristic of the liquid and is referred to as the *vapor pressure* of the liquid. Vapor pressure increases with an increase in temperature, and the volatility of a liquid has been shown to be roughly proportional to the vapor pressure and inversely proportional to the boiling point of the liquid.

These fundamental concepts of distillation have been appreciated for many years, and this knowledge has made it possible for researchers to develop more versatile distillation techniques and processes. The resolving power of modern distillation columns is remarkable. Multiple-component systems can be readily resolved when only minor differences of vapor pressure exist among the components. Fractions usually approach a high degree of purity except in the case of azeotropic mixtures.

Some closely related phenomena, simple volatilization and sublimation, can be considered along with distillation as a method of separation. Volatilization implies only the conversion of a solid or liquid into the gaseous state, whereas sublimation is the direct vaporization of a solid and the subsequent condensation of the vapor back to the solid state without passing through the intermediate liquid form.

Each process is dependent on the vapor pressure of either solids or liquids being great enough to effect a change in the physical state of the substance, but a simple change in physical state is not enough to effect a resolution. For resolutions to be complete, there also must be a mass transfer of at least one of the sample components. The versatility of volatilization techniques is based on the ease with which a mass transfer can be effected when the substance is in the gaseous state.

Each of these processes has found its greatest application in the field of organic chemistry. Volumes have been written describing distillation principles for organic separations; therefore, scant attention will be given separations in this area. Emphasis will be placed on the utility of vaporization and sublimation techniques for the separation of inorganics and metal organic coordination complexes.

1.4. Solvent Extraction. Solvent extraction as applied to solids is the selective dissolution of the soluble portion of a solid with an appropriate solvent. Such processes have been utilized for centuries by laymen and depend only on an appreciable difference in the solubility of the various solid substances involved. Formerly, leaching was used extensively to obtain lye from wood ashes and to recover salt from the debris of the smokehouse floor. Present commercial processes are numerous and include such varied procedures as extracting oil from fish and plant seeds, sugar from sugar beets, and precious metals from ores.

Liquid-liquid extraction is a physical partitioning process dependent on the favorable distribution of a given solute between two immiscible solvents. The distribution of a component between the two immiscible phases follows (in the ideal case) the distribution law when the system is at equilibrium.

$$\frac{C_1}{C_2} = K \qquad \text{distribution law}$$

C_1 and C_2 represent the concentration of the solute in the respective phases, and K is the distribution constant or partition coefficient. Frequently the distribution deviates considerably from this law owing to the association or dissociation of the solute in one or both phases, but a rigorous treatment of the distribution law can result in a correction for this anomalous behavior. At this point it becomes difficult to designate extraction as a physical method or chemical method because of these complicating factors. The solute particles may actually undergo a change in structure or composition as they change phases.

Gases can also be extracted from the gaseous phase into a liquid phase. The partitioning phenomenon here also follows the distribution law, but it is more common to express it as Henry's law:

$$\frac{m}{p} = K$$

where p is the partial pressure of the gaseous component in the atmosphere above the liquid and m is the concentration of the gas in the liquid phase.

The absorption of gases by a liquid often involves a chemical reaction, in which case the distribution law (Henry's law) does not apply.

Although the theoretical basis for extraction is known, the practical applications of liquid-liquid extraction are almost always empirical. This is owing to the varying degree of solvation, association, and dissociation exhibited by the solute in different solvent systems. Because of this, it is impossible to predict the distribution coefficient for a new solvent system from the physical constants we have available. Even solubility data are not useful for calculating distribution coefficients, except in the case of a solute that forms a saturated solution in both phases.

Extraction procedures also have been more widely accepted in the field of organic chemistry than in any other area. Nevertheless, applications of extraction procedures to inorganic analyses have burgeoned in recent years and have promise of effecting simply some otherwise difficult separations. More intense utilization of extractions can be expected as the quantity of known distribution coefficients increases.

1.5. Chromatography. Chromatography was first introduced in 1906 by the Russian botanist Tswett. The process consisted essentially in passing a sample solution through a column of solid adsorbent. The difference in adsorbability of otherwise very similar substances effected the resolution of the solutes and produced a chromatogram. Tswett separated the carotenes and several xanthophylls present in organic extracts of green leaves by passing the organic solution through a column of solid adsorbent, such as calcium carbonate. Although the process appeared particularly selective in its action, it was almost completely neglected for 25 years. In 1931, Kuhn, Winterstein, and Lederer reintroduced the chromatographic technique and proved its great resolving power.

Possibly no other separation technique has exerted so great an influence on organic chemistry and biochemistry as has chromatography. Without the isolation by chromatographic procedures of the various plant pigments, vitamins, viruses, and hormones, it would have been impossible for our knowledge in these areas to develop as rapidly as it did. Its effect on the field of inorganic chemistry was less spectacular, even though there have been thousands of publications relating chromatography to inorganic analyses.

Chromatography is not on a rational theoretical basis yet, as are distillation and extraction. One still cannot predict accurately what components will produce a suitable chromatogram. The field is empirical, or one relies mainly on experience. Applications have forged ahead of theory because once a separation has been effected, there is no need to delve further into that particular case.

The principles of adsorption chromatography have been considerably extended and now embrace paper chromatography and gas- or vapor-phase chromatography. The latter technique is rapidly replacing some of the more conventional methods of gas analysis.

The separation of charged or ionic mixtures by differential migration under the driving force of an electrical potential has been developed along two different lines—migration in a free homogeneous medium and migration in a porous or stabilized medium. The former is generally referred to as free electrophoresis, and the latter as ionophoresis, ionography, zone electrophoresis, and the preferred term electrochromatography. As far as separations are concerned, electrochromatography offers so many advantages over free electrophoresis that the latter will not be considered in detail in the text.

1.6. Ring-oven Technique. The ring-oven technique has evolved from a proved pseudochromatographic technique of testing single drops of solution for several components on filter paper. The single drop of test solution is applied to the center of a filter-paper disk, and one or several sample components are fixed in the paper by a precipitant. The soluble components are then washed from the center of the paper toward the edges of the disk with an appropriate solvent. As the solution nears the edge of the paper, the solvent is evaporated, leaving the soluble components concentrated in a ring which is completely separated from the original spot.

By the judicious selection of precipitants, solvents, and specific test reagents, up to 20 or 30 components in a single drop can be separated and determined. The method is particularly applicable to microanalytical separations and most likely will receive greater attention in the future.

1.7. Zone Melting. In zone melting, a narrow cross-sectional molten zone is produced in a solid material and slowly moved through the entire length of the solid. Solutes which are rejected by the freezing interface of the zone are carried along with the zone and deposited in one end of the solid. The process is quite selective, and with a number of molten zones passed through the material, an unusually high purity can be achieved in the solid. The reduction of impurities in metals to less than 1 part in 10^9 is not at all unusual with zone-melting techniques. It is unbelievably effective in separating impurities from some materials.

In passing, it might be worth noting the similarity between zone-melting and ring-oven techniques. In each case solutes are collected at one end of the migration path by repeatedly passing either a molten zone or solvent through the sample matrix. The zone or solvent selectively takes up the soluble components and deposits them at the end of the migration path, thus forming a concentrated zone of the soluble material.

1.8. Ion Exchange. Ion-exchange phenomena have been observed and studied for well over one hundred years. Some early observations of ion exchange were noted by agricultural chemists who were studying the uptake of fertilizers by soil. They showed that, when ammonia was adsorbed by certain soils, lime was released. By 1854 it was well established that the exchange of ions in soils involved equivalent quantities and that aluminum silicates were responsible for the exchange. Later it was demonstrated that exchange materials could be synthesized from soluble silicates and alum.

The practical significance of such an exchange phenomenon was not recognized immediately, and it was not until the first part of the twentieth century that natural or synthetic ion exchangers were widely known. By then a number of relatively pure minerals (zeolites and clays) were found or synthesized that exhibited exchange characteristics. Water containing calcium, magnesium, and heavy-metal ions was percolated through filter beds of these minerals. The calcium, magnesium, and heavy-metal ions exchanged with the sodium or potassium ions naturally occurring in the mineral, and the water was softened. This was not a demineralization of water because the obnoxious soap-consuming ions were simply replaced with sodium or potassium ions. The minerals or zeolites were converted back to the sodium or potassium form by passing a concentrated solution of a sodium or potassium salt through the filter beds. Because of this possible regeneration, exchangers can be used over and over again.

Serious limitations to the use of natural or synthetic mineral exchangers were soon recognized. None of the exchangers was capable of softening large volumes of water without a regeneration step, and most of the exchangers had to be in a finely divided state. Also, attempts to use these exchangers for the complete demineralization of water were not really successful.

In 1935 a completely new type of ion-exchange material was recognized and developed by the English chemists Adams and Holmes. Some synthetic high-molecular-weight organic resins were observed to exchange ions with an aqueous solution. This suggested the possibility that exchange substances might be produced that would overcome the difficulties associated with the use of the natural and synthetic zeolites. These newly discovered exchange resins were high-molecular-weight organic polymers that contained a large number of ionic functional groups as an integral part of the resin. Sulfonic acid and carboxylic acid groups were the ionic groups most used for cation-exchange resins, whereas primary, secondary, tertiary, and quaternary amine groups were responsible for anion exchange. These ionic functional groups were completely responsible for the exchange characteristics of the resin.

The actual ion-exchange process can be represented in the following manner using a sulfonic acid cation exchanger. If R is used to represent the large insoluble polymeric structure of the resin and —SO_3H the functional (sulfonic acid) ionic group, then the exchange with sodium ion is as follows:

$$R—SO_3H + Na^+ \rightleftharpoons R—SO_3Na + H^+$$

The hydrogen of the sulfonic acid group readily detaches itself from the functional group and is replaced by Na^+ or some other cation present in solution. The resin can then be regenerated to the original hydrogen form by washing the resin with a solution of acid, which releases the sodium ion. The exchange proceeds by the release and takeup of chemically equivalent quantities of the materials in the interior of the resin particle.

Similarly, anion exchange can be represented in the following manner:

$$R—NH_3 \cdot OH + Cl^- \rightleftharpoons R—NH_3 \cdot Cl + OH^-$$

The exchange proceeds by chemical equivalents, and the resin can be regenerated in the hydroxyl form by washing with a solution of strong base.

The analytical applications of ion exchange are manyfold, but in general, the applications fall into one of four categories:

1. The concentration of dilute solutions
2. The fractionation of ions
3. The deionization of aqueous solutions
4. Miscellaneous

Thousands of technical articles on the applications of ion exchangers have been published since 1946, but as so frequently happens, the practical applications have far surpassed the advances in theory. All the theories of ion exchange are similar, inasmuch as the exchange must proceed by equivalents or satisfy the law of electroneutrality. The difference in the various theories is usually in the mechanism of exchange.

For practical work a rigorous mathematical treatment of the theory is not necessary. Besides, none of the present theories explains all the observed phenomena, but an insight into the practical theory and kinetics of ion exchange is essential if one is to select and utilize exchange processes to the greatest advantage.

1.9. Ion Exclusion. Physical properties of the new synthetic ion-exchange materials have opened up a completely new area for diffusion separations. Water readily diffuses throughout these resins, and dissolved species are free to migrate into and out of the resin phase also. If an aqueous solution is left in contact with the resin for a short period of time, it has been observed that nonionics distribute themselves in such a way as to favor the resin phase, whereas under identical conditions, ionic substances are apparently excluded from the resin phase. Techniques utilizing the *ion-exclusion* principle have been devised that are very effective in resolving ionic and nonionic components of aqueous solutions. Admittedly many difficulties and limitations are associated with this new operation, but there are certain favorable characteristics about it that need to be considered also. Ion-exchange resins can be used for separations where a regeneration is not necessary.

1.10. Dialysis. Osmosis is probably the most familiar diffusion separation process and is the term used to describe the spontaneous flow of a solvent through a membrane from a dilute solution to a more concentrated one. The earliest recorded experiments describing this phenomenon date back to the middle of the eighteenth century. For an ideal system, the membrane permits the passage of the solvent particles only and prevents the migration of the solute particles from one solution to the other. Numerous biological metabolic processes are known to rely on osmotic processes, yet analytical applications of the osmotic process are seldom encountered.

Dialysis, another differential-migration process, differs from osmosis in that the membrane separating the two liquid phases is semipermeable to solute particles. Solute particles migrate through the membrane to a solution of lower concentration. Although dialysis and osmosis usually occur simultaneously within a system, the two processes are not to be confused.

Since its evaluation in the mid-nineteenth century, dialysis has become a practical means of separating salts from colloidal suspensions. The smaller ions diffuse rapidly through some membranes that actually prevent the diffusion of the larger colloidal particles. In more recent years, synthetic membranes have been so refined that they are capable of distinguishing among urea, glycerol, and glucose molecules, with molecular weights of 60, 92, and 180, respectively. Dialysis has been used most fully in the areas of colloid chemistry and biochemistry, but with the development of more selective membranes it appears that dialysis may have a significant place in the separations of inorganics other than colloids.

Further refinements in the development of synthetic semipermeable membranes have resulted in ion-exchange membranes. These membranes reject ionized particles on the basis not only of their size or volume but also of the *sign* of the charge. Cation- and anion-exchange membranes are very efficient in preventing the diffusion of anions and cations, respectively. Judicious combinations of cation- and anion-exchange membranes in electrodialysis cells make it possible to desalt saline waters and to separate many ionic mixtures.

1.11. Precipitation, Coprecipitation, and Adsorption. Precipitation is the process by which a dissolved substance is converted into an insoluble form which can be separated from the bulk of the solution. Generally, precipitation implies that a chemical change occurred in the transition from the soluble to insoluble form. In this way, crystallization, a physical process dependent only on a change in the physical properties of the system, and precipitation are distinguished from each other.

Precipitation is probably the most versatile and universally used separation technique. Researchers in this area have expressed repeatedly that precipitation, as a tool for separating mixtures, has a greater potential value than any other method. To consider this seriously in view of the progress made in precipitation techniques prior to 1900 seems at first ridiculous. However, in relatively recent years, tremendous strides have been made in developing and improving precipitation methods. Greater resolution efficiency and versatility are the result.

To understand precipitation methods better it is necessary to know the effect that various factors have on the solubility of precipitates. Factors most frequently considered are:

1. Temperature
2. pH
3. Solvent characteristics
4. Salt effect
5. Complexation
6. Degree of supersaturation

The extent to which temperature, pH, complexation, and salts affect the solubility of a precipitate is determined by the dynamic chemical equilibria involved. Therefore, if the principles of thermodynamics and mass-action law are utilized, it is possible for one to calculate or predict the quantitative effect of these factors on the solubility of precipitates. The effect of solvent and the degree of supersaturation must be considered on a more empirical basis.

Impurities found in precipitates are usually the result of coprecipitation, postprecipitation, and/or adsorption. If one is not confined to the thought that the above phenomena are responsible for *errors* in gravimetric analysis, then it is possible to utilize these phenomena as effective methods of separations. Instead of attempting to reduce the *error* to a minimum, it may be advantageous to adsorb, coprecipitate, or postprecipitate as much of a component as possible to effect its separation from other sample constituents. The hydrous oxides of the heavy metals are frequently precipitated under conditions such that their contamination will be great. The scavenging action exhibited by the fresh precipitate then can be used to remove quantitatively trace quantities of substances that would not precipitate alone under identical conditions. The principle involved is the same as that used in water-treatment plants when a coagulant such as alum is added to remove colloidal matter and large soluble organic molecules.

Knowledge of the effects that various factors have on the solubility of precipitates and of the mechanism of adsorption, coprecipitation, and postprecipitation is very important to the analytical chemist. When this knowledge is applied, precipitates can be obtained quantitatively in pure form or precipitates can be used to separate quantitatively trace components from the remainder of the sample.

The technique of precipitating substances from a homogeneous medium also has been a great advance. Controlled precipitations by the slow internal generation of the precipitant have greatly enhanced the versatility of differential, fractional, exchange, and normal precipitation techniques.

Alone, the introduction of organic precipitants for inorganic substances was an impressive advance in gravimetry. Organic precipitants opened new vistas because for the first time there was promise of producing precipitants that would be specific in their action. Dimethylglyoxime was the first organic precipitant to gain a real recognition for specificity. Yet it is not truly a specific reagent because it is suitable for the precipitation of either nickel or palladium in ammoniacal or acidic medium, respectively. In the chemical literature considerable attention has been devoted to the synthesis and use of specific precipitants. Hence, only a few of the more common reagents will be discussed.

Considered altogether, the recent advances in precipitation technology have given a great impetus to the field of gravimetry. As these principles or concepts are refined, precipitation methods may well demonstrate their great potential value.

1.12. Flotation. Substances with a density much greater than that of the liquid enveloping them may be concentrated at the surface of the liquid. The phenomenon is known as *flotation* and is due entirely to surface or interfacial forces. The importance of interfacial tensions is illustrated in the case of a floated particle that is forcibly submerged; it will not spontaneously rise again to the surface. On the other hand, if it is brought to the surface, it may float again. The buoyancy of such a dense material is attributed to the stabilization of the particle in a gas-liquid interface.

Because it is practically impossible to bring large quantities of finely divided solids gently in contact with the surface of a solution, flotation is accomplished by rapidly bubbling air through the solution. A suspension is produced by the violent ebullition of air, and the solid particles come in contact with the bubble films. If the particle is stabilized in the gas-liquid interface, then it can be carried to the surface and efficiently skimmed off with the foam. A particle can be stabilized in the surface or at the gas-liquid interface if the contact angle between solid and liquid is finite. The difference in contact angles exhibited by various minerals frequently is sufficient to produce a separation by selective flotation. Similarly, solid particles can attach themselves to liquid-liquid interfaces.

Although flotation processes are used effectively and efficiently to separate thousands of tons of valuable minerals from worthless ore, there are only a few listed applications of flotation to analytical chemistry. These few applications, however, are noteworthy and point out the potentialities of the same principles when applied on a small laboratory scale. For example, a trace of nickel dimethylglyoximate suspended in aqueous solution can be made visible simply by shaking the suspension with kerosene. The precipitate is concentrated at the liquid-liquid interface, and a pink color can be observed.

1.13. Biological Methods. Biological activity usually is overlooked as a method of separation because most chemists do not have sufficient training or interest in the functions of biological systems. Yet the utilization of biological systems for analytical purposes will probably become more important because they will effect some of the most selective separations known. Consider, for example, the great selectivity of some bacteria, molds, yeasts, animals, and higher plants toward the metabolism of only one of a pair of optical isomers. Too often it is almost impossible to separate racemic mixtures by other means.

This great specificity of a biological system for a particular chemical species also has been observed for inorganic substances. Most of the practical applications derived from these observations have been limited to bioassays, however, and do not include actual separation techniques. Undoubtedly, though, biological systems can be used to concentrate trace inorganic components and to separate complex mixtures.

REFERENCE

1. Strain, H. H., T. R. Sato, and J. Engelke: *Anal. Chem.*, **26**, 91 (1954).

CHAPTER 2

FRACTIONAL DISTILLATION AND SUBLIMATION

2.1. Basic Principles of Distillation. *Distillation* is defined as the partial vaporization of liquid in a still or retort and the subsequent collection of the vapor as condensate in a separate vessel. Pure liquids as well as liquid mixtures can be distilled, but inasmuch as no separation of components is involved in the distillation of pure liquids, this discussion will be confined to the distillation of mixtures. For simplicity only binary mixtures will be considered.

Gibbs' phase rule provides a general and useful connection between the number of components C and the number of phases P in an equilibrium system and the number of independent variables F (degrees of freedom) which must be specified in order to characterize the system. The phase rule states that

$$F = C - P + 2$$

Thus according to Gibbs' phase rule a two-component system whose liquid and vapor phases are at equilibrium has two independent variables —temperature and pressure—which must be specified to describe the system completely. Since for an ordinary distillation process the pressure of the system is maintained constant, there must be an unequivocal relation between the composition of the liquid and vapor phase and the temperature. It is convenient to express this relationship as a temperature-composition diagram similar to that in Fig. 2.1 for a mixture of benzene and toluene at constant pressure, 760 mm of mercury. In this diagram, the curve ADB represents the boiling points of mixtures of benzene and toluene whose composition is expressed in mole fractions. The curve ACB represents the composition of the vapor which is in equilibrium with the liquid at a given temperature. By way of an interpretation, the diagram signifies that the composition of the vapor in equilibrium with a solution of composition D is given by C. That is, the vapor phase is richer in the more volatile component than the liquid phase in equilibrium with it.

In its broadest terms distillation is a separation process based on the difference in composition between a liquid and the vapor in equilibrium with it. The separation efficiency of a distillation process is thus directly proportional to this difference. It is highly desirable, therefore, to introduce a concept of *volatility* which expresses the relationship between the compositions of the liquid and vapor phases when the two phases are equilibrated.

The volatility V of a given component is defined by the equation

$$V = \frac{y}{x} \tag{2.1}$$

where x and y represent the mole fraction of the component in the liquid and vapor phases, respectively. Obviously, the volatility of a pure substance is unity, and the term has real significance only if applied to

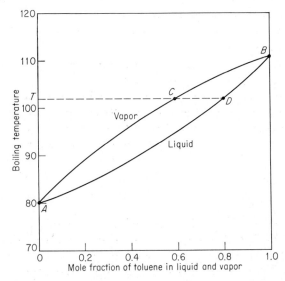

Fig. 2.1. Boiling-point-composition diagram for mixture of benzene and toluene at 760 mm mercury pressure.

mixtures. For a simple binary mixture, then, the volatility of the two components can be expressed as

$$V_1 = \frac{y_1}{x_1} \quad \text{and} \quad V_2 = \frac{y_2}{x_2}$$

A more useful term in distillation work is the *relative volatility* defined as

$$\alpha = \frac{V_1}{V_2} = \frac{y_1 x_2}{x_1 y_2} \tag{2.2}$$

Upon rearrangement

$$\frac{y_1}{y_2} = \alpha \frac{x_1}{x_2}$$

Then since

$$x_2 = 1 - x_1 \quad \text{and} \quad y_2 = 1 - y_1$$

Eq. (2.2) reduces to

$$\frac{y_1}{1 - y_1} = \alpha \frac{x_1}{1 - x_1} \tag{2.3}$$

which is probably its most useful form. It is customary to let x_1 snd y_1 represent the mole fraction of the more volatile constituent in the liquid and vapor, respectively. In this way α is conveniently set greater than unity.

The concept of relative volatility is widely employed, since it provides a direct measure of the separability of a binary mixture by distillation. It is also a basic component in almost every equation used to calculate the distillate composition under various circumstances.

Clearly, it would be desirable if α could be calculated from known physical properties of the pure compounds and not have to be determined by an actual analysis of vapor and liquid phases in a state of equilibrium. There are several approaches by which α can be approximated from physical constants which are quite useful in laboratory work. If Raoult's law holds for the solution and if Dalton's law of partial pressures is applicable to the vapor phase, the relative volatility can be shown to equal

$$\alpha = \frac{P_1}{P_2} \tag{2.4}$$

where P_1 and P_2 are the vapor pressures of the two pure components at the temperature of the system. This equation implies that for a perfect or near-ideal system one can calculate the vapor-liquid-composition diagram such as that given in Fig. 2.1 if the vapor pressures of the pure components are known.

The relative volatility can be approximated also for an ideal or near-ideal system in terms of the normal boiling points of the constituents. When an approximate form of the Clapeyron equation is combined with Trouton's rule, the following expression can be derived[1] for solutions which boil at atmospheric pressure:

$$\log \alpha = 8.9 \frac{T_B - T_A}{T_A + T_B} \tag{2.5}$$

T_A and T_B are the normal boiling points of the two constituents in absolute degrees. The equation holds only for ideal systems, but it does give a satisfactory estimation of α for mixtures of chemically similar liquids, such as o- and p-xylene. Thus, for mixtures which boil near 150°C, the relative volatility would be 1.049, 1.102, and 1.214 for a 2, 4, and 8° difference in boiling points of the constituents.

More complex relationships involving activity coefficients are available for predicting the relative volatility of nonideal mixtures.[2,3]

2.2. Theory of Fractional Distillation. Since the vapors obtained by boiling a solution differ in composition from the original liquid, the vapor being richer in the more volatile component, a separation of components

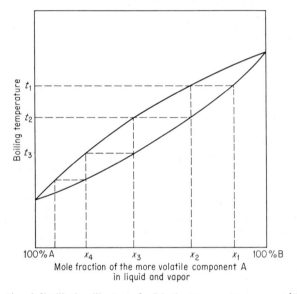

FIG. 2.2. Fractional distillation illustrated with the temperature-composition diagram.

can be achieved by condensing the vapors and then boiling off a portion of the condensate. The second vapors would contain a still higher concentration of the more volatile constituent. Thus, through successive distillations a pure product can eventually be obtained. The yield is quite small, though, unless the residual liquid from each vaporization can be returned to the preceding distillation chamber. This is what a distillation column does mechanically. The process is referred to as *fractional distillation*.

The simplest case of a fractional distillation of a miscible binary mixture is illustrated in Fig. 2.2. Suppose that a mixture of composition x_1 were partially volatilized at temperature t_1 and a portion of the vapor in equilibrium with the liquid were condensed at t_2 to give a liquid of composition x_2. The change in liquid composition from x_1 to x_2 corresponds to the change in one equilibrium stage. If the liquid of composition x_2 in its turn was partially vaporized, the composition of the new condensate would be x_3, etc. Hypothetically these successive distillations could be repeated until an infinitely small sample of very pure A was obtained.

Fortunately, the enrichment of finite samples can be achieved by using a distillation column so designed that excellent contact is made between vapor rising through the column and condensate (*reflux*) falling through the column. The efficiency of such columns is usually expressed in terms of the number of theoretical plates in the column, a *theoretical plate* being

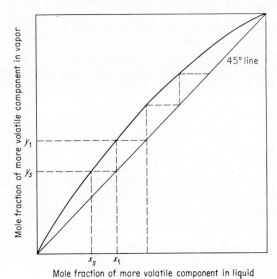

Fɪɢ. 2.3. Vapor-liquid-composition diagram for system at constant pressure.

that length of column required to give the same change in the composition of liquid as that brought about by one equilibrium stage in the temperature-composition diagram. Thus, distillation equipment capable of bringing about a change in composition from x_1 to x_3 in Fig. 2.2, if no product were removed, would be said to have an efficiency of two theoretical plates. The height equivalent of a theoretical plate (HETP) would then be given by

$$\text{HETP} = \frac{\text{length of column}}{\text{total number of plates in column}}$$

It is more common in distillation practice, however, to use a similar stepping-off process for determining the number of theoretical plates with a vapor-liquid-composition diagram such as that shown in Fig. 2.3. In this diagram the mole fraction of the more volatile component in the vapor is plotted against the mole fraction of this component in the equilibrium liquid. The diagonal in the diagram thus is the locus of all points at which liquid and vapor have the same composition and does not correspond to equilibrium conditions. The diagram is interpreted in the following manner: If the composition of the boiling liquid in the still is x_s, the vapor in equilibrium with it has a composition y_s. Condensate from this vapor then has composition x_1, which is equal to y_s. Vapor in equilibrium with x_1 will have a composition y_1, etc.

Theoretically, any two liquids can be separated by fractional distillation if their vapor pressures are different at a given temperature or if their boiling points are different at a given pressure. There are, however, practical limitations to the efficiency of fractional distillations which will become apparent in the subsequent discussion.

One of the major factors affecting the efficiency of separation is the proportion of condensate returned to the still pot as reflux. This proportion is referred to as the *reflux ratio* and is defined as the ratio of the moles of reflux per unit time to the moles of product withdrawn from the top of the column per unit time. That portion of the original liquid introduced into the still pot which is actually in the column as vapor or reflux at any given time is known as *holdup*. *Throughput* is the rate at which vapor is passing up the column. There is a maximum throughput at which the pressure drop through the column becomes so great that the velocity of rising vapors is sufficient to prevent the normal flow of reflux. The major purpose of a mathematical treatment of the distillation process is to show the relationship that exists between the sharpness of separation and the number of theoretical plates in a column, reflux ratio, holdup, and relative volatility.

There are in general two methods of fractional distillation—continuous and batch.

In continuous distillation the preheated material to be fractionated is fed into the middle of the column while the lower boiling fractions are withdrawn from the top and the higher boiling fractions from the bottom. The rate of sample introduction is adjusted so that the volume of feed is equal to the total volume of takeoff from the top and bottom of the column. Under such conditions the composition of phases will be constant at any given point in the column during the course of the distillation. Such a steady-state condition is amenable to mathematical treatment. For this reason continuous distillation will be considered first, although it is of very limited practical value in the usual laboratory separations. One has to go to industrial distillation processes to find continuous distillation widely used.

In batch distillation a definite amount of sample is placed in the still and distillation continues until the pot is nearly dry. Since the more volatile material is withdrawn from the top of the column, the composition of phases at any given point in the column will be continuously changing. The number of variables is so great that an exact mathematical treatment of batch distillation is impossible. However, if the column is operated at total reflux, namely, *all* the distillate is returned to the top of the column, again a steady-state condition is obtained analogous to that for continuous distillation and the process can be treated mathematically. One must keep in mind, though, that batch distillation with total reflux yields no product and is of no practical importance.

The equations derived for a column operating under total reflux are only approximations when applied to a true batch distillation. For this reason, then, the theory is useful chiefly as a general guide and cannot be used to predict column performance accurately.

2.3. Analysis of the Steady-state Condition (Continuous Distillation). Bear in mind that the purpose of any mathematical analysis of the distillation process is, first of all, to determine the conditions existing at any point in the column at any given time and, knowing these conditions, to predict the optimum operating conditions for the distillation and the results. The steady-state condition will be investigated first, since it is amenable to mathematical treatment. The conclusions drawn from the analysis of a steady-state condition can then be applied with some reservations to a batch distillation in which product is withdrawn. Several analyses of the steady state follow.

Fenske[4] and Underwood[5] independently derived an expression which relates the distillate composition to the relative volatility of the components, number of theoretical plates in the column, and the still composition when the column is operated under total reflux, that is, in a steady state. The derivation is merely the analytical equivalent of the graphical stepping-off technique described earlier for determining the number of theoretical plates required for a given separation, but it is interesting and deserves attention.

First, it is necessary to assume that α is constant over the range of concentrations considered. Then let x_s and y_s be the mole fractions of the more volatile component in the liquid and vapor, respectively. Under these conditions

$$\frac{y_s}{1 - y_s} = \alpha \frac{x_s}{1 - x_s} \tag{2.6}$$

represents the equilibrium relationship attained between the liquid in the still (see Fig. 2.4) and the vapor entering the base of the column. Assuming that the vapor entering the first plate of the column is condensed and in equilibrium with the vapor y_1 entering the second plate of the column,

$$\frac{y_1}{1 - y_1} = \alpha \frac{y_s}{1 - y_s} = \alpha^2 \frac{x_s}{1 - x_s}$$

A repetition of this reasoning process yields

$$\frac{y_2}{1 - y_2} = \alpha^3 \frac{x_s}{1 - x_s}$$

for the equilibrium between the liquid in plate 2 and the vapor rising to plate 3. The general expression for the equilibrium at the nth plate would be

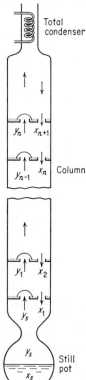

$$\frac{y_n}{1 - y_n} = \alpha^{n+1} \frac{x_s}{1 - x_s} \qquad (2.7)$$

The equation (generally referred to as the Fenske equation) infers that a column operated under total reflux with n theoretical plates will give a distillate of composition y_n when the still composition is x_s. From this equation one can calculate the minimum number of plates required to achieve the desired separation of a binary mixture *or* one can calculate from the known distilland and distillate compositions the number of theoretical plates in the column.

The Fenske equation thus provides the means for calculating the efficiency of a column. All that is necessary is to distill a mixture of normal solvents whose relative volatility is known and then analyze the distillate and distilland by withdrawing small samples while the column is operating under total reflux. Column efficiency is usually evaluated experimentally with a mixture of n-hexane and methylcyclohexane, for which very accurate vapor-liquid equilibrium data are available. Admittedly, the Fenske equation does not give the number of theoretical plates in the column when distillate is withdrawn from the system, but in practice the equation gives a good approximation to the number of theoretical plates if the column is operated with a high reflux ratio. Subsequent equations will bear this out.

FIG. 2.4. Illustration of distillation column operated under total reflux in a steady-state condition.

Sorel[6] and Lewis[7] derived an *operating-line* equation of great practical value by applying a material and thermal balance between two adjacent plates when the column is operated at partial reflux. It is assumed that the column is operated adiabatically and that there is no heat of mixing exhibited by the liquids. The heat necessary for vaporization of each plate is provided by the condensation of descending vapors. A total condenser is placed in the top of the column, but part of the condensate from the last plate is refluxed and the remainder returned directly to the still. A steady-state condition is reached in time, however, since no product is removed from the system as a whole. The relation between the composition of the liquid in the still and the condensate at the top of the column under these conditions is the same as that which might exist at some instant during the course of a batch distillation at partial reflux. The system in a steady-state condition is illustrated in Fig. 2.5.

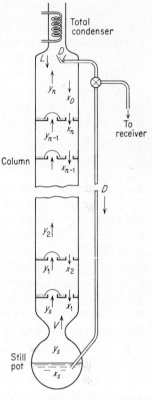

The operation can be described mathematically if L represents the moles of reflux and D the moles of distillate (returned directly to the still) per unit time. The reflux ratio R_D is then defined by

$$R_D = \frac{L}{D} \qquad (2.8)$$

The total number of moles V of vapor leaving the top plate per unit time is then given by

$$V = L + D \qquad (2.9)$$

FIG. 2.5. Operation of a column at partial reflux under steady-state conditions.

if a material balance is maintained. The amount of the more volatile component leaving the column at the top is Dx_D moles per unit time, which must equal $Vy_s - Lx_1$ moles per unit time entering the base of the column.   Therefore

$$Dx_D = Vy_s - Lx_1 \qquad (2.10)$$

or
$$y_s = \frac{L}{V} x_1 + \frac{D}{V} x_D = \frac{L}{L+D} x_1 + \frac{D}{L+D} x_D \qquad (2.11)$$

Under these same steady-state conditions a material balance can be applied between any two adjacent plates to give

$$y_1 = \frac{L}{V} x_2 + \frac{D}{V} x_D$$

and
$$y_2 = \frac{L}{V} x_3 + \frac{D}{V} x_D$$

and the general equation

$$y_{n-1} = \frac{L}{V} x_n + \frac{D}{V} x_D \tag{2.12}$$

This equation is known as the operating-line equation.

An algebraic analysis of equilibrium conditions from plate to plate is possible with the operating-line equation, but the method is tedious and time-consuming. For example, one can calculate the number of theoretical plates needed to achieve a desired degree of separation at a given reflux ratio if the relative volatility is known. Substitute into the general expression for the relative volatility

$$\frac{y_n}{1 - y_n} = \alpha \frac{x_n}{1 - x_n} \tag{2.13}$$

and calculate x_n, keeping in mind that with a total condenser in the top of the column, $x_D = y_n$. The value of y_{n-1} then can be calculated from the operating-line equation. In an analogous fashion calculate x_{n-1} and y_{n-2}, etc., until the calculated value for x corresponds to the composition x_s of the liquid in the still. The number of steps involved in the calculation will give the number of plates needed for the separation.

McCabe and Thiele[8] have devised a graphical method to circumvent the tedious calculations involving the operating-line equation when a large number of plates are encountered. The method is based upon the fact that the locus of points for the operating-line equation is a straight line with slope L/V which intersects the 45° line of the vapor-liquid-composition diagram at the point (x_D, y_n), since $x_D = y_n$, and the y axis at $(D/V)x_D$. When the reflux ratio, the relative volatility (namely, the vapor-liquid composition diagram), and the desired values of x_D and x_s are known, it is a relatively simple matter to step off the number of plates necessary to come to the composition of the residue in the still. The graphical method is illustrated in Fig. 2.6.

The McCabe-Thiele method is more generally applicable than the Fenske equation for determining the number of theoretical plates because it can be applied to nonideal mixtures for which the equilibrium line does not obey the equation

$$\frac{y}{1 - y} = \alpha \frac{x}{1 - x}$$

provided the equilibrium line has been plotted from experimental data.

A close inspection of Fig. 2.6 shows clearly the result of increasing the reflux ratio L/D so that it approaches total reflux. As D decreases, the slope of the operating line increases and fewer plates are needed to achieve the same degree of separation. It is important to recognize that under conditions of total reflux, namely, when $D = 0$ and $L/V = 1$, the operating-line equation reduces to

$$y_{n-1} = x_n$$

which is the 45° line in the vapor-liquid composition diagram. The minimum number of plates would be needed if the column were operated under total reflux. Keep in mind, though, that practical distillation processes cannot be operated under total reflux.

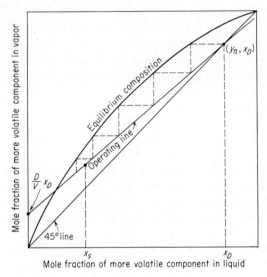

FIG. 2.6. Illustration of the graphical method of McCabe and Thiele.

On the other hand, if the reflux ratio is decreased, the slope of the operating line decreases and the point of intersection of the operating line and the equilibrium line shifts to the right. The minimum allowable reflux ratio $R_{D,\min}$ then is that which will cause the operating line to intersect the equilibrium curve at x_s. Under such conditions an infinite number of plates would be required to obtain a distillate x_D from the mixture x_s in the still. At still smaller values of R_D, the operating line would intersect the equilibrium line to the right of the still composition x_s and not even an infinite number of plates would achieve the desired separation.

The minimum allowable reflux ratio is easily calculated, since the slope L/V of the operating line would then be given by

$$\left(\frac{L}{V}\right)_{\min} = \frac{y_n - y_s}{x_D - x_s} = \frac{x_D - y_s}{x_D - x_s} = \frac{L_{\min}}{L_{\min} + D}$$

$$= \frac{(L/D)_{\min}}{(L/D)_{\min} + D/D} = \frac{R_{D,\min}}{R_{D,\min} + 1} \tag{2.14}$$

Solving for $R_{D,\min}$ it is found that

$$R_{D,\min} = \frac{x_D - y_s}{y_s - x_s} \qquad (2.15)$$

Thus, the minimum reflux ratio can be expressed in terms of the terminal compositions x_D, x_s, and y_s.

From the above considerations it is obvious that there is some relationship between the number of theoretical plates and the reflux ratio required to effect a given separation. All fractionations must be performed under conditions between those of a minimum number of plates at total reflux and an infinite number of plates at the minimum reflux ratio. Several equations[9] have been derived which express the relation between R_D and n, but Rose[1] has summarized it well by stating that the optimum number of plates should about equal the reflux ratio and is given by the following equation:

$$n = R_D = \frac{2.85}{\log \alpha} = \frac{T_2 + T_1}{3(T_2 - T_1)} \qquad (2.16)$$

where T_1 and T_2 are the absolute boiling points of the two components. This is not the criterion, however, for obtaining a pure distillate but represents the conditions needed to achieve a standard separation in which the first 40 per cent of the distillate collected from a 50-50 mole per cent mixture will have an average purity greater than 95 per cent. The same studies have indicated that there is a practical limit in the usual laboratory distillation beyond which an increase in the number of plates utilized gives only a slight increase in separative power. This limit is conveniently expressed as

$$n_{\max} = \frac{3.6}{\log \alpha} \qquad (2.17)$$

There is thus a narrow range of values of n which will accomplish the desired standard separation. Within this range a lower value of n can be partially compensated for by an increase in R_D, and higher values of n may allow use of smaller values of R_D.

A rather extensive treatment of these various relationships has been given by Rose and Rose.[10]

2.4. Analysis of Batch Fractional Distillation. The preceding discussion was restricted to an analysis of the steady-state condition in which the composition of vapor and liquid was constant at any given point in the column. In a true batch distillation, product is withdrawn from the still and the composition of vapors and liquid will vary continuously throughout the course of the distillation. The first distillate collected in a simple batch distillation would have the composition of the vapor in equilibrium with the original mixture. The distillate would be richer in the more volatile component. As the distillation proceeds, however, the concentration of the more volatile component in the distillate and distilland would decrease continuously. Therefore, the average distillate in a simple batch distillation cannot possibly be any richer in the more volatile component than the initial equilibrium vapor. Only a small measure of separation is possible. The separation efficiency can be greatly improved, though, if the vapors from the still are fractionated in a column.

The variation of the distillate composition during the course of a batch distillation with fractionation can be calculated with the Rayleigh equation[11]

$$\ln \frac{B_0}{B} = \int_x^{x_0} \frac{dx}{x_p - x} \tag{2.18}$$

which is based on a material balance on the more volatile component. B_0 is the moles of the initial charge to the still, B is the moles of charge remaining in the still after time t, x_0 is the concentration of the more volatile component in the initial charge and x is its concentration after time t, and x_p is the concentration of the more volatile component in the vapor at the bottom of the column for a given reflux ratio and a given number of theoretical plates.

The value of $\ln (B_0/B)$ can be determined only by a graphical integration which makes the calculation of the quantity B after a given time difficult. A graphical integration is performed by plotting $1/(x_p - x)$ versus x on a temperature-composition phase diagram and determining the area under the resulting curve between the limits corresponding to B_0 and B.

In most analytical work the distilling column is operated batchwise at a high reflux ratio. The most common way of expressing the results of such a distillation is by means of a distillation curve in which the boiling point, composition, refractive index, or some other physical property of the distillate is plotted against the percentage of the total sample distilled. A typical distillation curve is shown in Fig. 2.7. An ideal distillation curve would result in right-angled curves, but such a situation is impossible. Only in the case of easily separable mixtures or when very efficient equipment is used do the curves approximate the ideal. In the case of very complex mixtures a smooth irregular curve with no distinct plateaus may be obtained, which is indicative of an incomplete resolution. The concentration of each component in the original mixture is determined from the length of the plateau observed for that component in the distillation curve.

The shapes of the curves are too complex to be expressed in a general algebraic form, but Rose and coworkers have shown how the curves can be calculated with[12,13] and without[14] simplifying assumptions. The actual sharpness of the curve is primarily a function of the magnitude of the relative volatility, the HETP, and the reflux ratio. Holdup and throughput are of lesser importance. The approximate relationships between the sharpness of separation and the relative volatility, reflux ratio, and number of plates were given in Eqs. (2.16) and (2.17).

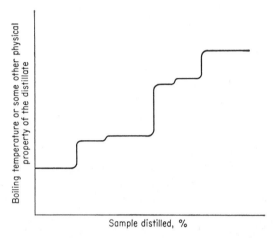

FIG. 2.7. Typical distillation curve obtained in the batch distillation of a multi-component mixture with sharp fractionation.

2.5. Apparatus. Laboratory distillation is probably the most convenient tool available to the chemist for the separation of mixtures of liquids because of the ease with which it is possible to obtain a large number of theoretical plates in a single column. Thus, relatively difficult separations can be carried out quickly in fairly simple apparatus.

Figure 2.8 illustrates a simple distillation unit which consists of a distilling flask, thermometer, water-cooled condenser, and receiving flask. Keep in mind that such a unit has very little resolving power, since the enrichment of the distillate with the more volatile component is probably no greater than that achieved with one theoretical plate.

The introduction of a rectifying or fractionating column in the simple equipment is illustrated in Fig. 2.9. Since the actual separation of components is effected in the column, this discussion will be centered about the several basic column designs usually employed in laboratory equipment.

There are, in general, two types of columns encountered—the film and the plate. The film column can be exemplified in varying degrees of complexity starting with a vertical open tube and progressing through various modifications of the shape and length of path in which the ascending vapor and descending liquid are kept in intimate contact. The plate column consists of a tube containing a series of equally spaced horizontal plates which impede the downward flow of the reflux. Liquid collects on the upper surface of each plate until it reaches a predetermined overflow level. In such a column there are definite increments in the

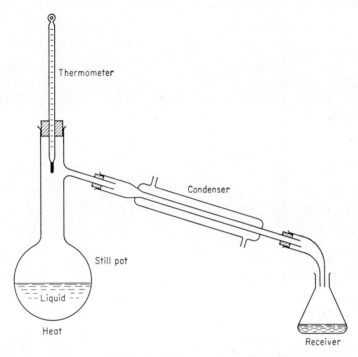

Fig. 2.8. Apparatus suitable for a simple distillation.

composition of liquid from plate to plate. Advantages and disadvantages are associated with the use of both types of columns.

One of the simplest film columns is the Vigreux illustrated in Fig. 2.10. It is made up from a cylindrical glass tube with indentations projecting inside it according to a definite pattern. The indentations occur in sets of three or four around the circumference of the tube. Alternate sets of indentations are pointed downward at a 45° angle with the other sets horizontal. Each set of indentations is rotated slightly with respect to the set above it to give a somewhat spiral arrangement of the drip points. Columns 1 m in length may have up to about 12 theoretical plates. The holdup is quite small, and there is a very low pressure drop through the column.

The spiral columns illustrated in Fig. 2.11 provide vapor and liquid paths considerably longer than they would be in an empty-tube column of the same length. The spiral column in various modifications is still very popular.

The most widely used film column is the *packed* column, which consists of a vertical tube filled with a porous packing which breaks up the direct

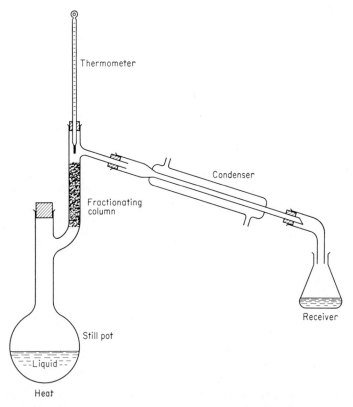

Fɪɢ. 2.9. Basic laboratory equipment for fractional distillation.

path through the tube and provides a large liquid surface for contact between the vapor and reflux.

Packing material for laboratory columns should be of small dimensions (generally 2 to 8 mm) and must be readily wetted by the liquid and inert to the liquids and vapors. Most packings are glass, porcelain, or metal. For general use the columns are packed with hollow open-end cylinders (Raschig rings) of approximately equal height and diameter, hollow open-end cylinders with a central partition (Lessing rings) to increase the surface area, Berl saddles, helices, or beads. The promiscuous arrangement of the various packings in a column provides a rather tortuous path through the column which assures intimate contact between ascending vapors and reflux. At the same time the packing is porous enough that little pressure is built up between the top and bottom of the column.

Because of the large contact surfaces provided by packed columns, the columns are usually quite efficient, having as many as 20 to 40 theoretical

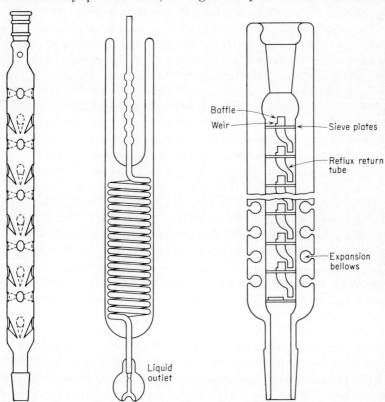

Baffle
Weir
Sieve plates
Reflux return tube
Expansion bellows
Liquid outlet

FIG. 2.10. Vigreux column.

FIG. 2.11. Simple spiral column.

FIG. 2.12. Oldershaw sieve-plate column.

plates per meter of column length. Compared with a Vigreux column of the same size, packed columns have a higher separating power, a larger holdup, and a much larger pressure drop in the column.

The Oldershaw[15] sieve-plate column shown in Fig. 2.12 is an example of a well-designed plate column. A column 1 m in length containing 30 sieve plates can possess as many as 15 to 18 theoretical plates, giving a fairly high resolving power. Operating conditions with such a column are highly reproducible, but the holdup per theoretical plate is greater than that for a theoretical plate in a packed column.

Since the effectiveness of a column depends upon the height as well as upon the packing or internal construction of the column, the efficiency is frequently expressed in terms of the height equivalent of a theoretical plate (HETP) for direct comparisons.

In the final selection of fractionating equipment for laboratory use a compromise must be found which combines high separating power per unit length of column (a low HETP) and high capacity with low holdup. If the absolute quantity of material to be separated is small, there is, of course, a definite limit on the holdup that can be tolerated. The holdup must not be of the same order of magnitude as the material to be resolved, and preferably it should be less than 10 per cent of the amount of material to be separated.

There is not much point in trying to use apparatus with more than 40 or 50 theoretical plates for normal laboratory work because of the unusually long time required for the column to come to equilibrium and the difficulty of operating such columns efficiently.

The Podbielniak automatic distillation apparatus[16] removes much of the tedium associated with the fractional-distillation process by automatically recording the boiling point as a function of the volume of distillate over a temperature range from 190 to 300°C. It is excellent for the efficient separation of all but the closest boiling components.

For more detailed information on packing materials, column designs (including spinning band columns), column evaluation, and the very necessary auxiliary equipment which complements the column, the interested reader is referred to the selected bibliography at the end of this chapter.

2.6. General Applications. Fractional distillation is used for a number of purposes in the laboratory, the most important of which are qualitative and quantitative analysis, the preparation of pure compounds, and the fractionation of complex mixtures into pure substances or classes of substances. Since the purely determinative applications of fractional distillation are far less important now than before the emergence of gas chromatography as an analytical tool, the discussion will be directed along the lines of utilizing distillation as a general separation technique of wide applicability, especially when sizable quantities of material must be handled. The distillation of a pure substance is of no interest because a separation of components is not involved.

Fractional distillation is widely used for the analysis and fractionation of complex mixtures of hydrocarbons, fluorocarbons, petroleum products, etc. It is a particularly powerful tool used with great success when coupled with other separation methods such as adsorption and partition chromatography, solvent extraction, crystallization, azeotropic distillation, and extractive distillation. One must recognize, though, that only through a knowledge of the limitations of fractional distillation and the other techniques can judicious combinations of these techniques be made which will result in the successful fractionation of mixtures. Specific examples of separations achieved with fractional distillation are given in the following section to illustrate the resolving power of the process when used alone and in conjunction with other methods. The illustrations employed in Sec. 2.7 will be confined to organic systems, since almost all the literature on fractional distillation pertains to the separation of organics.

It is interesting to note, though, how extensively fractional distillation has been used to fractionate inorganic materials. The general subject of the separation of isotopes falls outside the realm of this study, but it is worthwhile to mention that isotopic separations by distillation of hydrogen, helium, oxygen, carbon, boron, and lithium as elements or compounds are of much interest.[17] Recently, distillation methods for the purification of arsenic, titanium, tellurium, niobium, hafnium, zirconium, yttrium, and scandium have been devised which utilize either the elements or their halides.[18] In addition, many inorganics, including the metals and pseudometals, form compounds which can be volatilized from aqueous solutions and which are useful in the isolation and purification of the parent element[19,20] It is this last group of elements that has commanded the greatest attention of analytical chemists.

Section 2.8 is devoted to a discussion of the isolation of inorganic substances from aqueous solutions by volatilization techniques. Only those separations which can be effected in a simple still or volatilization chamber will be mentioned, since these are the only ones which have been widely accepted by the analyst. In general, less sophisticated equipment is employed for inorganic separations than for organic separations because the difference in volatility of similar inorganic species is usually rather great. It is not customary to use a highly efficient column for inorganic separations, but it is feasible.

2.7. Fractional Distillation of Organics. A classic example of the successful fractionation of complex mixtures by distillation is the work dealing with the composition of petroleum sponsored by the American Petroleum Institute and done at the National Bureau of Standards.[21] This work is a remarkably fine example of what can be done with fractional distillation, but what is probably more important, it illustrates what a combination of fractional distillation and other separation techniques can accomplish.

Over 80 hydrocarbons have been separated from one petroleum by a combination of distillation, selective adsorption, extraction, and crystallization. The scheme utilized can be described as one in which the original petroleum (a mixture of paraffins, cycloparaffins, and aromatics) is first fractionated by distillation into groups of compounds of roughly equal molecular size. These groups are then further subdivided by type of compound by selective adsorption, azeotropic distillation, or distillation at reduced pressure. Final purification then is achieved by fractional crystallization or by high-efficiency distillation.

Simple distillation will serve only as a convenient means for the separation of petroleum into broad fractions roughly according to molecular weight, since, in general, the volatility of a compound is inversely proportional to its molecular weight and boiling point. These fractions are usually referred to as the gas, gasoline, kerosene, gas-oil, and lubricating-oil fractions. Although the properties of each fraction are rather distinct, it must be kept in mind that the general properties are simply the average of what might be extremely diverse values for the individual hydrocarbons in each fraction. For, as the molecular weight of organic materials increases, the number of possible compounds of similar volatility increases greatly and separations by fractional distillation become very difficult, if not impossible. The paraffin octane, for example, has 15 isomers, all of which may be present in a given sample. Added to this is the complication that compounds of different molecular type can have almost the same volatility and boiling points. For example, the six-carbon hydrocarbons benzene and cyclohexane boil at 80.1 and 80.8°, respectively.

Although a complete separation by fractional distillation often is impossible in such cases, it is possible to separate further the narrow-boiling fractions containing different molecular types by extractive or azeotropic distillation or by distillation at reduced pressure.

Azeotropic Distillation. In azeotropic distillation a solvent is added to the close-boiling mixture which will form a constant-boiling mixture or azeotrope with one or more of the components of the mixture. An azeotrope boils or distills without a change in composition and in general has a boiling point which is higher or lower than that of any of its pure constituents. Thus, the shift in the boiling point of a substance when it forms an azeotrope is often large enough to effect a further separation of close-boiling materials.

The two basic requirements for an azeotropic distillation are that the added component reduce the partial pressure of one of the original components more than the other and that it be easily removed from the distillate. Consider the separation of a close-boiling binary mixture AB. The addition to the still of a third component C capable of forming an azeotrope with A will yield a distillate containing A and C in a fixed ratio as long as both A and C are present. The quantitative removal of A is therefore dependent on the addition of an excess of C. By a careful selection of the entrainer solvent the entrainer and component B can then be resolved by distillation. The maximum boiling-point depression (most azeotropes exhibit a minimum boiling point) is obtained when the boiling points of the two pure solvents forming the azeotrope are the same, but practical considerations require that the boiling point of the entrainer be sufficiently different from the close-boiling mixture that the excess entrainer can then be separated from the residue in the still by a fractional distillation. With an entrainer which boils within 30° of the material to be separated, a 5° lowering of the boiling point of the azeotrope is not uncommon. Thus, the azeotrope AC can be distilled off, leaving a mixture of B and C which can be resolved by fractional distillation.

The separation of an azeotrope from a nonazeotrope or from another azeotrope can be calculated by the conventional methods by simply treating the azeotrope as a pure component. In many instances, though, the separations are appreciably better than the calculations indicate they should be.

Two noteworthy cases of azeotropic distillation familiar to the analytical chemist are the preparation of constant-boiling hydrochloric acid and anhydrous ethyl alcohol. The preparation of anhydrous alcohol will illustrate the method well.

At atmospheric pressure water and ethyl alcohol form a constant-boiling mixture (bp 78.15°C) which is 95 per cent alcohol. Since water is a major component in the commercial preparation of alcohol, pure alcohol cannot be recovered by a simple fractional distillation. If, however, benzene is added to the alcohol-water azeotrope, a new lower-boiling (65°C) ternary azeotrope is formed among benzene, water, and alcohol (74 per cent benzene, 18.5 per cent alcohol, 7.5 per cent water). Distillation of the ternary azeotrope accomplishes the quantitative removal of water from the system but leaves the alcohol contaminated with benzene. The benzene and alcohol in turn form an azeotrope (67.6 per cent benzene and 32.4 per cent alcohol, bp 68.3°C) which distills over, leaving anhydrous ethyl alcohol which can be collected at 78.5°C.

In petroleum analyses, a given entrainer may form azeotropes with each type of hydrocarbon in a given boiling range or be somewhat specific in its action. For example, paraffins, naphthenes, olefins, and aromatics boiling in the range 100 to 110°C form minimum-boiling azeotropes with methanol whereas paraffins, olefins, and naphthenes (but not toluene) form an azeotrope with methyl ethyl ketone. Thus, the judicious selection of entrainer liquids (azeotrope formers) can facilitate the separation of complex mixtures. Tables of known azeotropes can be consulted for practical purposes.[22,23]

Specifically, acetic acid can be used to separate ethyl benzene from vinyl benzene (styrene), and butyl acetate is good for the dehydration of acetic acid.

Another logical development in the application of fractional distillation is the modification of the volatilities of sample components by the addition of certain solvents (extractive distillation) and by distillation at reduced pressures.

Extractive Distillation. Extractive distillation is a technique used to separate close-boiling ideal and nonideal mixtures, including azeotropes. It involves the addition of a relatively nonvolatile liquid to the sample mixture which enhances the relative volatility of the components to be separated. The added component acts as a preferential solvent for one of the components, thus lowering the vapor pressure of the dissolved material and raising the relative volatility of the two-component mixture to be separated. In effect, a nonideal system is deliberately created to enhance the separability of the two substances. This is a little-used technique in the laboratory but one quite versatile for industrial distillations. The following examples will indicate the effectiveness of the method.

Benedict and Rubin[24] resolved a mixture of paraffins and toluene by extractive distillation using phenol as the solvent. Without the phenol, the relative volatilities of the components were unity and no separation was possible. With phenol, the relative volatility increased to 3.7, giving a boiling-point difference of about 80°C for the two fractions collected.

Dicks and Carlson[25] using a single column were able to increase the column efficiency for the separation of *n*-heptane and methylcyclohexane from 13.1 theoretical plates to an effective 51.9 plates by changing from a normal fractional-distillation technique to an extractive distillation using aniline as the solvent. By the same method, using aniline as solvent, a constant-boiling mixture of cyclohexane and benzene (47 mole per cent cyclohexane) can be broken so as to give a pure cyclohexane distillate.

Distillation under Reduced Pressure. The chief advantage to distillation under reduced pressure is that the boiling point is usually lowered considerably. As a consequence, it is a widely used technique for the separation of compounds which would change chemically or distill too slowly at the temperature needed for a normal atmospheric-pressure distillation. It is significant also that the ratio of the vapor pressure of two substances (i.e., the relative volatility of two substances) should increase as the boiling temperature decreases. As a result, separations frequently are more effective when performed at reduced pressures.

2.8. Fractional Distillation of Inorganics. The elements which are generally recognized as being volatile under normal conditions and those which form compounds that can be volatilized from aqueous solution are outlined in Fig. 2.13. The form in which these elements are volatilized from aqueous solution is listed below.

FRACTIONAL DISTILLATION AND SUBLIMATION

The inert gases, hydrogen, oxygen, and the halogens can be volatilized completely in the elemental or molecular form. Carbon, sulfur, nitrogen, ruthenium, osmium, and rhenium form volatile oxides. Boron, carbon, nitrogen, phosphorus, sulfur, selenium, tellurium, and the halogens may escape from solution as the volatile acids, HBO_3, HNO_3, H_2Se, etc. Germanium, arsenic, antimony, tin, mercury, selenium, tellurium, and gold form volatile chlorides. Boron and silicon form volatile fluorides. Nitrogen, phosphorus, arsenic, and antimony form the volatile hydrides NH_3, AsH_3, etc.

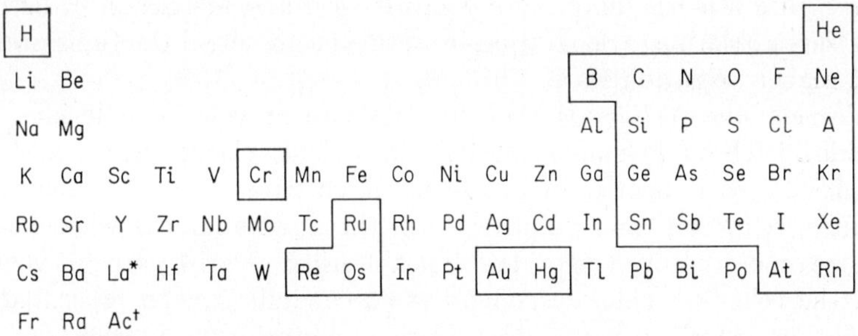

H																	He
Li	Be											B	C	N	O	F	Ne
Na	Mg											Al	Si	P	S	Cl	A
K	Ca	Sc	Ti	V	Cr	Mn	Fe	Co	Ni	Cu	Zn	Ga	Ge	As	Se	Br	Kr
Rb	Sr	Y	Zr	Nb	Mo	Tc	Ru	Rh	Pd	Ag	Cd	In	Sn	Sb	Te	I	Xe
Cs	Ba	La*	Hf	Ta	W	Re	Os	Ir	Pt	Au	Hg	Tl	Pb	Bi	Po	At	Rn
Fr	Ra	Ac†															

* Also elements 58 through 71.
† Also elements 89 through 103.

Fig. 2.13. Elements outlined in blocks can be volatilized from aqueous solutions in either compound or elemental form.

Since the conditions under which volatilization is attempted determine the completeness of separation for each of the elements, the optimum conditions are specified in the following paragraphs for the elements most commonly isolated from mixtures by volatilization procedures.

Nitrogen. Perhaps the best-known inorganic distillation separation is the volatilization of nitrogen as ammonia from a wide variety of materials by the Kjeldahl procedure. The method is fairly rapid and quantitative.

Fluorine. The only really satisfactory way of separating fluoride from elements that interfere in its determination is by steam distillation of SiF_4 or H_2SiF_6 from sulfuric or perchloric acid solutions containing silica.[26] The temperature must be at least 125°C. Of more limited applicability is the distillation of BF_3 from a 20 per cent perchloric acid solution saturated with boric acid.

Boron. Boron is often removed from mixtures containing borates by distillation as methyl borate,[27,28] CH_3BO_2. A quantitative distillation of boron can be achieved by placing a small amount of methyl alcohol and concentrated hydrochloric acid in the sample and distilling in a stream of methanol vapor.   Boron may also be lost as BF_3 from solutions containing fluoride.

Silicon.   Silicon can be removed from aqueous solutions or from solids by evaporation to dryness in a hydrofluoric-sulfuric or hydrofluoric-perchloric acid mixture.   The silicon is lost in each case as SiF_4.   A more versatile technique involves the removal of silicon as H_2SiF_6 by steam distillation from a hydrofluoric-perchloric acid medium.

Germanium.   The best method for the separation of germanium from complex mixtures is by distillation of $GeCl_4$ from concentrated hydrochloric acid solution in a closed system with condenser.[29]   The distillate is very pure if a fractionating column is used and arsenic is oxidized to As(V) with chlorine.   Separation from tin is complete if the tin is present in its higher oxidation state.

Selenium and Tellurium.   Both metals form volatile chlorides and oxychlorides.[30,31]   Selenides and tellurides yield volatile $SeCl_2$ and $TeCl_2$ and $TeCl_4$ when heated in a stream of chlorine gas.   The selenates, selenites, tellurates, and tellurites form these same halides when heated in a stream of hydrogen chloride.   The tellurium chlorides are less volatile than the selenium chlorides, and the two metals can be separated by distillation from concentrated sulfuric acid solution heated near its boiling point (300°C) if a stream of hydrochloric acid is passed through the mixture.

Arsenic, Antimony, and Tin.   These all form volatile chlorides which can be separated by distillation.   The boiling points of the chlorides are as follows: $AsCl_3$ 130°, $SbCl_3$ 220°, $SnCl_2$ 603°, $SnCl_4$ 114°.   A fractional- or successive-distillation separation of the three metals is described by Scherrer[32] and Mogerman.[33]   Arsenic distills below 112° and is accompanied by germanium.   Antimony distills at higher temperatures (155 to 165°).   Tin is prevented from distilling by the addition of phosphoric acid.   Arsenic can also be quantitatively separated from mixtures as AsH_3, arsine.   The arsine is readily formed in dilute sulfuric acid solutions containing zinc.   Under the same conditions antimony compounds form the volatile stibine, SbH_3.

Ruthenium and Osmium.   These two metals can be separated from each other and from other metals in spectroscopic purity by distillation from aqueous solutions.[34,35]   Osmium is distilled quantitatively as OsO_4 from a boiling nitric acid or nitric-sulfuric acid mixture.   Ruthenium tetroxide is not distilled under these conditions but can be if a strong oxidizing agent such as bromate, perchlorate, or permanganate is introduced.   Ruthenium tetroxide can be distilled also from a hot alkali hydroxide solution saturated with chlorine through which one draws a current of air or chlorine.

Rhenium.   Rhenium heptoxide, Re_2O_7, is volatilized from fuming

(200°C or higher) perchloric or sulfuric acid solutions but is not volatilized from boiling solutions containing only hydrochloric acid, nitric acid, or aqua regia.

Gold. Gold is volatilized to an appreciable extent from rapidly boiling solutions of aqua regia and from such solutions treated with sulfuric acid and evaporated to the point that copious fumes of SO_3 are evolved.

Chromium. Chromium is volatilized as chromyl chloride, CrO_2Cl_2, from hot hydrochloric-perchloric acid mixtures if a stream of hydrochloric acid is passed over the hot solution.[36,37]

Mercury. $HgCl_2$ is quite volatile in a sulfuric acid medium at temperatures above 300°C if a stream of chlorine or hydrochloric acid is passed through the solution.

2.9. Molecular Distillation. In conventional distillation processes, distillation occurs at a well-defined temperature, namely, at the boiling point of the material being distilled, and continues with the ebullition of the liquid. A dynamic equilibrium exists between the vapor phase and liquid phase, causing a large proportion of the evaporated molecules to return to the liquid phase. Use is made of this equilibrium tendency in establishing a fractional-distillation process with improved separating powers.

In contrast to conventional distillation, a distillation in high vacuum (less than 0.001 mm of mercury) does not commence at any well-defined temperature but occurs at any temperature as long as there is a thermal gradient between the evaporator and condenser. In distillations in high vacuum the mean free path of molecules of the distillate is relatively long (5.09 cm for air at 25°C and 0.001 mm of mercury) compared with that at atmospheric pressure (6.7×10^{-6} cm). Consequently, the distilling vapor molecules pass directly from the vaporizing surface to the condensing surface with very few vapor molecules ever returning to the distilland if the distance between evaporator and condenser surfaces is less than the mean free path of the vapor molecules. No equilibrium exists between the vapor and liquid phases. Ideal distillation conditions are attained when the rate of evaporation is equal to the rate of condensation.

Distillation in high vacuum goes under several names, the more common of which are *molecular distillation* and *evaporative distillation*. The former seems preferable here.

Strictly speaking, a *molecular still* can be defined as any still in which the distance between the evaporating surface and the condenser surface is less than the mean free path of the vapor molecules. A simple form of the apparatus (Fig. 2.14) is that in which a cooled condensing surface is supported a few centimeters (or millimeters) above a thin, heated layer of liquid and the whole is enclosed in a highly evacuated chamber. Since the mean free path of large molecules is appreciably less than that for air, the distance between the condenser and evaporator surface is usually reduced to several millimeters and the temperature of the condenser is kept quite low to reduce the rebound of vapor molecules from the condenser surface.   Liquid air and dry-ice–acetone mixtures are common condenser coolants.

Whereas Fig. 2.14 represents an apparatus particularly well suited for the distillation (sublimation) of solids, the still depicted in Fig. 2.15 is better suited for the distillation and collection of high-boiling liquids where it is necessary or desirable to collect the distillate in successive fractions.

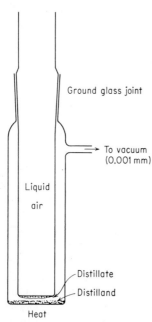

For apparatus of the type described above the rate of distillation is determined by the rate at which the liquid surface can produce vapor.   According to Langmuir the theoretical rate of distillation (and condensation under ideal conditions) is given by the expression

$$Q = \frac{P}{(2\pi MRT)^{1/2}} \qquad (2.19)$$

where Q = moles of substance evaporating per second per square centimeter of liquid surface

M = molecular weight of the distilling substance

R = molar gas constant

P = vapor pressure of the distilling substance, dynes per sq cm measured at absolute temperature T

Fig. 2.14. Basic features of simple molecular still. The distance between distilland and condensing surface is limited to several millimeters.

In practice, lower values for Q are obtained than predicted because of the rebound of some vapor molecules from the condenser surface and molecular collisions.   To take these factors into account the general equation is usually written as

$$Q = \frac{\alpha P}{(2\pi MRT)^{1/2}} \qquad (2.20)$$

where α is an efficiency factor.   A simplified form of the equation useful to the chemist is

$$W = \frac{0.0583P}{(M/T)^{1/2}} = \frac{0.0583PT^{1/2}}{M^{1/2}} \qquad (2.21)$$

where W is the distilling rate in grams per second per square centimeter of liquid surface and P is the vapor pressure in millimeters of mercury. The constant 0.0583 is the resultant of combining the molar gas constant and various conversion factors.

It is apparent from the general equation that the rate of evaporation at any given temperature is a function of the ratio of P/M and that the relative quantities of different sample constituents distilling are given by the ratios

$$\frac{P_1}{M_1^{1/2}} \qquad \frac{P_2}{M_2^{1/2}} \qquad \cdots \qquad \frac{P_n}{M_n^{1/2}}$$

where P is the partial pressure of the constituent. By contrast, in conventional distillation the relative quantities of each constituent dis-

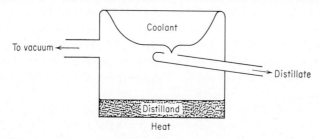

Fig. 2.15. Schematic of a simple molecular still suitable for fractional distillation through control of distillation temperature.

tilling over are proportional to their partial pressures; that is, the effect of the molecular mass is not involved.

The simplest separation to achieve by molecular distillation is the distillation of the desired substance from a residue of higher molecular weight. Owing to the temperature dependence of the rate of distillation, a fractionation of substances with different molecular weights can be effected by holding the temperature constant until the more volatile constituent is removed. Then the temperature is raised sufficiently to give a practical distillation rate for the less volatile substance, etc.

The degree of separation effected by molecular distillation is comparable to that produced by a simple batch distillation and is greatest when components differ in boiling point by 50° or more. Where fractionation is not complete in a single distillation, a greater degree of separation can be attained by redistillation of the distillate, the operation being repeated as many times as necessary to give the desired purity.

Since the fractionating power of the molecular still is restricted to the preferential evaporation of the most volatile constituents from the surface layer of the liquid, it is imperative that the surface layer be continually replenished. Any condition which leads to the removal of a volatile constituent more rapidly than that component can diffuse to the surface of the distilland reduces the efficiency of the distillation. "Flowing film" stills and others that continually replenish the distilland surface are well described in the literature by Perry.[38]

Several other devices have been proposed for increasing the fractionating efficiency of a molecular still. One[39] interposes a semipermeable barrier between the evaporator and condenser to retard the least-volatile molecules while allowing the more volatile molecules to reach the condenser. Another method[40] provides for multiple redistillations, and still another[41] for countercurrent reflux.

The great advantage of molecular distillation is that the "boiling point" of high-molecular-weight, high-boiling substances is greatly reduced (in some cases as much as 200 to 300°), making it possible to distill these substances without the thermal decomposition attendant upon their distillation at higher temperatures and atmospheric pressure. Molecular distillation is particularly adapted to the purification of a substance which is difficult or impossible to distill at ordinary pressures. Frequently, it is the only satisfactory method for the isolation of heat-labile substances and polymers.

Numerous references to the fractionation of fats and oils, fatty acids, esters of fatty acids, monoglycerides, phthalate esters, polymeric substances, sterols, tall oil, uranium chlorides, vitamins A and E, whale oil, etc., can be found in the work by Rose and Rose.[42]

2.10. Sublimation. Separations by volatilization are not limited, however, to the fractional distillation of liquids. Many solids also can be vaporized and separated in the vapor state from less volatile constituents. The usual technique is by *sublimation*, namely, the process involved when a solid is vaporized without melting and the vapor (upon cooling) is condensed directly back to the solid state. The initial solid is referred to as the *sublimand*, and the product as the *sublimate*.

One generally expects that, upon heating, a solid will eventually melt and then boil rather than sublime. The conditions for boiling and subliming, though, are somewhat different. A solid will sublime if its vapor pressure reaches atmospheric pressure below the melting point. Thus, theoretically at least, any substance which can be distilled without decomposition can also be sublimed at an appropriate temperature and pressure. This is dependent on the fact that the vapor pressure of a substance is directly proportional to the temperature whereas its melting point is almost independent of any change in atmospheric pressure.

The prerequisites for sublimation become apparent in a careful study of the typical triple-point phase diagram of a pure substance illustrated in Fig. 2.16. The curve AP indicates the temperatures and pressures at which the solid and liquid phases can be in equilibrium; that is, it repre-

sents the variation of the melting point with pressure.   Line BP represents the variation of the boiling point with pressure, and the line CP
represents the conditions under which solid and vapor are in equilibrium.
The point P at which the vapor-pressure curves intersect is known as the
triple point and specifies the condition under which the three states of
matter can coexist in a state of equilibrium.

Obviously, if a vapor at temperature T_1 and pressure P_1 is cooled to
temperature T_2, the vapor will pass first to the liquid state and finally at
the melting point to the solid state.   On the other hand, if a vapor at a

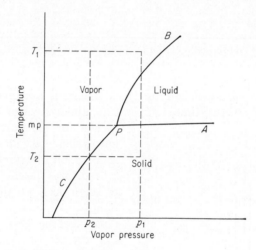

Fig. 2.16. Triple-point phase diagram for a pure substance.

pressure P_2, which is below the triple-point pressure, is cooled sufficiently,
the vapor will condense directly to the solid state without forming the
intermediate liquid phase.   Similarly, a solid can be completely vaporized
without passing through the liquid state provided the pressure of the
vapor is not allowed to exceed the triple-point pressure.   Clearly, if the
triple-point pressure is fairly high, it will be easy to establish the conditions necessary for sublimation to occur.   Not only that; the higher the
vapor pressure, the higher the rate of vaporization.

The temperature at which the vapor pressure of the solid equals
atmospheric pressure is frequently referred to as the *subliming point*.   It
is as characteristic of a particular substance as is the boiling point or
melting point.   Like the boiling point, the subliming point is influenced
by the presence of other vapors and varies greatly with the pressure in the
system.

The temperature at which a sublimate first becomes noticeable in a
given system is often referred to as the *sublimation temperature*, but this

TABLE 2.1. EFFECT OF REDUCED PRESSURE ON THE SUBLIMATION
TEMPERATURE OF SOME COMMON SUBSTANCES*

Compound	Melting point, °C	Sublimation temperature, °C	
		At 760 mm	At 0.5 to 1 mm
Anthracene............	215	77–79	28–31
Urea.................	132	59–61	49–52
Iodoform.............	119	43–45	30–34
Naphthalene..........	79	36–38	25
Benzoic acid..........	120	43–45	25
β-Naphthol...........	122	43–45	33–35

* After R. S. Tipson, Sublimation, in "Technique of Organic Chemistry," A.
Weissberger (ed.), vol. IV, p. 611, Interscience Publishers, Inc., New York, 1951.

temperature is so dependent on the dimensions and geometry of the
sublimation apparatus, time, temperature, and system pressure that it is
useless for comparative purposes unless these variables are standardized for all measurements. Table 2.1 indicates the effect that reduced pressure has on the sublimation temperature of a number of common substances.[43]

There are two basic approaches to the practical sublimation of substances. One approach is to evacuate the system while holding the temperature below the melting point of the sublimand. At reduced system pressures the vapor pressure of the solid exceeds the pressure of the atmosphere above it and the substance sublimes. In the case of those substances which sublime at atmospheric pressure, there is, of course, no need to reduce the pressure. Otherwise the technique is the same. Figure 2.17 is a schematic diagram of a simple but useful cold-finger vacuum sublimator.

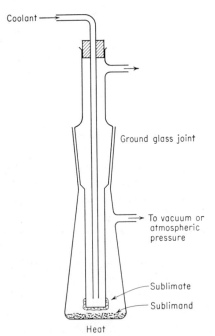

FIG. 2.17. Vertical vacuum sublimator with liquid-cooled condenser.

Coolant
Ground glass joint
To vacuum or atmospheric pressure
Sublimate
Sublimand
Heat

It can be operated over a wide range of pressure and temperature, and
sublimates are readily recoverable. There is, however, little chance with

apparatus of this type that substances with similar vapor pressures can be successfully fractionated, for, unlike distillation, there is no satisfactory way to increase the efficiency of the separation by way of producing reflux.

To accomplish a fractional sublimation, some degree of preferential vaporization and/or condensation must be exhibited by the solids. That is, there must be a pronounced difference in the vapor pressure of sample components at a given temperature. At any given pressure, then, a fractionation of components can be effected with a graded change in temperature of either the evaporative or condensing surface. With a controlled source of heat, the temperature of the still can be gradually raised with the collection of successive fractions of sublimate or the temperature of the still can be held above the sublimation temperature of the least-volatile component with fractionation effected by controlled deposition of the vapors on graded temperature condensing surfaces.

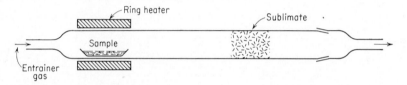

Fig. 2.18. Horizontal sublimator with air-cooled condenser tube.

Admittedly, the rate of sublimation may be quite low if the vapor pressure of the solid is low. Sublimation differs from distillation in that the surface layers of the solid gradually vaporize, exposing new surfaces, whereas in distillation a new liquid surface is continually being produced by evaporation, diffusion, and convection currents. In order to obtain the maximum rate of sublimation the surface area of the sublimand should be as great as possible and the distance between the sublimand and condensing surface should be short. Sublimations in high vacuum (less than 0.001 mm) follow closely the principles laid down in the discussion of molecular distillation in Sec. 2.9.

The second approach to the practical sublimation of substances entails the use of an inert gas as a "carrier" or "entrainer." With the inert gas moving slowly over the sublimand the partial pressure of the sublimand vapor is brought below the triple-point pressure and the sublimand vapor is swept along (entrained) by the carrier gas. A simple vacuum sublimation frequently can be speeded up by using an entrainer, since the sublimand vapor is moved as rapidly as it is formed from the vicinity of the sublimand. The apparatus illustrated in Fig. 2.18 is suited for entrainer sublimation techniques at either atmospheric or reduced pressures.

An added advantage to entrainer sublimation techniques is the possibility that solids with somewhat similar vapor pressures can be resolved by establishing a temperature gradient along the condenser tube or by fixing the temperature of finite portions of the condenser, as illustrated in Fig. 2.19. With each successive condenser section held at a lower temperature, the least-volatile constituents should condense first, etc., resulting in a fractionation. Apparatus of this type has been used in the author's laboratory to separate quantitatively four- and five-component mixtures. Separations of other complex mixtures should be just as effective by this technique if there is a great enough difference in constituent vapor pressures or if the temperature gradient along the condenser can be carefully controlled. Descriptions of fractional sublimation equipment can be found in a number of works.[44-48]

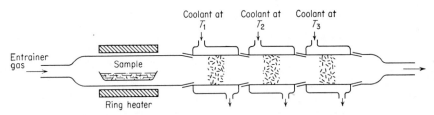

Fig. 2.19. Horizontal entrainer sublimator with graded temperature condensing surfaces.

Separations by sublimation appear to be limited to the separation of volatile crystallizable compounds from nonvolatile substances and from volatile substances which do not condense under the conditions existing at a given point in the system. But even with this restriction there are some rather interesting separations effected by sublimation procedures. Several sublimation separations are indicated below which indicate the versatility of the method.

The number of organic substances which are readily purified by simple sublimation under normal pressure is comparatively small but nonetheless important. Yields of high purity are usually obtained for naphthalene, anthracene, benzoic acid, salicylic acid, camphor, β-naphthol, hexachloroethane, saccharin, acetanilide, DL-alanine and many α-amino acids, urea, caffeine, iodoform, hexamethylenetetramine, quinine, coumarin, barbital, cholesterol, acetylsalicylic acid, atropine, phthalic anhydride, lauric acid, myristic acid, palmitic acid, stearic acid, and the quinones.

At reduced pressures many more substances can be sublimed and more sophisticated separations can be effected. For example, 1-hydroxyanthraquinone can be separated from 2-hydroxyanthraquinone by sublimation of the former at 130° and 0.009 mm. Subsequently, the 2-hydroxy compound can be sublimed at 180°. Mixtures of benzoic acid and saccharin can be resolved by sublimation of the acid at 50° and 1 mm. Saccharin sublimes readily at 150° at the same pressure. Fractional vacuum sublimation has proved especially effective in the examination of drugs.[49]

Simple sublimation also is an effective purification technique for the following inorganic substances: iodine, sulfur, arsenic, arsenic oxide, and the chlorides of mercury, magnesium, calcium, cadmium, zinc, silver, manganese, lithium, and aluminum.

Fractional sublimation of inorganics is encountered less frequently than for organic substances, but the following examples are worth mentioning.

Chaigneau[50] has reported on the separability of niobium and tantalum by a sublimation of their halides. Mixtures of Nb_2O_5 and Ta_2O_5 are heated with the appropriate aluminum halide in a closed tube to convert the oxides to the halide. The niobium and tantalum are then separable, owing to their different volatilities. Recorded vacuum sublimation temperatures are: $TaCl_5$ 150°, $NbOCl_3$ 230°, $NbBr_5$ 220°, $TaBr_5$ 300°, TaI_5 540°, NbI_3 (nonvolatile at atmospheric pressure).

Jacque and Dumez[51] have described a fractional-sublimation technique suitable for the enrichment of mixtures of hafnium and zirconium bromide.

There have been numerous reports in the chemical literature on the volatility of various metal chelates, but there have been few systematic studies which could be used for predicting the separability of various metals by sublimation. The studies of Berg and Truemper[52] on the volatility of various metal β-diketone chelates led to the prediction and ultimate separation of four- and five-component metal mixtures by a simple entrainment sublimation procedure. Volatility data collected by Charles and Langer[53] on various metal chelates derived from 8-hydroxy-quinoline also open the door to the selective separation of some metals by sublimation techniques.

Admittedly, fractional sublimation does not have a great resolving power but it does offer some distinct advantages over the more conventional distillation techniques. The main advantage is the ease with which sublimations can be effected in inert atmospheres at temperatures appreciably lower than those required for distillation.

2.11. Selected Bibliography

Carney, T. P.: "Laboratory Fractional Distillation," The Macmillan Company, New York, 1949.

Coulson, E. A., and E. F. G. Herington: "Laboratory Distillation Practice," George Newnes, Ltd., London, 1958.

Kirschbaum, E.: "Distillation and Rectification," translated by M. Wulfinghoff, Chemical Publishing Company, Inc., New York, 1948.

Leslie, R. T., and E. C. Kuehner: *Anal. Chem.*, **32**, 27R (1960).

Rose, A., and E. Rose: "Distillation Literature Index and Abstracts 1953–54," Applied Science Laboratories, Inc., State College, Pa., 1955.

Weissberger, A. (ed.): "Technique of Organic Chemistry," vol. IV, Distillation, Interscience Publishers, Inc., New York, 1951.

Zuiderweg, F. J.: "Laboratory Manual of Batch Distillation," Interscience Publishers, Inc., New York, 1957.

REFERENCES

1. Rose, A.: *Ind. Eng. Chem.*, **33**, 594 (1941).
2. Carlson, H. C., and A. P. Colburn: *Ind. Eng. Chem.*, **34**, 581 (1942).
3. Clark, A. M.: *Trans. Faraday Soc.*, **41**, 718 (1945).
4. Fenske, M. R.: *Ind. Eng. Chem.*, **24**, 482 (1932).
5. Underwood, A. J. V.: *Trans. Inst. Chem. Engrs.* (*London*), **10**, 112 (1932).
6. Sorel, E.: *Compt. rend.*, **108**, 1128, 1204, 1317 (1889).
7. Lewis, W. K.: *Ind. Eng. Chem.*, **1**, 522 (1909); **14**, 492 (1922).
8. McCabe, W. L., and E. W. Thiele: *Ind. Eng. Chem.*, **17**, 605 (1925).
9. Smoker, E. H.: *Ind. Eng. Chem.*, **34**, 509 (1942); *Trans. A.I.Ch.E.*, **34**, 165, 583 (1938).
10. Rose, A., and E. Rose: Distillation, in "Technique of Organic Chemistry," A. Weissberger (ed.), vol. IV, pp. 1–174, Interscience Publishers, Inc., New York, 1951.
11. Lord Rayleigh: *Phil. Mag.*, **8**, 534 (1904).
12. Rose, A., and L. M. Welshans: *Ind. Eng. Chem.*, **32**, 668 (1940).
13. Rose, A., L. M. Welshans, and H. H. Long: *Ind. Eng. Chem.*, **32**, 673 (1940).
14. Rose, A.: *Ind. Eng. Chem.*, **32**, 675 (1940).
15. Oldershaw, C. F.: *Ind. Eng. Chem., Anal. Ed.*, **13**, 265 (1941).
16. Podbielniak, W. J.: *Ind. Eng. Chem., Anal. Ed.*, **13**, 639 (1941).
17. London, H.: *Proc. Intern. Symposium on Isotope Separation* (*Amsterdam*), 1957 (published 1958).
18. Leslie, R. T., and E. C. Kuehner: *Anal. Chem.*, **32**, 27R (1960).
19. Hoffman, J. I., and G. E. F. Lundell: *Natl. Bur. Standards J. Research*, **22**, 465 (1939).
20. West, T. S.: *Anal. Chim. Acta*, **25**, 405 (1961).
21. Rossini, F. D.: *Anal. Chem.*, **20**, 110 (1948).
22. Horsley, L. H.: *Anal. Chem.*, **19**, 508 (1947); **21**, 831 (1949).
23. "Advances in Chemistry Series," no. 6, Azeotropic Data, American Chemical Society, Washington, 1952.
24. Benedict, M., and L. C. Rubin: *Trans. A.I.Ch.E.*, **41**, 353 (1945).
25. Dicks, R. S., and C. S. Carlson: *Trans. A.I.Ch.E.*, **41**, 789 (1945).
26. Schrenk, W. T., and W. H. Ode: *Ind. Eng. Chem., Anal. Ed.*, **1**, 201 (1929).
27. Wilcox, L. V.: *Ind. Eng. Chem., Anal. Ed.*, **2**, 358 (1930).
28. Hague, J. L., and H. A. Bright: *Natl. Bur. Standards J. Research*, **21**, 125 (1938).
29. Dennis, L. M., and E. G. Johnson: *J. Am. Chem. Soc.*, **45**, 1380 (1923); C. J. Rodden, "Analytical Chemistry of the Manhattan Project," p. 374, McGraw-Hill Book Company, Inc., New York, 1950.
30. Lenher, V., and D. P. Smith: *Ind. Eng. Chem.*, **16**, 837 (1924).
31. Dudley, H. C., and H. G. Byers: *Ind. Eng. Chem., Anal. Ed.*, **7**, 3 (1935).

32. Scherrer, J. A.: *Natl. Bur. Standards J. Research*, **16**, 253 (1936); **21**, 95 (1938).
33. Mogerman, W. D.: *Natl. Bur. Standards J. Research*, **33**, 307 (1944).
34. Hillebrand, W. F., H. A. Bright, and G. E. F. Lundell: "Applied Inorganic Analysis," 2d ed., p. 354, John Wiley & Sons, Inc., New York, 1953.
35. Gilchrist, R., and E. Wichers: *J. Am. Chem. Soc.*, **57**, 2565 (1935).
36. Smith, F. W.: *Ind. Eng. Chem., Anal. Ed.*, **10**, 360 (1938).
37. Bricker, L. G., S. Weinberg, and K. L. Proctor: *Ind. Eng. Chem., Anal. Ed.*, **17**, 661 (1945).
38. Perry, E. S.: Distillation under High Vacuum, in "Technique of Organic Chemistry," A. Weissberger (ed.), vol. IV, pp. 495–540, Interscience Publishers, Inc., New York, 1951.
39. Hickman, K. C. D.: *Ind. Eng. Chem.*, **39**, 686 (1947).
40. Hickman, K.: U.S. Pat. 2,234,166, Mar. 11, 1941.
41. Brewer, A. K., and S. L. Madorsky: *Natl. Bur. Standards J. Research*, **38**, 129 (1947).
42. Rose, A., and E. Rose: "Distillation Literature Index and Abstracts 1953–54," p. 180, Applied Science Laboratories, Inc., State College, Pa., 1955.
43. Tipson, R. S.: Sublimation, in "Technique of Organic Chemistry," A. Weissberger (ed.), vol. IV, p. 611, Interscience Publishers, Inc., New York, 1951.
44. Bates, T. H.: *Chem. & Ind. (London)*, 1958, p. 1319.
45. Flaschentrager, B., S. M. Abdel-Wahhab, and G. Habib-Labib: *Mikrochim. Acta*, **3–4**, 390 (1957).
46. Thomas, J. F., E. N. Sanborn, M. Mukai, and B. D. Tebbens: *Anal. Chem.*, **30**, 1954 (1958).
47. Melhuish, W. H.: *Nature*, **184**, Suppl. 25, 1933 (1959).
48. Shibata, E., and S. Saito: *Nippon Kagaku Zasshi*, **80**, 604 (1959).
49. Weismann, F.: *Pharm. Acta Helv.*, **10**, 125 (1935); *C. A.*, **29**, 8237 (1935).
50. Chaigneau, M.: *Compt. rend.*, **244**(7), 900 (1957).
51. Jacque, L., and P. Dumez: French Pat. 1,148,715, Dec. 13, 1957; U.S. Pat. 2,944,878, July 12, 1960.
52. Berg, E. W., and J. T. Truemper: *J. Phys. Chem.*, **64**, 487 (1960).
53. Charles, R. G., and A. Langer: *J. Phys. Chem.*, **63**, 603 (1959).

CHAPTER 3

LIQUID-LIQUID EXTRACTION

3.1. Distribution Law. Extraction is a partitioning process based on the selective distribution of a substance in two immiscible phases. A third component, when added to a two-phase system, will distribute itself in the two phases in a definite manner. Gibbs' phase rule (see Sec. 2.1) helps to predict the behavior of a multiphase system and elucidates the equilibrium state obtained. Since, in general, in liquid-liquid extractions the liquid phases are not in equilibrium with the surrounding atmosphere, the above system would be described as a ternary, two-phase system. Therefore, three variables, temperature, pressure, and composition, must be specified in order to define the system. But at constant temperature and pressure only one variable, composition, must be specified to define the system completely. This means that the concentration of solute in one phase has a direct relationship to its concentration in the other phase. The distribution law states clearly what this relationship is.

Once an equilibrium state is established in the ternary, two-phase system, the phenomenon can be expressed mathematically by the distribution law.

$$\frac{C_{1,\mathrm{I}}}{C_{1,\mathrm{II}}} = K = \text{distribution coefficient} \qquad (3.1)$$

$C_{1,\mathrm{I}}$ and $C_{1,\mathrm{II}}$ express the concentration of the third component in the two phases, respectively, and K is a constant. Such an expression of the distribution law is valid only for ideal systems as can be seen from a thermodynamic derivation of the law.

The change in free energy in a system, is expressed by the differential

$$dF = \left(\frac{\partial F}{\partial T}\right)_{P,n_1,n_2,\,\ldots} dT + \left(\frac{\partial F}{\partial P}\right)_{T,n_1,n_2,\,\ldots} dP$$
$$+ \left(\frac{\partial F}{\partial n_1}\right)_{T,P,n_2,n_3,\,\ldots} dn_1 + \left(\frac{\partial F}{\partial n_2}\right)_{T,P,n_1,n_3,\,\ldots} dn_2 + \cdots \qquad (3.2)$$

Since, by definition

$$\left(\frac{\partial F}{\partial n_1}\right)_{T,P,n_2,n_3,\ldots} = \text{partial molar free energy} = \mu_1$$
$$= \text{chemical potential} \tag{3.3}$$

$$dF = \left(\frac{\partial F}{\partial T}\right)_{P,n_1,n_2,\ldots} dT + \left(\frac{\partial F}{\partial P}\right)_{T,n_1,n_2,\ldots} dP$$
$$+ \mu_1\, dn_1 + \mu_2\, dn_2 + \cdots \tag{3.4}$$

At constant temperature and pressure,

$$dF = \mu_1\, dn_1 + \mu_2\, dn_2$$

Since there is no change in the total amount of material involved in the partitioning phenomenon, the system is thermodynamically *closed*. One of the conditions of equilibrium for a closed system is that $dF = 0$ at constant temperature and pressure. Therefore,

$$\mu_1\, dn_1 + \mu_2\, dn_2 = 0$$

or

$$\Sigma\mu\, dn = 0 \text{ at equilibrium}$$

This condition applies to the entire closed system. If a small quantity of component 1 is moved within the system from phase I to phase II, then at equilibrium

$$-\mu_{1,\mathrm{I}}\, dn_1 + \mu_{1,\mathrm{II}}\, dn_1 = 0$$

and

$$\mu_{1,\mathrm{I}} = \mu_{1,\mathrm{II}}$$

That is, the chemical potential of a component distributed between two phases that are in equilibrium is the same in both phases.

The chemical potential of any solute in solution can be written as

$$\mu = \mu^0 + RT \ln a \tag{3.5}$$

where a is the activity of the solute in solution and μ^0 is the chemical potential of the solute in a specific reference state. μ^0 is a constant independent of composition but dependent on the temperature and pressure of the system. The chemical potential of a substance distributed between two phases in equilibrium can be expressed as

$$\mu_{1,\mathrm{I}} = \mu_{1,\mathrm{I}}^0 + RT \ln a_{1,\mathrm{I}}$$
$$\mu_{1,\mathrm{II}} = \mu_{1,\mathrm{II}}^0 + RT \ln a_{1,\mathrm{II}}$$

in phases I and II, respectively.

Since at equilibrium $\mu_{1,\mathrm{I}} = \mu_{1,\mathrm{II}}$ and μ_1^0 is a constant, the expression reduces to

$$\frac{a_{1,\mathrm{I}}}{a_{1,\mathrm{II}}} = P = \text{partition coefficient} \tag{3.6}$$

This is an exact expression of the distribution law and shows that the original form

$$\frac{C_{1,\mathrm{I}}}{C_{1,\mathrm{II}}} = \text{constant}$$

is only an approximation that holds true for dilute solutions and ideal behavior. For many practical applications the approximate form of the law is adequate.

3.2. Deviations from the Distribution Law. In practice distribution coefficients frequently vary appreciably because they are determined from the total concentration of the solute in each phase rather than from the concentration of a single molecular species. Since the distribution law is intended to express only the behavior of a single chemical species as it distributes itself between the two phases, any tendency for the solute to be distributed abnormally in either phase will show up as a divergence from the normal distribution coefficient. Invariably deviations are ascribed to the fact that the same molecular species is not present in both phases. Any tendency for the solute to change its form through reaction, association, or dissociation will produce anomalous behavior.

In a system where the distributed solute is dissociated in phase 1, a more complicated expression is needed for the distribution law. Consider the system involving species A that dissociates to give B and C and establishes the following equilibrium:

$$A \rightleftharpoons B + C$$

If α is the fractional amount of the solute A that dissociates, then the true concentration of the distributed species in that phase is given by the expression $C_1(1 - \alpha)$, where C_1 is the total concentration of A in phase 1. The dissociation constant for the system thus becomes

$$K_d = \frac{[\mathrm{B}][\mathrm{C}]}{[A]} = \frac{\alpha^2 C_1{}^2}{C_1(1 - \alpha)} \tag{3.7}$$

The partition coefficient is then more appropriately expressed as

$$K = \frac{C_1(1 - \alpha)}{C_2} = \frac{\alpha^2 C_1{}^2}{K_d C_2} \tag{3.8}$$

where C_2 is the total concentration of A in phase 2.

Consider also the possibility of having the distributed solute A associated in phase 2. The equilibrium established can be represented as

$$n\mathrm{A} \rightleftharpoons \mathrm{A}_n$$

Let C_1 and C_2 be the total concentrations of the solute A in each phase. The degree of solute association is given by β, and n is the number of solute molecules in the associated species.   The association constant for the solute in phase 2 can be represented as

$$K_a = \frac{[A_n]}{[A]^n} = \frac{\beta C_2/n}{[C_2(1 - \beta)]^n} \tag{3.9}$$

The distribution or partition coefficient is expressed then as

$$K = \frac{C_1}{C_2(1 - \beta)} = \frac{C_1}{(\beta C_2/nK_a)^{1/n}} \tag{3.10}$$

3.3. Triangular Coordinates.   Triangular coordinates are used to describe three-component systems.   The interpretation of triangular

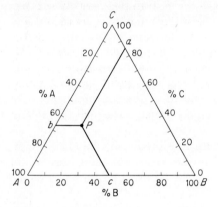

FIG. 3.1. Typical triangular coordinate system.

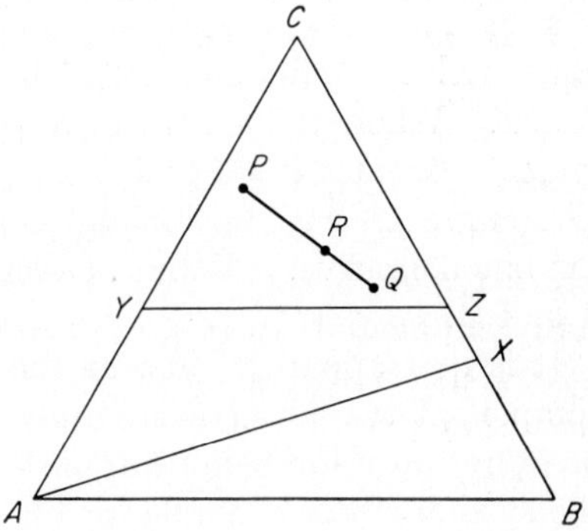

FIG. 3.2. Interpretation of triangular coordinates.

coordinate systems is based on the geometry of an equilateral triangle. Refer to Fig. 3.1.   The composition of any three-component mixture P is expressed completely by the triangular coordinate system.   Draw lines through P parallel to each side.   Then

$$aP + bP + cP = AC = AB = BC$$

where aP = fractional amount of A in mixture P
bP = fractional amount of B in mixture P
cP = fractional amount of C in mixture P

Drop a line from the vertex of the triangle to the opposite side in Fig. 3.2.   Any point on this line represents mixtures with a constant ratio of B to C and variable amounts of A.   Any mixture whose composition can be represented by a point on line YZ, drawn parallel to one side of the triangle, has a constant proportion of component C and a variable ratio of A to B.

P and Q represent any two mixtures of the three components. R represents a mixture of P and Q, and the relative amounts of each are given in the proportion

$$\frac{\text{Amount P}}{\text{Amount Q}} = \frac{\text{RQ}}{\text{RP}}$$

Two-phase systems are also readily depicted with triangular coordinates. If two solvents A and B are only partially miscible, they may separate into two phases when mixed in certain proportions. In Fig. 3.3 the binary mixture R is not homogeneous and consequently separates into two phases with compositions of a and b. Add a third component C that is miscible with both A and B. The resulting mixture Q will separate also into two phases with compositions a' and b'. The line $a'b'$ is a *tie* line. Its upward slope indicates that C is more soluble in the phase rich in component B. The tie lines become shorter as more C is added. When the ends of the tie lines meet at composition N, the system becomes homogeneous. N is the critical point or plait point. The curve aNb is the binodal curve, and M is the maximum point of the binodal curve. N and M coincide only when C is equally soluble in A and B.

It is now apparent, just as the phase rule predicted, that in a three-component two-phase system at equilibrium (constant temperature and pressure) only the composition of one phase needs to be stated to define the system. For example, in Fig. 3.3, the mixture P separates into two phases with compositions a'' and b''. If the composition of one phase is established, then the composition of the other phase is fixed by the point where the tie line and binodal curve intersect.

More completely, then, Fig. 3.3 represents a three-component system in which A and C and B and C are completely miscible but A and B are only partially miscible. Any mixture P of the three components with a composition that falls within the binodal curve will separate into two phases whose respective compositions are determined by a'' and b''. Mixtures whose composition falls outside the binodal curve are homogeneous (single phase). Some typical three-component systems that give two-phase systems are:

Acetic acid : chloroform : water
Ethyl alcohol : ethyl acetate : water
Alcohol : benzene : water

3.4. Choice of Solvent. The first problem encountered in choosing a solvent for extraction is its selectivity. This refers to its ability to extract one component of a solution in preference to another. Consider a typical ternary system ABC shown in Fig. 3.4. It is planned to separate a mixture M of A and C with solvent B. The addition of solvent B moves the composition of the mixture along MB to point S. Such a composition is not homogeneously stable and will separate into two phases. The composition of the two phases R and T will be determined by the tie line that passes through point S. Separate the two phases and independently remove solvent B from each. As the solvent is removed from solutions R and T, the composition of the mixtures varies along the lines RD and TE, respectively. The resulting solutions are

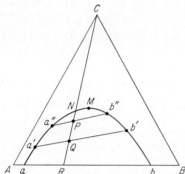

FIG. 3.3. Representation of a heterogeneous system on triangular coordinates.

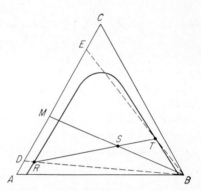

FIG. 3.4. Interpretation of extraction using triangular coordinates.

represented by D and E, respectively. Thus, by a single extraction with solvent B, the mixture M is resolved into two solutions D and E that are much richer in components A and C, respectively. The operation is most efficient when E and D are separated greatly.

Binary mixtures of A and C with compositions lying roughly between A and E thus conceivably can be resolved into fractions containing pure A and fractions enriched with component C. It is inconceivable that pure C could be isolated by extraction in the above system.

The use of phase diagrams is summarized in Fig. 3.5. In each case B can be used to resolve mixtures of A and C with compositions lying between A and M. Separations would be much more efficient in the system represented by Fig. 3.5a. For the same three-component system, A is a very poor solvent for the resolution of mixtures of B and C.

Although the selectivity of a solvent for a given component can be determined from phase diagrams, it is a little-used procedure in analytical chemistry. The principal difficulty is simply that too few phase diagrams exist in the literature. It would be a monumental piece of work that would produce the phase diagrams for even a very low percentage of the possible combinations of solute species and two-phase solvent systems. For the same reason, there are few published distribution coefficients. The result is that the choice of solvent for an extraction procedure is based on either experience or semiempirical considerations.

The choice of solvent need not be completely empirical if something is known about the polar or nonpolar character of the solute to be extracted. Intuitively, we accept the concept that like substances are miscible. Experience has indicated that use of such a generalization in extraction is

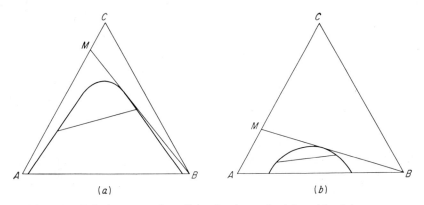

Fig. 3.5. Relative extraction efficiencies determined from binodal curves.

justified.   Polar solvents are used for the extraction of polar substances from nonpolar media and vice versa.   For example, the theory pertaining to the extraction of inorganic solutes from aqueous solutions with non-polar solvents postulates the formation of a neutral complex or molecule which is the species extracted.

Certainly the interactions of solute and solvent will have a bearing on the selectivity of the solvent.   If the solute is readily solvated by a given solvent, then it will be soluble in that solvent.   Hydrogen-bond formation between solute and solvent influences solubility and selectivity.

The distribution coefficient of the solute must be high if it is going to be readily extracted from one phase.   If the solute is to be separated from other solutes, then the solvent must be selective in its action.   That is, the distribution coefficients of the various solutes must be distinctly different.

Almost as important as the selectivity of the extractant is its recoverability.   Of more practical significance in analytical work is the recovery of the solute.   In either case it is necessary to separate extractant and solute after the distribution.   The removal of solvent by distillation or evaporation has been widely practiced provided the solute is nonvolatile and thermally stable.   Only one real difficulty exists here, and that is the frequent formation of azeotropic mixtures which prevent a complete resolution.

Since the solvent is usually present in a much greater quantity than the solute, it should be energetically simpler to remove the solute from the solvent. The removal of the solute from the final extract phase is called *stripping*. Since most analyses are still carried out in aqueous media, it would often be desirable to have the solute in an aqueous phase at the end of the extraction process. This is particularly true for inorganic species.

The principle of stripping is well illustrated in the recovery of inorganic ions that have been extracted into organic solvents as metal chelates, particularly if the formation of the extractable species is dependent on the pH of the original aqueous solution. If the extract is equilibrated with an aqueous solution at a pH unfavorable to the formation of the extracting species, the chelate can be destroyed and the metal ion extracted back into the aqueous phase. For example, the copper(II) chelate of 2-furoyl-trifluoroacetone forms readily in a neutral or slightly basic solution. The chelate is quantitatively extracted into methyl isobutyl ketone in a single equilibration. Later, however, the copper can be stripped from the organic solution simply by equilibrating the organic extract with a 1 N sulfuric acid solution.

Stripping is an effective recovery technique as long as the solute itself or some form of the solute can be favorably distributed between the original extractant phase and the desired solvent. Often this is the simplest recovery technique available.

The greater the difference in the solvent densities, the faster will be the rate at which the immiscible layers separate. Emulsions are more easily produced when the densities of the two solvents are similar. Sometimes troublesome emulsions can be broken by introducing a strong electrolyte, such as sodium sulfate, to the system. Emulsions formed with ethereal solutions can be broken with the addition of small quantities of ethanol or isopropanol.

Certainly some consideration should be given to the interfacial tension created between two solvents. At the critical point of a two-phase system, the interfacial tension γ_{AB} is zero. The interfacial tension is the difference between the surface tension of the two liquids; i.e.,

$$\gamma_{AB} = \gamma_A - \gamma_B \qquad (3.11)$$

Therefore, it would be desirable to select solvents that have a high interfacial tension for rapid separation of phases.

The most desired solvent characteristic is that it be mutually soluble with the solute to be extracted and be completely immiscible with the other solvent. Such an ideal system is rarely, if ever, obtained. Fortunately, the distribution coefficient is a practical value that is determined for a nonideal system. Consequently, solvent extraction is predictable once the partitioning coefficient is known.

3.5. Techniques of Extraction. Within certain limits the actual techniques of extraction are determined by theoretical considerations alone. One can show readily the relationship between extraction efficiency and the distribution coefficient. From this it is possible to determine the number of extractions required to effect a quantitative removal of the distributed solute. In order to calculate extraction efficiency, let

x = fractional amount of the solute extracted
V_o = volume of extractant
V_w = volume of raffinate
K = distribution coefficient

Then

$$K = \frac{x/V_o}{(1-x)/V_w} = \frac{xV_w}{(1-x)V_o} \qquad (3.12)$$

$$K(1-x)V_o = xV_w$$
$$KV_o - KxV_o = xV_w$$
$$x(V_w + KV_o) = KV_o$$

$$x = \frac{KV_o}{V_w + KV_o} = \frac{K}{K + V_w/V_o}$$

$$\text{Per cent extracted} = 100x = \frac{100K}{K + V_w/V_o} = \frac{100KV_o}{V_w + KV_o} \qquad (3.13)$$

For a volume ratio of extractant to raffinate of unity, the denominator reduces to $K + 1$. The relationship between K and per cent extraction is then graphically illustrated in Fig. 3.6. This is an important relationship because it points up the fact that for distribution ratios greater than 100 the extraction is essentially complete. Therefore, when extraction techniques are to be used for the quantitative removal of a solute species from solution, large variations of the distribution coefficient can be tolerated without affecting the completeness of the resolution. It is not at all uncommon to observe large differences in the measured distribution coefficients if the coefficient is large. Depending upon the accuracy of

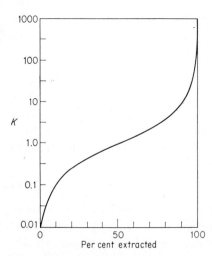

FIG. 3.6. Relationship between extraction efficiency and value of distribution coefficient.

the concentration measurements, K may vary as much as 50 per cent simply because one term is very large and the other very small. The slightest error in the measurement of the lower concentration is magnified in determining K.

It is often said that a single extraction with a large volume of solvent is much less efficient than two extractions using half of the solvent each time. This can be shown to be true with simple mathematics. Assume that w g of solute is to be extracted from V_w ml of solvent with V_o ml of extractant. If w_1 is the weight of solute remaining in the raffinate after the first extraction, then

$$K = \frac{(w - w_1)/V_o}{w_1/V_w} = \frac{(w - w_1)V_w}{w_1 V_o}$$

and

$$w_1 = w \frac{V_w}{KV_o + V_w} \tag{3.14}$$

After a second extraction with V_o of solvent then w_2 g of solute remains in the raffinate.

$$w_2 = w_1 \frac{V_w}{KV_o + V_w} = w \left(\frac{V_w}{KV_o + V_w}\right)^2 \tag{3.15}$$

After n extractions with V_o ml of solvent, the weight of solute w_n remaining in the raffinate is given by

$$w_n = w \left(\frac{V_w}{KV_o + V_w}\right)^n \tag{3.16}$$

A single extraction with $2V_o$ ml of solvent would have left a larger amount of solute, w_a, in the raffinate. For example

$$w_a = w \frac{V_w}{2KV_o + V_w} \tag{3.17}$$

Since $w_a > w_2$, greater extraction efficiency is obtained with two successive extractions using V_o ml each time than with a single extraction using $2V_o$ ml. The proof of this can be shown by comparing the values of w_a and w_2.

$$w \frac{V_w}{2KV_o + V_w} > w \left(\frac{V_w}{KV_o + V_w}\right)^2 \tag{3.18}$$

The expression can be simplified by assuming a volume ratio V_w/V_o of unity.

$$\frac{1}{2KV_o/V_w + V_w/V_w} > \left(\frac{1}{KV_o/V_w + V_w/V_w}\right)^2$$

or

$$\frac{1}{2K + 1} > \frac{1}{(K + 1)^2}$$

$$\frac{1}{2K + 1} > \frac{1}{K^2 + 2K + 1} \tag{3.19}$$

These calculations are based entirely upon ideal behavior of solute and complete immiscibility of solvents. Although the actual formulas cannot be used to calculate the efficiency of a separation, they are sufficiently accurate to serve as guiding principles in the development of extraction techniques.

If the distribution coefficients are large, then there is usually little need for multiple extractions. It is only when the extraction efficiency is low that multiple-extraction techniques are worthwhile.

To resolve mixtures containing two extractable species requires somewhat different considerations. The effectiveness of extraction techniques is usually exemplified by means of separation factors. The separation factor is

$$\beta = \frac{K_1}{K_2}$$

where K_1 and K_2 are the distribution coefficients of the two extractable species. From this it becomes immediately apparent that two species will not be resolved with one extraction unless K_1 and K_2 are grossly different.

3.6. Batch Extractions. This is the simplest of the extraction techniques and involves only a single equilibration of solute and solvents. The only equipment required is the simple separatory funnel illustrated in Fig. 3.7. The solution to be extracted is placed in the separatory funnel along with the extracting solvent. After the solutions have been thoroughly mixed and the two phases have separated, the denser phase is drained through the stopcock and collected in another vessel.

Batch extractions are quite limited in their usefulness for the resolution of complex mixtures. Unless the distribution coefficient of a solute is large, there is little chance that a quantitative removal will be effective in one or two extractions. Fortunately, many organic products can be quantitatively extracted from aqueous phases in one or two equilibrations. Also, many metallic coordination complexes have large distribution coefficients that will permit the isolation of the metal in a single equilibration. For example, many of the metal chelates formed with β-diketones, 8-quinolinols (oxines), and diphenylthiocarbazone (dithizone) can be isolated quantitatively in a single extraction. On the other hand, it is probably safe to say that only a few pure inorganic species can be completely extracted in a single pass. This is not too surprising, since the extraction of inorganic solutes is believed due to the formation of molecular or uncharged species. The predominant ionic character of most inorganic compounds thus excludes them as extractable species.

One immeasurable value of batch extraction is its use in the determination of distribution coefficients. The behavior of a solute can easily be determined in a single equilibrium by determining solute concentrations in the two phases. Constancy of the system is checked by varying factors such as total solute concentration, pH, volume ratio of solvents, complexing agent concentration, etc. From such data it is possible to predict the behavior of the solute when it is subjected to multiple equilibrations. This is most important when substances with similar distribution characteristics are to be separated. Even the type and number

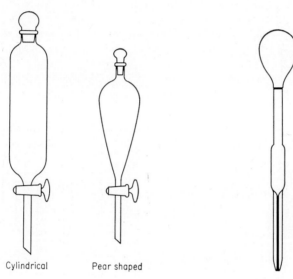

Cylindrical   Pear shaped

Fig. 3.7. Separatory funnels.   Fig. 3.8. Carlton pipet.

of multiple equilibria needed for a resolution can be calculated from the distribution coefficients or separation factors.

Carlton[1] suggested a simple modification of the batch-extraction technique that makes it possible for one to apply extraction procedures on a semimicroscale. The device is shown in Fig. 3.8. A 2- to 3-ml capacity pipet with a capillary delivery tip is fitted with a 10-ml rubber bulb. The heterogeneous system is drawn into the bulb of the pipet and mixed by drawing air through the mixture. After the two phases separate, the lower one can be expelled and collected in a separate vessel. The technique is particularly useful in spot-test analyses where small volumes of solutions are involved. It is also particularly useful in the empirical search for a solvent suitable for the extraction of a given chemical species, since many extractions can be completed on a small volume of sample in a matter of minutes.

In many instances an unfavorable distribution coefficient will require multiple extractions of the one sample to remove the desired solute.

Quantitative removal of solutes under such conditions is tedious, since so many manipulations of phases are involved. Kutscher and Steudel[2] eliminated the multiple steps by inventing a continuous extractor to be used with solvents lighter than water. The apparatus is shown in Fig. 3.9. The extracting solvent is added to the apparatus through a dropping

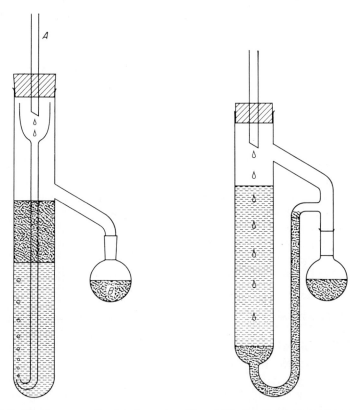

FIG. 3.9. Continuous extractor for solvents lighter than water. [*After F. Kutscher and H. Steudel, Z. physiol. Chem.,* **39,** 474 (1903).]

FIG. 3.10. Continuous extractor for solvents heavier than water. [*After S. Wehrli, Helv. Chim. Acta,* **20,** 927 (1937).]

funnel *A*. Solvent and solutes are collected continuously in *B* as the extractant overflows the extracting chamber.

Wehrli[3] adapted the continuous extractor for use with solvents heavier than water. The apparatus is shown in Fig. 3.10. A modification of the original Wehrli extractor for solvents heavier than water has been proposed by Pierce and Peterson.[4] The extractor assembly described gives a rapid rate of extraction by exposing a large surface area of fresh aqueous phase to the organic phase through the action of a rotating glass ball. The system is airtight, and there is little tendency for emulsions to form. There are numerous other designs of equipment that will permit continuous contact between the two solvents, but these two should be sufficient to illustrate the principle of continuous extraction.

Bewick, Currah, and Beamish[5] evaluated the efficiency of continuous extractions in terms of the "half-extraction volume." This is the volume of solvent required to reduce the solute concentration to one-half its original value.

3.7. Multiple Extractions. Bush and Densen[6] have described a multiple-extraction technique that will resolve solutes with similar distribution coefficients. The significant fact about this technique is that it can be completed using only small separatory funnels; no elaborate equipment is needed. Since the technique is not encountered too frequently in analytical work, some discussion is necessary.

Let XI_0 and YI_0 represent the initial portions of the aqueous phase and organic phase, respectively. Solute a can be considered as being present in either phase initially or simply added to the heterogeneous system. After the solute a has distributed itself between the two phases and equilibrium is attained, the phases are separated into raffinate XI_1 and extractant YI_1. Multiple fractional extractions are achieved by introducing fresh portions of the two solvents YII_0 and XII_0, which are added to the original raffinate and extractant, respectively. The various combinations, equilibrations, and separations of phases are carried out according to the extraction pattern given in Fig. 3.11. Subscripts denote the number of extractions the solution has passed through.

The fraction of solute a found in the raffinate phase after the first equilibration is designated by P_a. The fraction of solute transferred to the extractant must equal $(1 - P_a)$ or Q_a. The value of P_a can be determined in the following manner.

If V_x and V_y equal the total volume of raffinate and extractant, respectively, then

$$\text{Total amount of } a \text{ in } XI_1 = (\text{mg of } a \text{ per ml of } XI_1) V_x$$

and

$$\text{Total amount of } a \text{ in } YI_1 = (\text{mg of } a \text{ per ml of } YI_1) V_y$$

$$\frac{P_a}{1 - P_a} = \frac{(\text{mg of } a \text{ per ml } XI_1) V_x}{(\text{mg of } a \text{ per ml } YI_1) V_y} = K_a \frac{V_x}{V_y} \qquad (3.20)$$

By transposing and combining terms

$$P_a = \frac{K_a V_x}{K_a V_x + V_y} \qquad (3.21)$$

where K_a is the distribution coefficient of the solute.

The greatest fractional separation of several solutes is achieved if the same fraction of a is found in XI_1 as b in YI_1, that is, when

$$P_a = Q_b = 1 - P_b \qquad (3.22)$$

or

$$\frac{K_a V_x}{K_a V_x + V_y} = 1 - \frac{K_b V_x}{K_b V_x + V_y}$$

This expression can be simplified to show that the greatest fractional separation is attained if

$$\frac{V_x}{V_y} = \left(\frac{1}{K_a K_b}\right)^{\frac{1}{2}} \qquad (3.23)$$

The algebraic calculation of the fraction of solute found in each phase is shown in Fig. 3.11. The circled terms represent the fractional amount of a single solute found in that particular heterogeneous system, whereas the composition of any single phase is given below the appropriate circle in terms of p and q. For example, the composition of the raffinate which

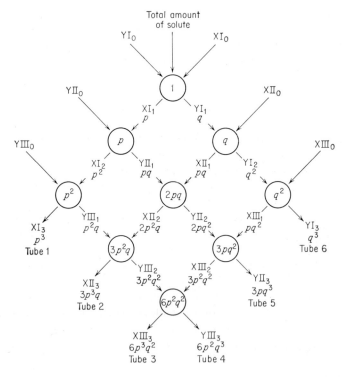

Fig. 3.11. Extraction pattern of Bush and Densen. [*M. T. Bush and P. M. Densen, Anal. Chem.*, **20**, 121 (1948).]

is collected in tube 1 is given by the term p^3, since the solute a has been partitioned among the solvents on three occasions. Ultimately, the solute concentrated in the raffinate phase appears in tubes 1, 2, and 3. The solute concentrated in the extractant appears in tubes 4, 5, and 6.

Bush and Densen have calculated the distribution of solutes for all values of P for the same extraction pattern, resulting in 12 or 20 fractions. The theory predicts a normal distribution of the solutes over a series of collected fractions.

Theoretical considerations are greatly simplified if a few assumptions are made. First, one must assume that the distribution coefficient does not vary with concentration and that the solute is not appreciably associated or dissociated in either phase. Second, there must be negligible adsorption of the solute on the apparatus or at the liquid-liquid interface. In dealing with mixtures of solutes, it must also be assumed that each solute is distributed independently of the other.

It was on these assumptions that the theoretical distribution curves were calculated. Obviously, these assumptions are not true in a nonideal system, but the deviations must be determined experimentally, since there is no method for calculating all the interactions. Probably the worst assumption was the first. Nevertheless, reasonable agreement can be observed between theoretical and experimental results.

Berg and Senn[7] have successfully applied this multiple-extraction technique to the separation of some heavy metals. The separation of rhodium and iridium will illustrate the technique and show the agreement between theory and practice.

The chloro complexes of rhodium(III) and iridium(IV) were partitioned between n-butyl phosphate and a hydrochloric acid solution saturated with sodium chloride. The variations of the distribution coefficients with acid concentration are shown in Fig. 3.12. Distribution coefficients of the two solutes differ most in 6 M hydrochloric acid; consequently, separations were attempted in 6 M acid solution. Perhaps it should be noted at this point that K_d is the reciprocal of K_a as defined in the theoretical treatment above.

A volume ratio of 14 ml of extractant to 15 ml of raffinate was established from theory as the optimum volume ratio. Ninety-nine per cent of the rhodium and 94 per cent of the iridium were recovered free of the other metal after only nine equilibrations. The predicted distribution of solutes is compared with the experimentally determined distribution in Fig. 3.13. Theory predicts a normal distribution of solutes, and a near-normal distribution is obtained.

The theory of multiple fractional extractions has been presented by Hunter and Nash[8] also.

3.8. Countercurrent Extraction. A true countercurrent extraction is one in which the two immiscible solvents are contacted as they flow through each other in opposite directions. The extractor designed by Kolfenbach[9] (Fig. 3.14) is a true countercurrent extractor of the continuous type. As the ether rises through the extraction chamber, it is

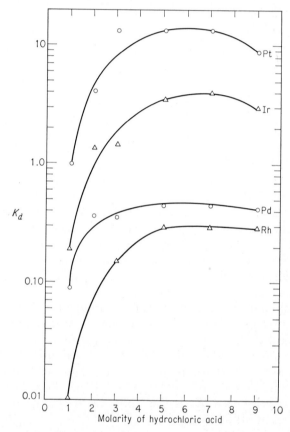

FIG. 3.12. Variation of distribution coefficient of chloro complexes with acid concentration.

contacted with the aqueous phase passing in the opposite direction. The extracted solute is concentrated in flask A. Extractors of this type are very efficient because fresh extractant is brought in contact with the solute-depleted aqueous phase and then the solute-enriched extractant is contacted with the fresh aqueous phase. Under these conditions an equilibrium state can be approached.

It is almost impossible to predict the efficiency of resolution that can be obtained in such continuous countercurrent devices because the theory is not too well defined. However, by utilizing an intermittent pseudo-countercurrent technique, it is possible to follow the extraction through every contacting stage and predict the efficiency of solute separation. Craig and Craig[10] have been most successful in the development of the theory and technique of countercurrent extraction. Craig set up a simple experiment to demonstrate the technique for a system involving equal volumes of raffinate and extractant and a solute distribution coefficient of 1.

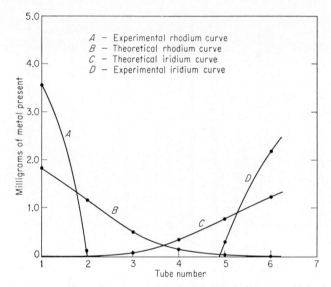

FIG. 3.13. Distribution curves for the separation of rhodium and iridium.

Consider a series of extraction tubes (Fig. 3.15) numbered 0, 1, 2, 3, . . . , r containing equal volumes of solvent L_0, L_1, L_2, L_3, . . . , L_r respectively. Initially, place all the solute in L_0 and contact L_0 with an equal volume of extractant U_0. All the solute is still present in tube 0, although it has distributed itself between the two phases. Half of the solute is in U_0 and half is in L_0. Thus after a single equilibration with no transfer of phases all the solute is in tube 0. If, however, the extractant U_0 is transferred and contacted with solvent L_1 in tube 1, then half of the solute is in tube 0 and half in tube 1. This is the condition after one transfer of solvents.

Now contact an equal volume of pure extractant U_1 with L_0 and equilibrate the phases in tube 0. Simultaneously equilibrate U_0 and L_1 in tube 1. Again transfer the extractants U_0, U_1, and U_2 so that they will contact solvents L_2, L_1, and L_0, respectively, in tubes 0, 1, and 2.

Thus, after two transfers there will be 0.25, 0.50, and 0.25 of the solute in tubes 0, 1, and 2, respectively.

Multiple extractions are achieved by the repeated equilibration and transfer of the two phases as illustrated. In effect it is a pseudocounter-current extraction because only one solvent is moved through the system.

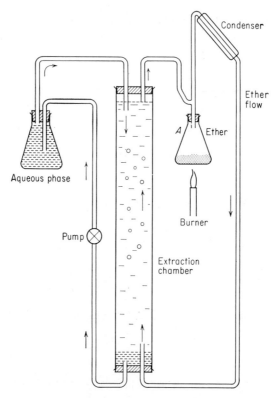

Fig. 3.14. Countercurrent extractor of Kolfenbach. [*J. J. Kolfenbach, E. R. Kooi, E. I. Fulmer, and L. A. Underkofler, Ind. Eng. Chem., Anal. Ed.,* **16,** 473 (1944).]

However, the solvents can be considered as moving in opposite directions relative to each other.

In effect, the progression of solute through the tubes is described by a binomial expansion

$$(x + y)^n = 1 \tag{3.24}$$

where $x = \dfrac{K_d}{K_d + 1}$ = fraction of solute transferred in moving phase

 $y = \dfrac{1}{K_d + 1}$ = fraction of solute remaining in stationary phase

In this example $x/y = K_d = 1$. Thus, the fraction of solute in each tube can be calculated from the binomial theorem. The general formula for calculating the fraction of solute $T_{n,r}$ found in tube r after n transfers is

$$T_{n,r} = \frac{n!}{r! \, (n - r)!} \left(\frac{1}{K_d + 1}\right)^n K_d{}^r \tag{3.25}$$

If the total concentration of solute in each tube is plotted versus the tube number, the solute can be seen to follow a normal distribution

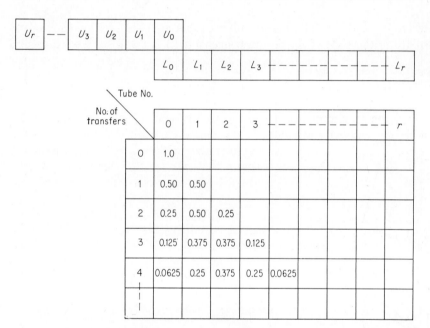

FIG. 3.15. Distribution of solute in countercurrent extraction process. [*From Craig and Craig, "Technique of Organic Chemistry," vol. III, part I, 2d ed., A. Weissberger (ed.), Interscience Publishers, Inc., New York, 1956.*]

pattern and appears to move through the system as a band at a rate which is directly proportional to the fraction of solute in the upper phase at equilibrium. For the situation where a large number of transfers is involved, it becomes quite laborious to calculate the distribution of solutes with Eq. (3.25), but a good approximation can be obtained with

$$T_{n,r} = \frac{1}{\sqrt{2\pi n K_d/(K_d + 1)^2}} \exp\left[\frac{-(r_{\max} - r)^2}{2n K_d/(K_d + 1)^2}\right] \tag{3.26}$$

which is essentially the normal error curve of statistics. The equation is valid provided $n > 25$. The quantity $r_{\max} - r$ represents the number of tubes that a particular tube r is removed from the tube of maximum solute concentration. Therefore, if one knows r_{max}, the distribution curve can be approximated by determining $T_{n,r}$ for several values of r to either side of r_{max}.

The tube number r_{max} containing the maximum solute concentration can be calculated with the equation

$$r_{max} = \frac{nK_d}{K_d + 1} \qquad (3.27)$$

where n is the total number of transfers involved. The fraction of solute in the tube of maximum concentration is given by the expression

$$T_{n,r,max} = \frac{1}{\sqrt{2\pi n K_d/(K_d + 1)^2}} \qquad (3.28)$$

Thus, the maximum concentration to be found in any one tube varies inversely with $\sqrt{n}$, which is to say that the spread of solute among the tubes increases with $\sqrt{n}$. Craig has shown, though, that the *relative* sharpness of the peaks actually increases with an increase in $\sqrt{n}$.

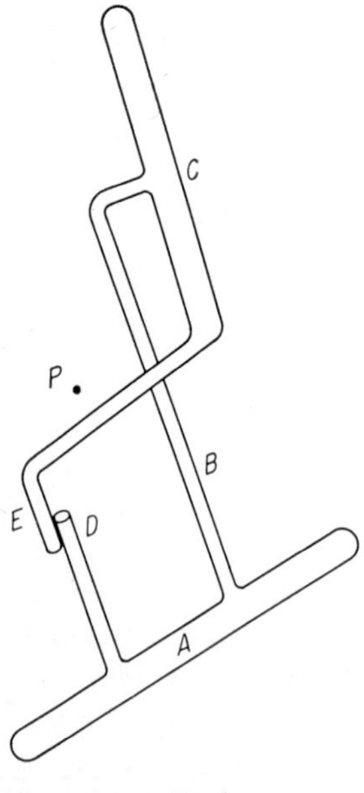

It should be noted here that Eqs. (3.24) to (3.28) hold equally well for unequal volumes of raffinate and extractant if K_d is multiplied in each instance by the volume ratio of the upper and lower phases. For example, the fraction of solute present in the upper phase of each stage is then given by the expression

$$\frac{K_d v}{K_d v + 1}$$

where v is the ratio of the volumes of the upper and lower phases.

Craig not only worked out the theory of countercurrent extraction but also developed an all-glass multiple-stage apparatus[11] for handling a large number of equilibrations and transfers. A single stage of the apparatus is shown in Fig. 3.16. The solvents and solute are introduced through D and equilibrated in A. After the two phases separate, the apparatus is pivoted about point P so that the upper phase is decanted through B and collected in C. When the apparatus is returned to a normal position, the

FIG. 3.16. Single stage of countercurrent extraction device designed by Craig and Post.

upper phase is transferred through E into the equilibration chamber of the next stage. In practice, the lower phase is added to all stages in an amount such that it will fill the chamber A up to arm B when A is in a vertical position. With all the solute in the first stage initially, the extractant is added to the first stage in equal volumes after each transfer. In effect, the extractant is forced through the apparatus by the intermittent addition of fresh extractant to the first stage.

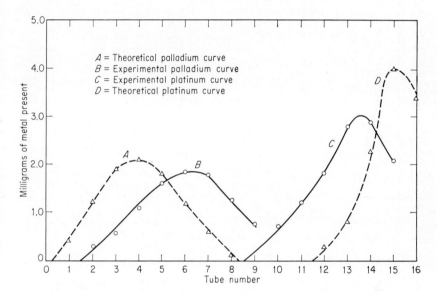

FIG. 3.17. Distribution curves for the separation of platinum and palladium.

Nichols[12] and Nelson[13] have described methods for calculating the number of transfers required to effect a given degree of separation between similar solutes by a countercurrent distribution process. Hollingsworth, Taber, and Daubert[14] used the theory of regular solutions and obtained equations that express the behavior of distribution ratios near the critical solution temperature of two-component systems and near the plait point of three-component systems.

Countercurrent extractions have been very effective in resolving organic solutes, but there have been only a few applications to inorganic systems. There is no inherent reason why the technique should not be just as effective for resolving heavy metals as it is for organic species.

Berg and Senn[15] reported the separation of mixtures of platinum and palladium and platinum and rhodium by countercurrent extraction. Distribution coefficients were determined for the partitioning of the chloro complexes of these metals between n-butylphosphate and various concentrations of hydrochloric acid saturated with sodium chloride. These data are given in Fig. 3.12. Theoretical calculations based on the experimentally determined distribution coefficients indicated that a 17-stage countercurrent-extraction device would resolve mixtures of platinum and palladium and platinum and rhodium in 6 M hydrochloric

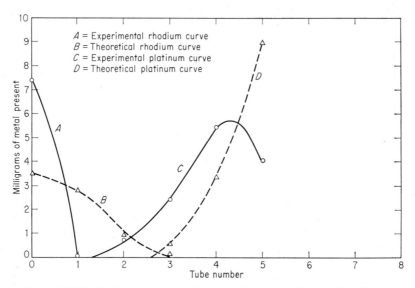

FIG 3.18. Distribution curves for the separation of rhodium and platinum.

acid. The theoretical recovery of the solutes is compared with the actual experimental recovery in Figs. 3.17 and 3.18.

A point for discussion in the extraction of the chloro complexes of the platinum-group metals is the type of species extracted. The theory pertaining to the extraction of inorganic solutes postulates the formation of an uncharged complex or neutral species which may form by coordination or ion association. Using iridium as an example, several extraction mechanisms can be suggested.

(a) raffinate | extractant
$$IrCl_6^{=} \rightleftharpoons 2Cl^- + IrCl_4 \rightleftharpoons IrCl_4$$

(b) raffinate | extractant
$$IrCl_6^{=} + 2H^+ \rightleftharpoons H_2IrCl_6 \rightleftharpoons H_2IrCl_6$$

Mechanism (b) appears to be more probable, since the variation of the distribution coefficient with hydrogen-ion concentration is very pronounced. Also, the known stability of the $IrCl_6^{--}$ almost precludes the formation of $IrCl_4$.

3.9. Extraction of Solids. Although the extraction or leaching of solids with a solvent is not a liquid-liquid partitioning phenomenon, it should be discussed along with liquid-liquid extraction. The principles are the same, and the techniques are similar. The digestion of solids with aqueous solutions is an extractive process that has been employed for centuries for the recovery of metals, sugars, salts, medicinals, and other products. Final physical separations are achieved by filtration and decantation. These primitive procedures are still used, but there have been numerous modifications in technique that place the extraction on an automatic and continuous basis.

Perhaps the most popular refinement of leaching processes is the Soxhlet extractor (Fig. 3.19) or some modification of it. A volatile solvent is introduced to the flask A, and the solid sample is placed in B. It is customary to encase the sample in a cloth, paper, or asbestos bag or thimble to prevent some of the solid form being carried over with the solvent. The solvent is vaporized, and the vapors pass through the side arm E and are condensed in the condenser C. The condensate drips onto the sample and finally immerses it. When sufficient solvent has accumulated in the extraction chamber, it is automatically filtered and siphoned through tube D. Dissolved solutes are concentrated in A as the solvent is recycled through the system. This is an intermittent type of multiple extraction on a batch sample. Numerous modifications of this equipment have been proposed in the chemical literature.

Soxhlet extractors are practically standard equipment in laboratories that analyze for fats and oils in biological samples. The method can be used in inorganic extractions but seldom is.

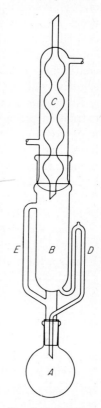

Fig. 3.19. Soxhlet extractor.

3.10. Advantages. The chief advantages of the extraction techniques are that the methods are usually rapid, fairly simple, and versatile. Separations can be achieved at low temperatures in inert atmospheres on a micro- or macroscale by a discontinuous or continuous process. The resolving power of solvent extraction is unusually great for such a simple process.

3.11. Disadvantages. Without consideration of the difficulties that arise in particular systems, there are few disadvantages associated with extraction procedures. The method is still empirical, although the theoretical background is reasonably well developed. There is a serious shortage of reliable data on partition coefficients and phase diagrams. As these data become more common and available, it will be possible to raise extraction applications above the empirical status.

3.12. Applications. The analytical applications of liquid-liquid extraction usually can be placed in one of two categories: extraction of a single chemical species for removal purposes and extraction for the fractionation of complex mixtures. Extraction for removal purposes is the simplest type. It depends on the use of a solvent that will extract only the desired solute from a given mixture. The isolation of the extractable species can be achieved by a batch extraction, multiple extractions, or continuous extraction. The method chosen is determined by the selectivity of the solvent and the distribution coefficient of the extractant.

Extraction for the fractionation of complex mixtures is the most difficult extraction process. Unless the separation factors are large, the sample may have to be fractionated a hundred or a thousand times to isolate the individual components. As a result, countercurrent-distribution techniques are usually employed and often required because they produce the highest overall selectivity of any extraction procedure. The success or failure of such separations may depend on a shift in the separation factor as low as 1.0 to 1.1.

Separation of Molecular Organic Species. Extraction techniques have been widely accepted in the fields of organic chemistry and biochemistry. Even so, there still are no general rules established for the selection of a solvent system that will be suitable for the isolation of a given compound. The most useful approach is still empirical; partition coefficients are determined in a variety of solvent systems. This is the basis, then, for selecting the system that is potentially most valuable.

Fats, oils, waxes, hydrocarbons, pigments, etc., can be concentrated by simple extraction from a multitude of natural and synthetic products. The removal of these constituents has long been a commonplace operation in the laboratory and industry. Except for these simpler separations that can be effected by continuous extraction, a single extraction, or a limited number of batch extractions, greater attention is being given to countercurrent-distribution processes.

The general applicability and selectivity of countercurrent extraction to the separation of molecular organic species can be illustrated with a few examples. Craig[16] has separated an artificial mixture of beef insulin (molecular weight 5733) and pork insulin (molecular weight 5777) by countercurrent distribution in a butanol–acetic acid–pyridine solvent system. Klenk and Lindlar[17] have effectively separated some C_{22} fatty acids on the basis of their containing one, two, three, or four double bonds. One of the most spectacular achievements of countercurrent distribution has been in the fractionation of the pituitary hormones. The ability of extraction techniques to separate fragile and heat-labile solutes such as the hormones and vitamins has not been surpassed by other separation techniques.

A fairly comprehensive review of the various systems resolved by extraction procedures can be found in the list of books and review articles located at the end of this chapter. Hundreds of references to apparatus, systems, theory, and technique can be found in this selected bibliography.

Separation of Metals. Extraction techniques, as they are applied to inorganic substances, have become so important that it is impossible to do more than emphasize the areas of greatest promise. The inherent potentialities of extraction techniques have not been so widely exploited for the separation of metals as for the separation of organic and biological samples. It is a field in which much improvement can be expected in the near future.

Most extractions of metals have been done in single-stage processes which inherently lack great selectivity. To increase the selectivity of the systems, complexing agents have been added under controlled conditions either to inhibit the extraction of some species or to enhance the extraction of other species.

The hypothesis has been that metals must exist in the form of a neutral or molecular species before they can be extracted into nonpolar solvents. This hypothesis holds well in practice. Almost all metals are extracted either in the form of molecular metal chelates or as ion-association species.

The β-diketones form very stable chelates with many different metal ions. Many of these chelates are easily formed, intensely colored, and quantitatively insoluble in water but soluble in common organic solvents. They form in a weakly acidic, neutral, or alkaline medium and are destroyed in a strong-acid medium according to the following equilibria.

$$
R - \overset{\overset{\text{O}}{\|}}{C} - CH_2 - \overset{\overset{\text{O}}{\|}}{C} - R' \rightleftharpoons R - \overset{\overset{\text{O}}{\|}}{C} - CH = \overset{\overset{\text{OH}}{|}}{C} - R'
$$

$$
2 \; R - \overset{\overset{\text{O}}{\|}}{C} - CH = \overset{\overset{\text{OH}}{|}}{C} - R' + M^{++} \rightleftharpoons \quad + 2H^+
$$

Acetylacetone (2, 4-pentanedione) forms chelates with over 60 metals, and many of them can be extracted into organic solvents. A few selected examples will illustrate this. The beryllium complex with acetylacetone[18] is extracted into chloroform at a pH of 7 to 8. If EDTA (ethylenediaminetetraacetic acid) is added to the sample prior to the extraction, then beryllium can be selectively separated from iron, aluminum, zinc, lead, copper, and some other heavy metals. Under different conditions, iron, manganese, copper, aluminum, indium, gallium, and some actinide metals can be extracted. Steinbach and Freiser[19] used the acetylacetone in a dual role as solvent and reagent in the extraction of copper, zinc, and beryllium. Several other researchers have tried this technique also.

β-Diketones prepared by substituting aromatic, heterocyclic, and perfluoro alkyl groups for the methyl groups of acetylacetone form metal chelates that are more soluble in organic solvents. The introduction of electronegative substituents to the β-diketone increases the stability and covalent character of the corresponding chelates. Except for this increased stability and decreased water solubility, the properties of the substituted chelates closely parallel those of the metal acetylacetonates. Thenoyltrifluoroacetone (TTA) has been an excellent ligand for producing extractable chelates with most of the common heavy metals and the actinide[20] metals. Huffman and Beaufait[21] partially resolved mixtures of hafnium and zirconium by extraction with TTA in benzene. McIntyre, Berg, and Campbell[22] reported on the extractability of a number of transitional metals with 2-furoyltrifluoroacetone.

8-Hydroxyquinoline (oxine) forms chelates with more than 40 metal ions. Many of the chelates are soluble in chloroform and can be extracted from aqueous solutions. The extractions are not very selective because numerous metals react under the same conditions. Chelate formation is dependent on pH in the following manner.

Trivalent ions usually react to give a complex with the empirical formula of $M(C_9H_6NO)_3$. If pH is carefully controlled and masking agents are used, the specificity for extraction can be increased greatly. Moeller[24] separated cobalt from iron, copper, and bismuth by extraction with oxine in chloroform solution. Below a pH of 3.5 cobalt is not extracted but iron, copper, and bismuth are. Aluminum and nickel are extracted with the cobalt. The magnesium-oxine complex[25] can be extracted into butyl cellosolve solution.

As a group, the α-dioximes have been effective complexing agents producing extractable species with nickel and palladium. Dimethylglyoxime is the most familiar α-dioxime and can be used to illustrate the class behavior.   The nickel complex forms in alkaline media and can be

$$2 \begin{array}{c} CH_3-C=NOH \\ | \\ CH_3-C=NOH \end{array} + Ni^{++} \rightleftharpoons \begin{array}{c} \text{nickel dimethylglyoxime complex} \end{array} + 2H^+$$

extracted into chloroform over a pH range of 4 to 12.[26,27]   The palladium complex forms in acid media and can be extracted into chloroform from strong-acid media.[28]   The other α-dioximes react similarly and form extractable species with nickel and palladium.

The extraction of metals as ion-association species is not so selective as the extraction of chelates.   The association of ions to form an extractable species simply is not a very selective process.   Numerous metals form extractable ion-association complexes with chloride, bromide, iodide, thiocyanate, and nitrate ions.   A few examples will suffice for illustration purposes.

Arsenic(III), antimony(V), gallium(III), germanium(IV), platinum(IV), palladium(II), rhodium(III), gold(III), iron(III), mercury(II), thallium(III), and a number of other ions form extractable species with the chloride ion.   Edwards and Voigt[29] separated Sb(V) from Sb(III) by extracting the pentavalent form from hydrochloric acid with isopropyl ether.   Under these conditions very little trivalent antimony is extracted. Iron[30] has been extracted as the chloro complex by many workers and is an important step in reducing the iron concentration in steel samples prior to the analysis of the nonferrous metals.

Fewer metals form extractable species with the bromide and iodide ions than with the chloride ions.   Gold(III), gallium(III), indium(III), thallium(III), antimony(V), and iron(III) form extractable bromides. McBryde and Yoe[31] reported the extraction of gold as bromoauric acid, $HAuBr_4$, with isopropyl ether.   The extraction is virtually complete and effects a separation of gold from the platinum-group metals.   West and Carlton[32] investigated the extraction of a number of metal iodides in different solvent systems.

A few nitrates are extractable species.   Bock and Bock[33] studied the extraction of uranyl nitrate, cerium(IV) nitrate, and thorium(IV) nitrate with ethyl ether.   Silver[34] has been extracted into toluene as the perchlorate.

Specker and Bankmann[35] quantitatively separated gallium from aluminum in one extraction from an acid thiocyanate solution using an ether-tetrahydrofuran mixture as solvent. Bock[36] has made an intensive study of the extractability of a number of metal thiocyanates.

The triphenylmethylarsonium cation forms salts that are soluble in organic solvents with anionic complexes of iron, antimony, cobalt, copper, and manganese. Gibson and White[37] utilized this knowledge to extract permanganate ion at the end point of permanganate titrations involving other colored species.

Long-chain tertiary amines such as dioctylmethylamine were first used for the extraction of sulfate and chloride[38] from aqueous solutions. The amine forms a salt that is preferentially soluble in chloroform. A single extraction can remove as much as 98 per cent of the chloride or sulfate provided strongly basic ions, such as Na and K, are absent. The amines have also proved useful for the separation of metals. Moore[39] has extracted the anionic complexes of polonium, plutonium, zirconium, and protactinium with long-chain amines in chloroform.

For additional references to the separation of metals by extraction consult the very excellent monograph by Morrison and Freiser and the numerous reviews given in the selected bibliography at the end of this chapter.

3.13. Selected Bibliography

Alders, L.: "Liquid-Liquid Extraction," Elsevier Press, Inc., New York, 1955.
Craig, L. C.: *Anal. Chem.*, **21**, 85 (1949); **22**, 61 (1950); **23**, 41 (1951); **24**, 66 (1952); **26**, 110 (1954); **28**, 723 (1956).
Craig, L. C., and D. Craig in "Technique of Organic Chemistry," 2d ed., A. Weissberger (ed.), vol. III, part I, Interscience Publishers, Inc., New York, 1956.
Irving, H. M.: *Quart. Revs. (London)*, **5**, 200 (1951).
McBryde, W. A. E.: *Analyst*, **80**, 503 (1955).
Morrison, G. H.: *Anal. Chem.*, **22**, 1388 (1950).
Morrison, G. H. and H. Freiser: "Solvent Extraction in Analytical Chemistry," John Wiley & Sons, Inc., New York, 1957.
Sandell, E. B.: *Anal. Chim. Acta*, **4**, 504 (1950).
Treybal, R. E.: "Liquid Extraction," 2d ed., McGraw-Hill Book Company, Inc., New York, 1962.
Welcher, F. J.: "Organic Analytical Reagents," vol. I, D. Van Nostrand Company, Inc., Princeton, N.J., 1947.
West, T. S.: *Anal. Chim. Acta*, **25**, 405 (1961).
West, T. S.: *Metallurgia*, **53**, 91, 132, 185, 234, 292 (1956); **54**, 47, 103 (1956).

REFERENCES

1. Carlton, J. K.: *Anal. Chem.*, **22**, 1072 (1950).
2. Kutscher, F., and H. Steudel: *Z. physiol. Chem.*, **39**, 474 (1903).
3. Wehrli, S.: *Helv. Chim. Acta*, **20**, 927 (1937).
4. Pierce, C. E., and R. E. Peterson: *Anal. Chem.*, **28**, 2029 (1956).
5. Bewick, H. A., J. E. Currah, and F. E. Beamish: *Anal. Chem.*, **20**, 740 (1948).
6. Bush, M. T., and P. M. Densen: *Anal. Chem.*, **20**, 121 (1948).

7. Berg, E. W., and W. L. Senn, Jr.: *Anal. Chim. Acta*, **19**, 109 (1958).
8. Hunter, T. G., and A. W. Nash: *Ind. Eng. Chem.*, **27**, 836 (1935).
9. Kolfenbach, J. J., E. R. Kooi, E. I. Fulmer, and L. A. Underkofler: *Ind. Eng. Chem., Anal. Ed.*, **16**, 473 (1944).
10. Craig, L. C., and D. Craig in "Technique of Organic Chemistry, 2d ed., A. Weissberger (ed.), vol. III, part I, Interscience Publishers, Inc., New York, 1956.
11. Craig, L. C., and O. Post: *Anal. Chem.*, **21**, 500 (1949).
12. Nichols, P. L., Jr.: *Anal. Chem.*, **22**, 915 (1950).
13. Nelson, E.: *Anal. Chem.*, **28**, 1998 (1956).
14. Hollingsworth, C. A., J. J. Taber, and B. F. Daubert: *Anal. Chem.*, **28**, 1901 (1956).
15. Berg, E. W., and W. L. Senn, Jr.: *Anal. Chim. Acta*, **19**, 12 (1958).
16. Craig, L. C.: "Ciba Foundation, Symposium on Internal Secretions of the Pancreas," J. and A. Churchill, London, 1956; *Anal. Chem.*, **28**, 724 (1956).
17. Klenk, E., and F. Lindlar: *Z. physiol. Chem.*, **301**, 156 (1955).
18. Adam, J. A., E. Booth, and J. D. H. Strickland: *Anal. Chim. Acta*, **6**, 462 (1952).
19. Steinbach, J. F., and H. Freiser: *Anal. Chem.*, **25**, 881 (1953).
20. Magnusson, L. B., and M. L. Anderson: *J. Am. Chem. Soc.*, **76**, 6207 (1954).
21. Huffman, E. H., and L. J. Beaufait: *J. Am. Chem. Soc.*, **71**, 3179 (1949).
22. McIntyre, R. T., E. W. Berg, and D. N. Campbell: *Anal. Chem.*, **28**, 1316 (1956).
23. Sandell, E. B.: "Colorimetric Determination of Traces of Metals," 2d ed., Interscience Publishers, Inc., New York, 1950.
24. Moeller, T.: *Ind. Eng. Chem., Anal. Ed.*, **15**, 346 (1943).
25. Luke, C. L., and M. E. Campbell: *Anal. Chem.*, **26**, 1778 (1954).
26. Sandell, E. B., and R. W. Perlich: *Ind. Eng. Chem., Anal. Ed.*, **11**, 309 (1939).
27. Nielsch, W.: *Z. anal. Chem.*, **150**, 114 (1956).
28. Young, R. S.: *Analyst*, **76**, 49 (1951).
29. Edwards, F. C., and A. F. Voigt: *Anal. Chem.*, **21**, 1204 (1949).
30. Wells, J. E., and D. P. Hunter: *Analyst*, **73**, 671 (1948).
31. McBryde, W. A. E., and J. H. Yoe: *Anal. Chem.*, **20**, 1094 (1948).
32. West, P. W., and J. K. Carlton: *Anal. Chim. Acta*, **6**, 406 (1952).
33. Bock, R., and E. Bock: *Z. anorg. Chem.*, **263**, 146 (1950).
34. Hill, A. E., and F. W. Miller, Jr.: *J. Am. Chem. Soc.*, **47**, 2702 (1925).
35. Specker, H., and E. Bankmann: *Z. anal. Chem.*, **149**, 97 (1956).
36. Bock, R.: *Z. anal. Chem.*, **133**, 110 (1951).
37. Gibson, N. A., and R. A. White: *Anal. Chim. Acta*, **12**, 115 (1955).
38. Smith, E. L., and J. E. Page: *J. Soc. Chem. Ind. (London)*, **67**, 48 (1948).
39. Moore, F. L.: *Anal. Chem.*, **29**, 1660 (1957).

CHAPTER 4

ADSORPTION CHROMATOGRAPHY

4.1. History. Present-day chromatographic processes, exclusive of paper chromatography, were originated by the Russian botanist Tswett. In 1906, Tswett[1] reported the results of some of his work on the separation of plant pigments. A petroleum-ether extract of plant leaves was percolated through a column of powdered calcium carbonate. The plant pigments were strongly adsorbed near the top of the column by the calcium carbonate and were formed into a variety of yellow and green zones. On further washing with petroleum ether alone, one of the pigments was washed out of the column while others were obviously resolved on the adsorbent. The column was drained, and the adsorbent extruded from the column. Individual pigments were then isolated by dividing the column of adsorbent into fractions containing the various pigments. The pigments were desorbed with alcohol and recovered by evaporation of the solvent. Although complete resolutions were not effected, it was a great advance in the development of new separation methods.

Tswett called the process *chromatography* after the Greek words *chromatus* and *graphein*, meaning "color" and "to write." Such a name was appropriate for the earlier applications of the new technique because mostly colored compounds were involved. Later applications showed that colorless substances also were separated by chromatography. The choice of name for the process thus is not so appropriate as first believed. Perhaps "adsorption analysis" would be a better name, but the name chromatography is apparently fixed in the chemical literature.

Tswett recognized the process as an adsorption phenomenon and was able to explain in a qualitative fashion the observed effects. The least strongly adsorbed pigments were washed through the column rapidly, whereas more strongly adsorbed pigments were immobilized by their adsorption; i.e., their migration rate through the column was greatly retarded. Essentially, then, chromatography is a differential-migration method of separation dependent on the selective adsorption of solute materials.   Adsorption is an unusually selective process and is responsible for the great resolving power of adsorption chromatography.

Unfortunately, 25 years elapsed before Tswett's adsorption process was recognized and exploited by chemists.   In 1931, Kuhn and Lederer[2] reintroduced the adsorption process and proved its worth by resolving plant carotene into its components.   From 1931 to 1943, there was a gradual acceptance of the new technique; from 1943 on, the number of publications referring to chromatography increased rapidly.   Now each year there are thousands of publications in a variety of scientific fields that refer to chromatographic separations.

H. H. Strain,[3] one of the noted workers in the field, has defined chromatography as "the study and the utilization of widely applicable, analytical procedures for the resolution of mixtures of solutes by differential migration from a narrow zone in porous media, the migration being produced by electrical potential or by flow of liquid or gas."   This more general definition of chromatography is preferred because nothing is said about the mechanism for producing differential-migration rates.   Since all differential-migration methods have much in common (see Sec. 1.2), what is true about adsorption chromatography generally applies to partition chromatography and gas- or vapor-phase chromatography.

4.2. Development of Chromatogram.   The characteristic feature of adsorption chromatography is the observed affinity between solute and adsorbent.   This affinity is not, however, the sole factor that determines solute migration rates; there is a dynamic equilibrium involving solute, solvent, and adsorbent.   The solvent as well as the solute is always adsorbed from solution.   There is a competition between the solute and solvent particles as they strive to occupy the surface of the adsorbent. The more strongly the solvent is adsorbed, the greater the competition for adsorption of the solute.   For the development of a chromatogram, the adsorbent must adsorb the solute reversibly and exhibit preferential or selective affinity for the different solutes.   Simultaneously, the solvent must dissolve the solutes and provide a driving force for the migration of the solutes through the column.   The difference in adsorbability of otherwise similar substances causes the solutes to migrate at different rates and produce a chromatogram.   Not all adsorption processes are reversible, as is shown by the nonmovement of some zones during the development of a chromatogram.

It is possible to follow qualitatively the mechanism by which a chromatogram is developed.   Consider, for example, the typical adsorption isotherm for solute A in Fig. 4.1a.   The equation for the adsorption isotherm is

$$m = Kc^{1/n}$$

where m = amount of solute adsorbed per unit mass of adsorbent
$\quad\quad\ c$ = equilibrium concentration of solute
$\quad\quad\ K$ = characteristic constant
$\quad\quad\ n$ = characteristic constant with value usually ranging between
$\quad\quad\quad\quad$ 1 and 2

From this equation it is possible to calculate the amount of adsorbent required to lower the concentration of A from c to c_1 and from c_1 to c_2, etc. A finite number of equilibrium steps would reduce the concentration of A to zero if the solution containing A were successively equilibrated with adsorbent, filtered, and equilibrated with fresh adsorbent. A situation analogous to this is responsible for the development of a chromatogram. Assume that the solution to be analyzed is passed through a column of adsorbent made up of thin layers of adsorbent as in Fig. 4.1b. Then, as the sample solution flows into the top of the column, the solute is equilibrated with the adsorbent in layer 1 and the concentration of solute A is reduced from c to c_1. Under the influence of gravity the depleted solution then comes in contact with layer 2, and again an equilibrium is established. The solute concentration is reduced further from c_1 to c_2. Successive equilibria occur as the depleted solution flows down the column contacting layers of fresh adsorbent until the solute has been completely adsorbed. This process builds up the zone of solute on the adsorbent. Then, as pure solvent is added, the solute in layer 1 is desorbed until an equilibrium is reestablished among solute, solvent, and adsorbent. The solute is carried down the column through multiple equilibria until fresh adsorbent is contacted, and then it is again deposited on the adsorbent. The net effect is that the solute migrates through the column under the flow of the liquid. Because of the inherent differences in solute adsorbability, evidenced by the characteristic adsorption isotherms, a different number of equilibria are required for the quantitative adsorption and desorption of each solute. Hence, each solute will migrate through the column at a characteristic rate.

With the introduction of several solutes to the solvent-adsorbent system, the theoretical considerations become very complex, but the relative migration rates are a measure of the interaction of solute, solvent, and adsorbent. A convenient measure of the relative migration rates for solutes was suggested by LeRosen.[4] The ratio of the distance traversed by the solute to the distance traversed by the solvent in the same length of time was designated as the R value. Some confusion arises from the use of this term because there is no portion of the zone designated for the point of measurement. An R_f value, as defined by Martin and Synge,[5] is preferred because it specifies the criterion for migration-rate measurements.

$$R_f = \frac{\text{distance traversed by leading edge of zone}}{\text{distance traversed by leading edge of solvent}}$$

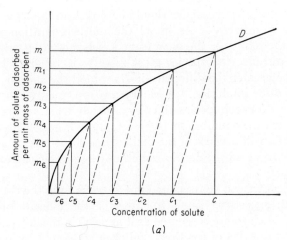

(a)

Fig. 4.1a. The diagram simulates the reduction in solute concentration from c to c_1, c_1 to c_2, etc., that would be achieved if the solution were repeatedly equilibrated with a given mass of adsorbent, filtered, and contacted with the same mass of fresh adsorbent. The reductions in concentration for successive equilibria are related to one another by the typical adsorption isotherm D which follows the equation $m = Kc^{1/n}$.

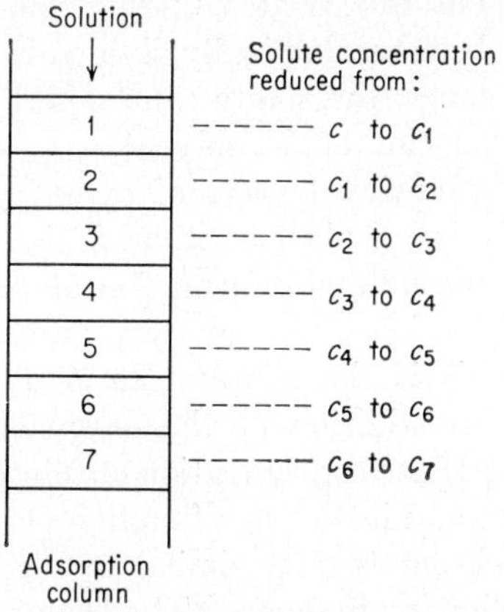

Solution

Solute concentration
reduced from:

Adsorption column	
1	------- c to c_1
2	------- c_1 to c_2
3	------- c_2 to c_3
4	------- c_3 to c_4
5	------- c_4 to c_5
6	------- c_5 to c_6
7	------- c_6 to c_7

(b)

Fig. 4.1b. The diagram simulates the reduction of solute concentration that would occur in a solution fed into an adsorption column if it is assumed that the depleted solution is equilibrated with each successive finite layer of the adsorbent that it contacts. A comparison with Fig. 4.1a clearly shows that some finite number of equilibria will quantitatively remove the solute from solution and in the case of an adsorption column form a zone of solute.

For a given solvent-adsorbent system, R_f values are characteristic and reproducible for each solute but are dependent on temperature, concentration of solute, and flow rate of solvent.

For the efficient resolution of mixtures in a column, the initial zone of adsorbed material should be narrow, the total solute concentration should be small, the rate of solvent flow should be slow, and the R_f values should be appreciably different. As in all differential-migration methods of separation, the narrower the zone from which migration originates, the shorter the distance the species must migrate in order to be resolved. Similarly, the greater the difference in R_f values, the shorter the column length needed for resolution. A binary mixture usually can be resolved if the R_f values for each species differ by as much as 0.1. Flow rates must be slow enough for equilibrium to be established, and solute concentrations must be small because of the limited adsorbent surface available for adsorption. Also, adsorption is sometimes more efficient at the lower concentrations.

Resolved solutes can be recovered in two ways. As the chromatogram is developed, successive small fractions of the effluent are collected separately. Each solute is isolated as it appears in the effluent in a single fraction or in a series of fractions and then recovered by removing the solvent. A plot of the solute concentration versus the volume of effluent collected is commonly called a *liquid chromatogram*. A second method employed for the recovery of solutes involves draining the solvent from the column once the chromatogram has been developed. Subsequently, the column of adsorbent is extruded intact from the tube. After the adsorbent column has been mechanically divided into fractions containing the individual solute zones, the solute can be eluted from the adsorbent and recovered by elimination of the solvent.

There are three conventional ways of operating a chromatographic column: frontal analysis, displacement analysis, and elution analysis. Each method gives some unique information about the sample solution.

4.3. Frontal Analysis. Frontal analysis was first introduced by Tiselius[6] in 1940. This is the simplest form of chromatography and requires the continuous addition of the original sample solution to a column of adsorbent. If the concentration of solutes in the effluent of the column is determined and plotted as a function of the volume of effluent, one obtains a liquid chromatogram similar to Fig. 4.2. The results are interpreted in the following manner. The least-adsorbed component A of the sample mixture will migrate through the column rapidly and appear in the effluent first. The second least-adsorbed component B will appear in the effluent next, etc. One step will be obtained in the elution curve for each solute material that appears in the effluent. The effluent will be a mixture of solutes after component B first appears, and the complexity of the effluent will increase with the appearance of each new solute until the effluent composition is identical with the influent.

The decrease in solute concentration in each step of the elution curve shown by the dashed lines in Fig. 4.2 can be explained in the following way: As the zone of solute A moves down the column, the adsorbent

becomes saturated with A.   The leading portion of the zone contains only
solute A, but farther up the column the adsorbent is saturated with A
and B; A, B, and C, etc.   Because of the competition for adsorption by
solute B and others, the saturation level of A decreases as one proceeds
up the column.   This variation in solute concentration along the column
shows up in the solute concentration of the column effluent.   The
manner in which the solute concentration varies in the effluent from the
column is illustrated by the dashed portion of the elution curve for each
solute in Fig. 4.2.   Keep in mind, though, that the sample solution is
added continuously to the column and eventually the solute concentration
in the effluent will fall to its level in the sample.

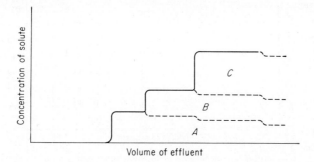

Fɪɢ. 4.2. Liquid chromatogram obtained by frontal analysis.

Frontal analysis yields a considerable amount of information about a
sample solution.   The number of steps in the elution curve designates the
minimum number of sample components even in a complex unknown
mixture.   The technique has the advantage that the solute does not have
to be eluted; thus, it can be used in the case of irreversible adsorption.
This is important because sometimes it is difficult to obtain adsorbents
that will give up adsorbed material quantitatively.   Frontal analysis
is not effective for resolving mixtures because only a limited portion of
the least-adsorbed component can be isolated in pure form.

4.4. Displacement Analysis.   Displacement analysis was introduced
by Tiselius[7] also, but not until 1943.   In displacement analysis, the
solutes to be separated are adsorbed from a small volume of sample near
the top of the adsorbent column.   This is followed by a solution of a
substance with a greater affinity for the adsorbent than any of the sample
components.   A chromatogram is developed as this second solution is
forced through the column.   The developing solution displaces all
adsorbed solutes, which, in turn, displace one another.   If the adsorbent
column is long enough for equilibrium to be approached, each component

will move through the column as a zone of pure material. The least absorbed will appear in the effluent first, followed by other sample components in the order of their increasing adsorption affinities. Last of all, the displacing substance will appear in the effluent. Figure 4.3 represents the typical elution curve obtained by displacement analysis when the concentration of solute is plotted against the volume of effluent. Under equilibrium conditions all zones move through the column at the same rate as the developer but they are not completely resolved. Even under near-ideal conditions the trailing edge of one zone will overlap the leading edge of the following zone. Ideally there is no overlap of zones; only an interface exists between the two zones.

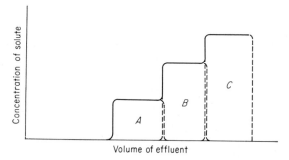

FIG. 4.3. Liquid chromatogram obtained by displacement analysis.

The method is theoretically limited to reversible adsorption systems because a solute that is irreversibly adsorbed will not appear in the effluent. Therefore, only the minimum number of sample components can be determined. Each component that appears in the effluent will produce a step in the effluent curve. Each component can be separated in a pure form, but not quantitatively. It is possible, though, to use the method for the quantitative determination of each substance. Under equilibrium conditions only a given amount of solute can be adsorbed per unit weight of adsorbent. Therefore, as the concentration of a sample component is increased, the length of the corresponding zone in the chromatogram is lengthened. This is reflected in the elution curve, Fig. 4.4. As the concentration of A is increased in the sample, the corresponding elution step (dashed line) becomes longer, not higher. The volume of effluent required to collect component A is directly proportional to the amount of A in the sample. Calibration of effluent volume with standard samples permits the quantitative determination of component A.

4.5. Elution Analysis. Elution analysis is essentially the method of analysis introduced by Tswett. This form of columnar chromatography is distinguished from the other types by the fact that the sample solutes are adsorbed from a small volume of sample near the top of the column and then washed down the column with a pure solvent. Each component will migrate down the column at a different rate depending on its adsorption affinity. The result is that this method can conceivably completely resolve even complex mixtures. Figure 4.5 is a typical elution curve obtained in elution analysis.

Theoretically, elution analysis is applicable to reversible adsorption systems only, and as in displacement analysis, it is possible to determine

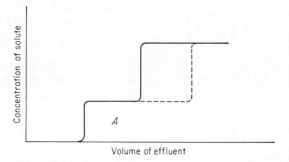

Fig. 4.4. Effect of concentration on the liquid chromatogram developed by displacement analysis.

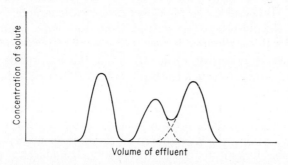

Fig. 4.5. Liquid chromatogram obtained by elution analysis.

the minimum number of sample components. Advantages of the method are that components can be quantitatively resolved and then determined by conventional means. The greater versatility of elution analysis is responsible for its being the most widely used form of chromatography.

4.6. Gradient Elution Analysis. Gradient elution analysis was introduced by Alm, Williams, and Tiselius[8] in 1952. Essentially, the method consists in adsorbing the sample solutes in a small zone near the top of the column and eluting with a liquid mixture the composition of which is continually changed. Solvent characteristics are changed in the direction of increased eluting power by gradually adding and mixing a more polar component to the developing solvent in a chamber which drains into the column. Usually the polar component is added at the same rate as the developing solvent is added to the column.

Alm, Williams, and Tiselius contend that in many instances sharper zones are obtained with this technique because tailing is greatly reduced or even eliminated. The method should be most useful with solutes which have very curved adsorption isotherms. The increased eluting power of the solvent will tend to reduce the tailing of zones and produce sharper resolutions. Williams[9] also tried a temperature gradient along the column with gradient elution analysis.

4.7. Present Status of Theory. Because of the inherent slight differences in adsorbability of different substances, it should be theoretically possible to separate any solute mixture by chromatography. With such immense potentialities involved, it is no wonder that many people have tried to develop the theory of the adsorption phenomenon. Still, there has been no great breakthrough in the theory, and chromatography remains an empirical science. Well-designed experiments are essential when difficult separations are attempted.

There are two factors, about which little is known, that almost prevent further progress in chromatography theory. These are the connection between adsorption and chemical structure and the lack of reproducible adsorbents. It is difficult to reproduce adsorbent characteristics exactly even when the adsorbent is derived from the same source. Partly responsible for this is the great influence that small quantities of impurities have on such large active surfaces. Even the adsorption of minute quantities of water by an adsorbent will alter the adsorbent characteristics greatly.

Fortunately, there are some clues to the adsorption mechanism that may be of help in raising chromatography above its empirical status. One is Traub's rule, which predicts the variation of adsorption affinity with molecular weight for the members of a homologous series. The work of adsorption increases with each methylene (CH_2) group added. Thus, when members of a homologous series are being chromatographed, it is possible to predict the relative adsorption sequence or the order of decreasing R_f values.

The relative order of the adsorption affinity of a series of solutes is fairly constant for different adsorbents. Two examples involving completely different types of solutes will illustrate this interaction of solute and adsorbent. The plant pigments α-carotene, β-carotene, and xanthophyll appear in that order in the effluent from a chromatographic column when calcium carbonate, magnesium oxide, or alumina is used as the adsorbent. Similarly, when the iron(III), cobalt(II), nickel(II), copper(II), and manganese(II) chelates of 2-thenoyltrifluoroacetone are chromatographed on cellulose, starch, silicic acid, or alumina, the adsorption sequence is the same. The R_f values of the metal chelates are in decreasing order: Fe > Cu > Ni > Co > Mn. It is possible, though, for the relative adsorption affinities or R_f values to be reversed when different adsorbents or solvents are used or temperatures are changed. Strain[10] has listed a number of systems that show a reversal in the adsorption sequence with small changes in the nature of the adsorbent, temperature, and the composition of the solvent.

There is a pronounced regularity noted in the increasing adsorption affinity of various solvents as the solvent polarity is increased. This change in adsorption affinity is so regular that often it is possible to predict qualitatively the effect of changing the solvent. Particularly impressive is the use of mixed solvents in empirically arriving at the correct solvent-solute-adsorbent system. When a nonpolar and a polar solvent, such as benzene and methanol, are miscible in all proportions, it is a simple matter to vary solvent polarity by adjustment of solvent composition.

The fourth clue is the preparation of adsorbents that are specific in their actions. Most of the commonly used adsorbents are inherently selective in their actions, but in certain instances it has become possible to increase the specificity greatly. Freshly precipitated silica gel will adsorb methyl orange readily, but the specific affinity of the adsorbent for methyl orange can be greatly increased. Dickey[11] has shown that, if the silica gel is precipitated and dried in the presence of methyl orange and the adsorbed or occluded dye is eluted, then the adsorbent has a greater affinity for methyl orange. Bernhard[12] has shown also that silica gel prepared in the presence of propyl orange has a greater adsorption affinity for this dye than for the methyl, ethyl, or butyl analogues. Possibly there is some steric relationship between solute and adsorbent that may be enhanced and will produce unusual specificity in adsorbents. Certainly, the recent development of ion-exchange resins was an advance in the preparation of more selective and specific adsorbents. We can look forward to the introduction of many new and powerful adsorbents.

Molecular sieves are a relatively new group of inorganic crystalline adsorbents that have a rather unusual specificity for certain substances. They are crystals of metal-alumina silicates which retain their three-dimensional crystalline character without collapsing or ionic rearrangement when dehydrated. The dehydrated crystals are quite porous, but unlike other common porous adsorbents the pores and cavities are precisely uniform in size, are of molecular dimensions, and make up almost 50 per cent of the total volume of the crystals. Only those molecules (solutes) which are small enough to diffuse through the pores of the crystal can enter the structure and be adsorbed on the walls of the cavities. This screening or sieve action combined with the adsorption affinity of the crystal matrix makes it possible for molecular sieves to separate molecules smaller than the size of the pores from those which are larger.   One type of sieve that is available commercially will permit only molecules smaller than about 4 A to enter the cavities and be adsorbed. For example, ethane with a diameter of about 4 A is readily adsorbed by the sieve while propane (almost 5 A diameter) is not.   A second type of sieve has a pore opening of approximately 5 A and will adsorb straight-chain hydrocarbons like n-hexane but not branched-chain iso-hexanes or cyclic hydrocarbons like cyclohexane and benzene.

The sieves have an unusually high affinity for unsaturated hydro-carbons and polar compounds.   The combination of selective factors makes it possible to separate ethanol and n-propanol from n-butanol and higher molecular-weight normal alcohols and to separate ethylene, acetylene, and propylene from butene and higher molecular-weight normal olefins.   The adsorbed compounds will remain confined by the sieve until released by heat or displaced with another adsorbable material. As might be expected, the sieves have an unusually great affinity for water and adsorb it more strongly than any other substance.   Thus, water can be used to displace all other adsorbates.   The affinity is so great that the sieves will adsorb 15 weight per cent of water from an atmosphere with only 1.3 per cent relative humidity at 100°C.

Their strong affinity for water plus their selectivity based in part on molecular size adds up to a unique adsorber.   Adsorbers of the molecular-sieve type have great promise in the analytical laboratory because of their ability to distinguish among solutes on the basis of size.

LeRosen[13] and coworkers tried a semiempirical approach to relate the R value and molecular structure of the solute to the type of bond formed in the adsorption process.   It was recognized that any equation developed would have to take into consideration the dynamic equilibrium among the solute, solvent, and adsorbent.   To place his ideas on a formal basis, LeRosen proposed a rate equation for relating R to the adsorption process.

$$f = ks = \frac{T_a}{T_s} = \frac{1 - R}{R}$$

In this equation R has its usual significance and

$\qquad k$ = equilibrium constant for adsorption process

$\qquad s$ = surface area of adsorbent expressed as moles per unit of adsorbent

$\qquad T_s$ = statistical average time a particle spends in solution between adsorptions

$\qquad T_a$ = statistical average time a particle spends on adsorbent between adsorptions

$\qquad f$ = proportionality factor in adsorption isotherm that will give amount of substance adsorbed from unit volume of solvent when multiplied by concentration of solute in solution

It was assumed that the interactions of the solute, solvent, and adsorbent in an equilibrium system were determined mainly by the relative electron-donor or acceptor strength and hydrogen-bonding capacity of the three components. The rate equation was then semi-empirically expressed in terms of the bonding abilities of the three components.

$$f = \frac{1}{M_{sc}} \left(\frac{A_a D_s}{D_d} + \frac{D_a A_s}{A_d} + \frac{D_a{}^H H_s}{H_d} + \frac{H_a D_s{}^H}{D_d{}^H} \right) = \frac{1 - R}{R}$$

where M_{sc} = sum of molecular weights of all side chains in solute molecule

D = relative donor strength as compared with standard electron pair. Subscripts a, d, and s refer to donor strength of adsorbent, solvent (developer), and solute, respectively

A = relative acceptor strength as compared with standard electron pair

D^H = relative donor strength of electron pair donated to a hydrogen atom in hydrogen-bond formation as compared with a standard

H = relative acceptor strength of hydrogen-bonding hydrogen for electron pair as compared with a standard

Relative values for the donor and acceptor strengths of solutes were determined experimentally after some standards were arbitrarily selected. The electron pair of a tertiary nitrogen represented an electron-donor unit, and the unfilled orbital of a boron atom in an alkyl-boron was an electron-acceptor unit. The hydrogen of an alcohol was selected as the standard hydrogen-bond hydrogen unit. Relative values for the donor and acceptor strengths of the solvents were based on petroleum ether as the standard unit. Chromatograms were developed with petroleum ether and other solvents while using the same adsorbent-solute system. From these data, the relative interaction tendencies of the other solvents were calculated. In an analogous fashion the relative donor and acceptor strengths of a few adsorbents and solutes were determined (see Table 4.1).

In aromatic amines the donor strength of the nitrogen is determined by the fractional number of the major resonance forms that show the electron on the nitrogen atom. The agreement between calculated R values and the observed R values was very good for the limited number of systems to which it was applied. Where there was lack of agreement, there was usually an obvious reason. The development of LeRosen's ideas stopped with his untimely death. The theory is promising and should be extended further.

4.8. Adsorbents. Virtually complete insolubility of the adsorbent in the solvent is necessary to prevent the dissolution of the column as solvent is percolated through it. This requirement greatly restricts the number of adsorbents that are suitable for both organic and aqueous solvents. As a result, only the more chemically inert adsorbents, such as charcoal, alumina, and complex silicates, are widely used in all the common solvents. There are, however, numerous inorganic substances and a few organic substances that are used as adsorbents in nonpolar solvent

TABLE 4.1. RELATIVE DONOR AND ACCEPTOR STRENGTHS OF SOME COMMON SOLVENTS, ADSORBENTS, AND SOLUTES*

	A	D	D^H	H
Solvents:				
Petroleum ether............	1†	1†	......	1†
Benzene.................	25	5.8	......	4.3
Adsorbents:				
Special filtrol..............	14,000	1,333	1,300	
Merck reagent silicic acid....	4,800	2,570	120	
Florisil.................	2,000	1,160	260	
Merck heavy powder calcium				
carbonate..............	33	224	26	
$CaHPO_4 \cdot 2H_2O$.............	77	....	42	
Magnesium oxide..........	47	3,350	190	
Calcium hydroxide.........	40	11,500	23	
Solutes:				
Amino N.................	....	1†		
Alkyl B..................	1†			
Alcohol H................	....	....	1†	
Alcohol O................		0.17		
Acid or ketone O...........	....	0.20		
Nitro group..............	....	0.04		
Aromatic ring............	....	0.002		

* After A. L. LeRosen, P. H. Monaghan, C. A. Rivet, and E. D. Smith, *Anal. Chem.*, **23**, 730 (1951).
† Standards.

systems. For reasons to be considered shortly, chromatograms are usually developed with nonpolar solvents.

The adsorbent must not interact (except for the adsorption mechanism) with solvent or solute. Usually some knowledge of the sample constituents is required if an adsorbent is selected that will not interact. These are the obvious reactions between acidic solutes and the common basic adsorbents such as magnesia, calcium oxide, and calcium carbonate. The neutralization of alkaline solutes with acidic adsorbents is less frequently encountered. Precipitation reactions are sometimes involved, particularly when metal ions are the solutes. Of particular interest is the isomerization of molecular species brought about by contact with the strong adsorbents. Alumina will isomerize β-carotene to pseudo-α-carotene readily and will cause acetone to dimerize. Since some adsorbents are very efficient drying agents and catalysts, one can also expect to encounter dehydration and polymerization reactions. Engel[14] discusses some of these reactions that may take place in column chromatography.

Although it is still a desirable characteristic, the adsorbents need not be colorless or white. With the light-colored adsorbents it is easy to follow the development of the chromatogram visually if colored solutes are involved. This will often give assurance that the chromatogram is being developed evenly under near-equilibrium conditions. When it is impossible to locate the solutes visually, then varied physical and chemical means are employed to detect solutes in the effluent or on the adsorbent. Chromatography will effectively resolve colored or colorless solutes on colored or colorless adsorbents. The problem is to determine the position of the different zones.

Undoubtedly most solids would be effective adsorbents for certain sample mixtures, but they must be cheap enough to be discarded after only one application. Economy becomes important when one considers that, relative to the amount of solutes resolved, large volumes of pure adsorbent are required. Cost is not too important a consideration if the adsorbent can be recovered and used over and over again. For some reason yet unexplained, many adsorption processes are not completely reversible and used adsorbent may be contaminated. The effect of even minute traces of impurities on adsorbent characteristics was noted earlier.

At times it has been impossible to get identical results with the same adsorbents obtained from different sources. This also has been a difficulty with adsorbents obtained from the same manufacturer. Common practice has been to start experimental work with enough adsorbent obtained from a single source to complete the work. Except for the more exacting procedures, this is not necessary. A history of the previous treatment received by an adsorbent will often explain the observed differences. The strength of adsorption exhibited by common adsorbents is usually greatly affected by moisture content. Therefore, controlled heat treatments in the preparation of adsorbents is important in obtaining reproducible adsorbents. Methods are now available for standardizing adsorbents, and it is possible to buy commercially standardized adsorbents.

Brockmann and Schodder[15] determined the relative adsorption activity of different alumina preparations by observing the adsorption behavior of mixtures of dyes. The position and sequence of the adsorbed zones of dyes permitted a classification of activity. In general, it was observed that adsorption activity decreased as the adsorbent was exposed to damp air for longer periods of time. Müller[16] has prepared alumina of any

desired degree of activity by controlling its moisture content.   Through
calorimetric measurements he has obtained much evidence to indicate the
role of water in the deactivation of adsorbents.   Wilkie and Jones[17]
determined quantitatively the adsorbent strength of magnesia and
magnesia-Celite mixtures by adding an excess of a standard petroleum-
ether solution of a food dye to a given weight of adsorbent.   After
equilibration, the excess dye was determined spectrophotometrically.
The amount of dye adsorbed was a measure of the adsorbent strength.

The physical properties of an adsorbent should be such that the solvent
can be percolated through the adsorbent bed at a reasonable rate.   Two
conflicting factors, particle size and adsorbent surface area, are involved.
The capacity of a given adsorbent is inherently small, but it is directly
proportional to the surface area exposed and inversely proportional to
the particle size.   One manufacturer advertises a magnesia adsorbent
with 120 sq m per g of material.   The large surface area is due partly to
a porous structure and is not entirely the result of small particle diameters.
Every effort must be made to provide a large uniform adsorbent surface
for the adsorption process.   At the same time, practical considerations
make it necessary to use a large enough particle size that flow rates are
reasonable.   When very small adsorbent particles are used, an incon-
venience arises in operation.   The force of gravity must be supplemented
with a pressure differential between the ends of the column to speed up
flow rates.   The compromise on particle size seems to cover the range
from about 100- to 300-mesh size.   Even so, the smaller particles give
such low flow rates that a filter aid is required.   Diatomaceous earths,
kieselguhr, and certain forms of silica are good filter aids and go under
the trade names of Celite and Hyflo Supercel.   These filter aids are
finely divided, weak adsorbents, inert and quite porous.   When mixed
with a stronger adsorbent they act as an inert diluent and increase the
overall porosity of the adsorbent bed.   These filter aids are mixed with
the adsorbent in weight ratios as high as 1:1 to obtain a porous bed
without appreciably affecting the adsorption characteristics.

The adsorbents used are almost without exception oxygen containing
organic or inorganic compounds.   They are hydrophilic with a high
capacity for adsorbing water and only a slight tendency to adsorb nonpolar substances.   They are not alike in activity or in their capacity for
adsorbing solutes.   As a rule, though, solutes are adsorbed in the same
sequence on different adsorbents.   Table 4.2 lists some of the more
common hydrophilic adsorbents in the order of increasing strength of
adsorption.   The relative positions of these adsorbents in the table were
determined for the activated adsorbents which are obtained by drying at
elevated temperatures.   Their positions in the series can be changed by
first equilibrating the adsorbent with small amounts of water.

TABLE 4.2. COMMON HYDROPHILIC ADSORBENTS LISTED IN ORDER OF
INCREASING STRENGTH OF ADSORPTION*

Sucrose
Cellulose
Starch
Inulin—polysaccharide resembling starch
Magnesium citrate
Sodium carbonate
Potassium carbonate
Calcium carbonate
Calcium sulfate
Calcium phosphate
Magnesium carbonate
Calcium oxide
Silicic acid
Magnesium silicates
Charcoal
Magnesium oxide
Aluminum oxide
Fuller's earths

* From F. Feigl, "Chemistry of Specific, Selective and Sensitive Reactions,"
p. 596, Academic Press, Inc., New York, 1949.

4.9. Adsorption Sequence of Functional Groups. The adsorption
affinities of different solutes for an adsorbent should have some relationship with molecular structure or functional groups. Experience indicates that the adsorption affinities of organic compounds are particularly
influenced by the polarity of the molecules. Table 4.3 gives the order of
decreasing adsorption affinity exhibited by some of the more common
functional groups.

TABLE 4.3. ORDER OF DECREASING ADSORPTION AFFINITY OF SOME
COMMON FUNCTIONAL GROUPS

1. Acids and bases
2. Hydroxy, amino, thio, and nitro compounds
3. Aldehydes, ketones, and esters
4. Halogen compounds
5. Unsaturated hydrocarbons
6. Saturated hydrocarbons

* F. Feigl, "Chemistry of Specific, Selective and Sensitive Reactions," p. 597,
Academic Press, Inc., New York, 1949.

The influence of polarity on adsorption affinities explains why water
and low-molecular-weight alcohols are such good eluting agents. They
are preferentially adsorbed and displace less strongly adsorbed solutes.

Other factors that definitely influence the adsorption sequence of
solutes are the position of the functional groups and the size or weight of
the molecules. Traub's rule and other general adsorption rules predict

this and the effect.   Winterstein and Schön[20] determined the adsorption sequence for the following:

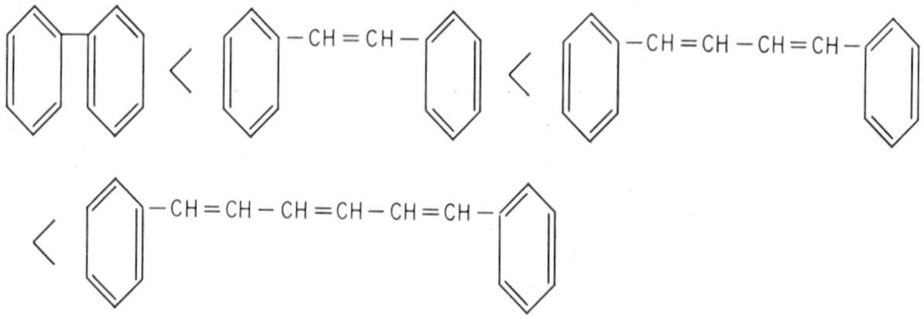

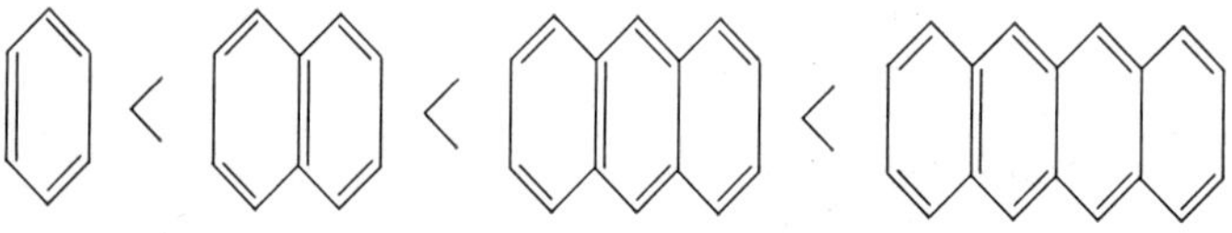

$-CH=CH-$ $<$ $-CH=CH-CH=CH-$

$<$ $-CH=CH-CH=CH-CH=CH-$

$<$ $<$ $<$

Karrer and Nielsen[21] reported the following adsorption sequence on alumina for the isomers of nitrophenol and nitroaniline:

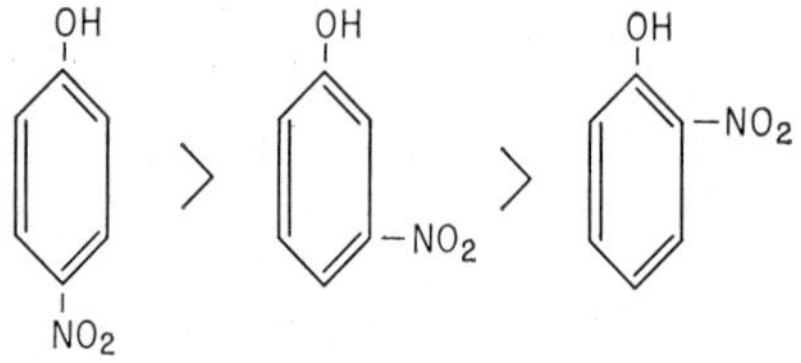

OH / NO_2 $>$ OH / $-NO_2$ $>$ OH / $-NO_2$

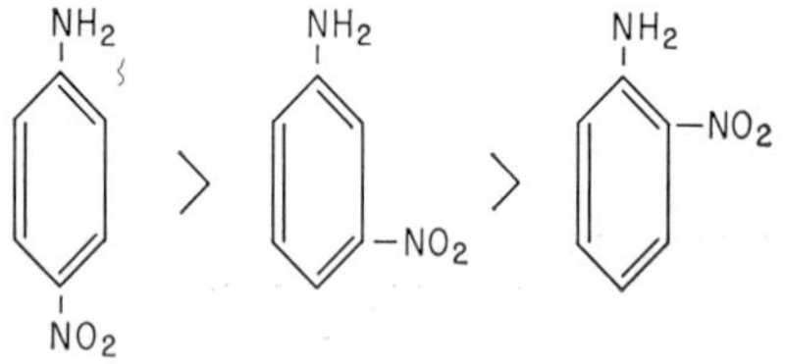

NH_2 / NO_2 $>$ NH_2 / $-NO_2$ $>$ NH_2 / $-NO_2$

4.10. Solvents.   From a theoretical point of view there is no difference between solute and solvent, since the adsorbent acts on both.   Thus, when the above considerations are applied to solvent-adsorption sequences, it should be possible to predict which of the common solvents are most strongly attracted to the adsorbent.   Table 4.4 lists the more common solvents in the order of increasing self-adsorption.   Note that the adsorption affinity increases with a definite increase in solvent polarity.

4.11. Apparatus.   One of the greatest advantages associated with the chromatographic technique is the simplicity of apparatus design.   The basic equipment is illustrated in Fig. 4.6.   The chemical literature is full

TABLE 4.4. ORDER OF INCREASING SELF-ADSORPTION FOR THE
MORE COMMON SOLVENTS

Petroleum ether
Carbon tetrachloride
Cyclohexane
Carbon disulfide
Diethyl ether
Benzene
Esters
Chloroform
Dichloroethane
Alcohols
Water
Pyridine
Organic acids
Inorganic acids and bases

of modifications of this basic design, and it appears that the researchers'
imaginations have run rampant. Cassidy, Strain, Zechmeister, and
Lederer (see Selected Bibliography, Sec. 4.16) have each written an
excellent treatise on chromatography that adequately covers the design
of apparatus.

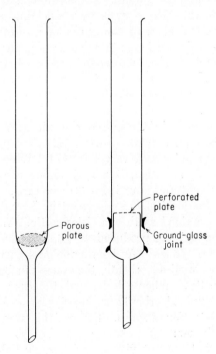

FIG. 4.6. Simple adsorption chromatographic equipment.

Modifications consist mainly in the alteration of column dimensions, receiving vessel, and solvent reservoir. The ratio of column length to column diameter is usually at least 4:1 and often is as great as 100:1. There are reports in the literature of columns up to 52 ft long and diameters from about 1 mm to 1 m. Samples can be conveniently handled on either a microscale or a macroscale by altering column dimensions without changing the basic design.

The flow rate of solvents through a column is dependent on adsorbent particle size, length of the column, and the viscosity of the solution. If a long adsorbent column is needed to resolve the sample components, then flow rates may be reduced to the point of being impractical. To alleviate this situation, a partial vacuum can be applied to the receiving flask to increase the pressure differential across the adsorbent bed and speed up the flow rate. This is impractical for highly volatile solvents, so pressure may have to be applied to the solvent reservoir to force the solvent through the column. Both the receiving flask and solvent reservoir design have been altered primarily to produce a pressure differential across the bed of adsorbent.

Bean[22] has designed a device for maintaining a constant hydrostatic head on a chromatographic column. Gevantman et al.[23] have achieved a constant flow rate through columns by connecting a 3-mm glass tube packed with powdered glass to the outlet of a chromatographic tube. The flow rate was adjusted by suitable changes in the dimensions of the small glass tube and the grain size of the powdered glass.

Columns can be packed with adsorbents in several ways. Each method has its merits, and the selection of a method is usually based on a personal preference. Granular adsorbents can be poured into the tube to form a uniform porous bed if the sides of the tube are tapped gently and a partial vacuum is applied to the lower end. Dry packing of columns in this fashion is popular and very effective. When finely divided or powdered adsorbents are used, it may be more convenient to form a slurry with the solvent and pour it into the column. If the liquid level never falls below the level of the adsorbent in the tube, then a uniform adsorbent bed is obtained as the particles settle. When air enters the adsorbent bed, channels are produced.

4.12. Detection of Zones. As long as colored components are being resolved on light-colored adsorbents, the zones can be detected visually without any difficulty. When colorless substances are chromatographed or when dark colored adsorbents are used, some other means must be available for the detection of zones. Some of the more common detection devices are listed below:

1. Substances that are not visible under white light or natural light will often fluoresce when exposed to ultraviolet radiation and thus be

made visible. The technique is simple and has proved to be very useful in the detection of zones on dark adsorbents like charcoal.

2. The detection of colorless substances is facilitated if a colored component is present or can be introduced whose behavior is known relative to the colorless component. It has been observed that Indicator Red 33 is adsorbed in the same part of the column as vitamin D3. Consequently, it is possible to locate the vitamin on an adsorbent column by visually locating the indicator. Graf and Skau[24] applied phenol red to a column of magnesia as a means of following the separation of mixtures of long-chain fatty acids.

TABLE 4.5. STREAK REAGENTS*

Reagents	Compounds detected	Zone color
Dimethylglyoxime.................	Ni	Red
$KMnO_4$.........................	Oxidizable compounds, olefins	Green
Na_2S............................	Inorganic cations	Black, brown, yellow
Schiff's reagent...................	Aldehydes	Violet
$SbCl_3$ in $CHCl_3$.................	Vitamin A	Blue
Aqueous solution of diazonium salt...	Naphthols, benzidine, amines	Green or red

* A. L. LeRosen, R. T. Moravek, and J. K. Carlton, *Anal. Chem.*, **24**, 1335 (1952), and A. L. LeRosen et al., *Anal. Chem.*, **22**, 809 (1950).

3. Colorless substances are readily detected by converting them to a colored or fluorescent material. The heavy-metal ions are easily detected on most adsorbents by extruding the adsorbent from the column intact and exposing it to hydrogen sulfide. Most of the heavy-metal sulfides are intensely colored and qualitatively identify the metal. When a thin streak of the color-producing reagent is applied to the extruded column with a small brush, it is referred to as *streaking*. LeRosen[25,26] and coworkers developed this technique rather fully and published a list of streak reagents (Table 4.5) useful in detecting many colorless organic compounds. The technique has been refined, and now it is customary to spray the reagents on the adsorbent.

4. A very powerful technique used for the detection and determination of colorless substances is the development of a liquid chromatogram. Successive small fractions of the column effluent are collected and tested individually for the different sample components. Automatic fraction collectors are available commercially, and a few easily assembled ones have been described in the literature.[33-38] An automatic collector is almost indispensable if a large number of fractions must be collected for analyses. If only a determination and not a separation of components is required,

then a continuous record of the chemical or physical characteristics of the column effluent may be more appropriate. Specific chemical tests can be applied to each fraction conveniently, but it is very difficult to obtain a continuous record of the chemical properties of a system. As a result, most tests applied to the effluent on a continuous basis are measurements of some specific physical property. Physical properties that have proved useful in testing individual fractions and recording continuous liquid chromatograms are the following:

a. Radioactivity
b. Absorbance (optical density)
c. Refractive index
d. Absorption spectrum
e. Dry weight of each fraction
f. pH
g. Conductivity
h. Dielectric constant
i. Biological activity

4.13. Applications. It is virtually impossible to mention all the areas in which chromatography has been applied successfully. Generally, though, the remarkable selectivity of the chromatographic process has been used for qualitative and quantitative analysis, the resolution of mixtures, and the concentration of dilute solutions.

Chromatography can be used indirectly for qualitative analysis by giving a local accumulation of the unknown on an adsorbent prior to identity tests with streak reagents and physical tests. More direct qualitative tests are the comparison of R_f values of known and unknown. Fillinger[27] and a number of workers have recommended chromatographic qualitative schemes for the determination of inorganic substances. The sensitivity of such methods is comparable to or exceeds the more conventional qualitative schemes.

The homogeneity of a substance can be checked reliably by chromatography. If the substance gives a single well-defined zone when chromatographed on two or three different adsorbents, it can be assumed that a homogeneous substance is involved. Although the method is not fool-proof, it certainly provides an easy checking procedure. Considering the great selectivity of adsorption processes, it is not surprising that this test is effective.

Ovenston[28] has shown that the formation of a double zone by a single substance is more likely if the column is treated with a strong developing solvent first, followed by a weaker developer. It is suggested that water on the adsorbent is partially eluted, leaving a wet intermediate zone between two more strongly adsorbing zones. Some comments are made on the best method of applying the homogeneity test.

Substances also can be identified by the use of a "mixed chromatogram." For this method to be effective, it is necessary to have some idea about the identity of the unknown. The substance to be identified is mixed with pure material thought to be the same substance. If only a single well-defined zone results when the mixture is chromatographed on two or three different adsorbents, the identity of the unknown is verified. The method is analogous to mixed melting-point determinations and is of comparable value to the researcher.

The resolution of α- and β-carotene is probably as striking an example of the resolving power of chromatography as there is. These isomers are resolved readily by chromatographing a petroleum-ether extract of the pigments on calcium carbonate. α-Carotene washes through the column rapidly and can be collected in the effluent before the β isomer is eluted. The empirical formula of the isomers is $C_{40}H_{56}$ with the following structural formula:

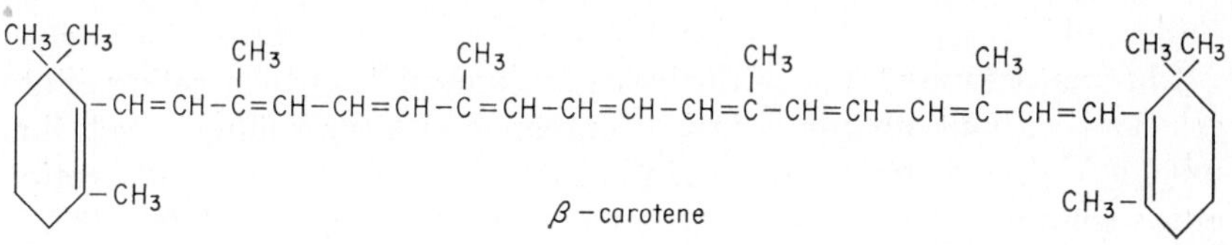

β – carotene

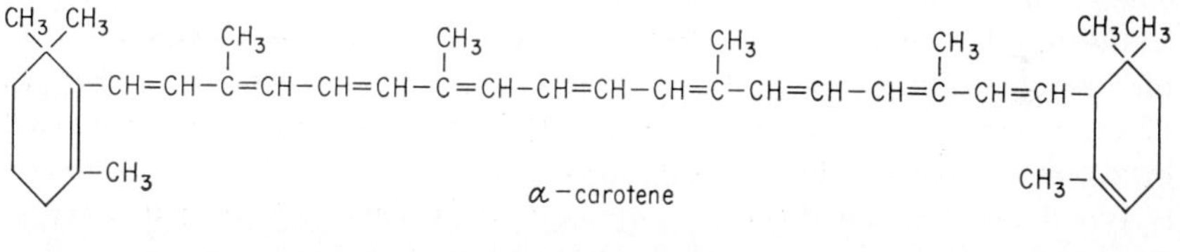

α – carotene

The two high-molecular-weight isomers differ only in the position of a double bond, yet they are readily resolved. Shifting the double bond destroys the conjugated system, though, and this probably has a marked effect on the adsorbability of the α-carotene.

Karagunis and Coumoulos[29] reported the resolution of the optical isomers of triethylenediammine chromic chloride on columns of d- or l-quartz.

Weil[30] discusses the work done at the National Bureau of Standards on the separation of hydrocarbons by preferential adsorption or elution in a column of silica gel. Pure hydrocarbons have been separated from mixtures of branched-chain paraffins and alkyl-benzenes. Gasoline, kerosene, and gas-oil fractions were divided into fractions of paraffins and napththenes, mononuclear species, and mixed aromatics in a single pass through the column. A number of references are listed for review purposes.

Schwab and Jockers[31] separated on alumina a number of the common heavy-metal ions. They are listed in the order of decreasing adsorption affinity:

$$Hg(II)$$
$$As(III), Sb(III), Bi(III), Fe(III), UO_2{}^{++}, Pb(II),$$
$$Cr(III)$$
$$Ni(II)$$
$$Ag(I), Zn(II), Co(II), Tl(I), and Mn(II)$$
$$Cd(II)$$

The series is very pH dependent, and the relative adsorption affinities are altered by complexation.

Of the 36 possible binary mixtures made from the nine basic dyes, 32 can be resolved by chromatography.

Even though adsorption chromatography does possess a remarkable resolving power, attempts to resolve the rare earths have not been successful.

Chromatography is one of the best ways of rapidly concentrating dilute solutions without applying heat. Compared with the volume of solution used, a relatively small volume of adsorbent is required for the adsorption of the solute. The solute can then be recovered from the adsorbent in a small volume of eluting agent, thus greatly concentrating the original solution. Koschara[32] concentrated the flavins from 5000 liters of urine on 4 kg of Floridin. The flavins were eluted and collected in 10 to 15 liters of aqueous pyridine. Further purification steps resulted in the isolation of 220 mg of recrystallized uroflavin.

Wohlleben[33] reduced the ethanol content of chloroform to below 0.005 per cent by a slow percolation of the chloroform solution through a highly activated column of alumina.

Hesse and Schildknecht[34] purified cyclohexane and n-heptane for use in ultraviolet spectroscopy by treating the solvents with concentrated sulfuric acid followed by filtration through a column of silica gel and alumina.

Oshchapovskii[35] concentrated nickel on a column of dimethylglyoxime by precipitation chromatography. As low as 0.5 μg of nickel was reported detected in the presence of 5000 times as much cobalt.

Milligram quantities of the plant xanthophylls and carotenes in a liter of petroleum-ether extract can be greatly concentrated and resolved by adsorption on a small chromatographic column.

The quantitative determination of substances by chromatography is based mainly on the measurement of specific chemical or physical properties of the column effluent. An adequate discussion of quantitative techniques appears in the sections dealing with displacement analysis and the detection of zones.

Chromatography has been applied to the analysis of foods, condiments, drugs, dyes, and a host of other substances. Forensic science has successfully applied chromatographic procedures to the analysis of inks, cosmetics, etc. The monographs by Lederer and Lederer, Strain, and Zechmeister and the review articles listed in Sec. 4.16 will give a nearly complete bibliography of articles dealing mainly with chromatography. These sources should be consulted before a separation is attempted, because the work may already be reported.

4.14. Advantages and Disadvantages. The advantages of adsorption chromatography are summed up briefly in the following outline. The apparatus is simple compared with that used in distillation and extraction and most instrumental methods. Unskilled technicians can readily develop the skills needed to operate chromatographic columns. Chromatography can be applied over a wide temperature range, but it is particularly effective for resolving heat-labile substances at low temperatures. If necessary, the entire operation can be carried out conveniently in an inert atmosphere. The procedure will detect small traces of impurities in a substance and sometimes give a quantitative estimation of the amount present. Complex mixtures of organic or inorganic substances can be quantitatively resolved. Very dilute solutions can be concentrated easily and quickly.

The main disadvantages associated with chromatographic analyses are the following: Substances may undergo chemical change when subjected to adsorption on the active adsorbents. Changes most frequently encountered are isomerization, hydrolysis, neutralization, decomposition, and precipitation. Adsorbents have low capacity for adsorbing solutes. The method is still empirical, although judicious selections of solvent-adsorbent systems are usually possible.

4.15. Partition Chromatography. Partition chromatography is distinguished from adsorption chromatography by the use of two solvents. One is fixed on or in the adsorbent, and the other passes over it. This can be accomplished by impregnating a solid adsorbent, such as silica gel, with a solvent that is immiscible with the sample solvent. As the solutes are washed through the column, they are continuously partitioned between the immobile liquid phase and the moving solvent phase, thus producing a differential migration of various solutes. Martin and Synge[5] introduced partition chromatography with the separation of a mixture of amino acids on silica gel holding about 50 per cent water. The developing solvent was a mixture of chloroform and butanol.

Partition chromatography is actually a pseudocountercurrent-extraction phenomenon, and solute behavior can be fairly well predicted from the known distribution of the solute between the two solvent phases.   In fact, Martin and Synge derived an expression to relate the movement of a zone with the partition coefficient, namely,

$$R_f = \frac{A_L}{A_L + \alpha A_s}$$

where $R_f = \dfrac{\text{distance solute zone migrates}}{\text{distance solvent front migrates}}$

A_s = cross-sectional area of immobile phase

A_L = cross-sectional area of mobile phase

α = partition coefficient = $\dfrac{\text{solute concentration in immobile phase}}{\text{solute concentration in mobile phase}}$

The R_f values of some amino acids were shown to agree well with those calculated from known partition coefficients.   Thus, the theory of partition chromatography is better established than that of adsorption chromatography.

TABLE 4.6. EXAMPLES OF ADSORBENT-SOLVENT SYSTEMS USED FOR PARTITION CHROMATOGRAPHY

Adsorbent	Immobile phase	Mobile phase	Solute	Reference
Silica gel..........	Aniline	Isopropyl alcohol and benzene	Paraffins and cycloparaffins	36
	Water	Butanol-chloroform	Amino acids	5
	Methanol-water-H_2SO_4	Skellysolve B	Aromatic acids	37
Cellulose..........	Water	Alcohols	Amino acids	38
	Water	Organic	Inorganic species	39
Starch............	Water	Butanol–benzyl alcohol	Amino acids	40
Kieselguhr........	Methanol-water	Ligroin-methanol	C_7 acids	41
Celite............	Aqueous NaOH	Benzene	Diols	42
Silica............	Methanolic NaOH	Isooctane	Aliphatic acids	43
Powdered rubber...	Butanol	Aqueous buffers saturated with butanol	Amino acids	44
Hyflo Super Cel....	Silicone	Chloroform–Skellysolve S–water–methanol	C_6-C_{12} fatty acids	45

Although partition chromatography is a pseudocountercurrent-extraction phenomenon, it will be considered as a chromatographic process. Operating techniques are the same as for adsorption chromatography; only the mechanism for retarding the flow of solutes is different. The important technical differences are that the solid adsorbent must not act as an ordinary adsorbent and it must absorb or hold a substantial volume of the immobile solvent phase.

Generally, the adsorbents used as a supporting medium for the immobile solvents are weak adsorbents with a very porous structure. Examples of different solvent-supporting mediums are listed in Table 4.6 with the appropriate solvent-solute system and the literature reference. Since the techniques, apparatus, and applications are the same as for adsorption chromatography, no further discussion will be given to partition chromatography.

4.16. Selected Bibliography

Brimley, R. C., and F. C. Barrett: "Practical Chromatography," Reinhold Publishing Corporation, New York, 1953.

Cassidy, H. G.: Fundamentals of Chromatography, in "Technique of Organic Chemistry," A. Weissberger (ed.), vol. X, Interscience Publishers, Inc., New York, 1957.

Lederer, E., and M. Lederer: "Chromatography," 2d ed., D. Van Nostrand Company, Inc., Princeton, N.J., 1957.

Pollard, F. H., and J. F. W. McOmie: "Chromatographic Methods of Inorganic Analysis," Academic Press, Inc., New York, 1953.

Smith, O. C.: "Inorganic Chromatography," D. Van Nostrand Company, Inc., Princeton, N.J., 1953.

Strain, H. H.: "Chromatographic Adsorption Analysis," Interscience Publishers, Inc., New York, 1942.

Strain, H. H., et al.: *Anal. Chem.*, **21**, 75 (1949); **22**, 41 (1950); **23**, 25 (1951); **24**, 50 (1952); **26**, 90 (1954); **28**, 687 (1956).

Zechmeister, L.: "Progress in Chromatography, 1938 to 1947," Chapman & Hall, Ltd., London, 1950.

Zechmeister, L., and L. V. Cholnoky: "Principles and Practice of Chromatography," 2d ed., John Wiley & Sons, Inc., New York, 1943.

REFERENCES

1. Tswett, M.: *Ber. deut. botan. Ges.*, **24**, 384 (1906).
2. Kuhn, R., and E. Lederer: *Naturwissenschaften*, **19**, 306 (1931); *Ber. deut. chem. Ges.*, **64**, 1349 (1931).
3. Strain, H. H., T. R. Sato, and J. Engelke: *Anal. Chem.*, **26**, 95 (1954).
4. LeRosen, A. L.: *J. Am. Chem. Soc.*, **64**, 1905 (1942).
5. Martin, A. J. P., and R. L. M. Synge: *Biochem. J.*, **35**, 1358 (1941).
6. Tiselius, A., and S. Claesson: *Arkiv Kemi, Mineral. Geol.*, **B 15**(18) (1942).
7. Tiselius, A.: *Arkiv Kemi, Mineral. Geol.*, **A 16**(18) (1943).
8. Alm, R. S., R. J. P. Williams, and A. Tiselius: *Acta Chem. Scand.*, **6**, 826 (1952).
9. Williams, R. J. P.: *Analyst*, **77**, 905 (1952).
10. Strain, H. H.: *Ind. Eng. Chem., Anal. Ed.*, **18**, 605 (1946).

11. Dickey, F. H.: *Proc. Natl. Acad. Sci.*, **35**, 229 (1949).
12. Bernhard, S. A.: *J. Am. Chem. Soc.*, **74**, 4946 (1952).
13. LeRosen, A. L., P. H. Monaghan, C. A. Rivet, and E. D. Smith: *Anal. Chem.*, **23**, 730 (1951).
14. Engel, C.: *Chem. Weekblad.* **48**, 766 (1952).
15. Brockmann, H., and H. Schodder: *Ber. deut. chem. Ges.*, **74**, 73 (1941).
16. Müller, P. B.: *Helv. Chim. Acta*, **26**, 1945 (1943).
17. Wilkie, J. B., and S. W. Jones: *Anal. Chem.*, **24**, 1409 (1952).
18. Feigl, F.: "Chemistry of Specific, Selective and Sensitive Reactions," p. 596, Academic Press, Inc., New York, 1949.
19. Feigl, F.: Ref. 18, p. 597.
20. Winterstein, A., and K. Schön: *Z. physiol. Chem.*, **230**, 146 (1934).
21. Karrer, P., and N. Nielsen: *Zanger Festschr.*, Zurich, 1934, p. 954; F. Feigl, "Chemistry of Specific, Selective and Sensitive Reactions," p. 599, Academic Press, Inc., New York, 1949.
22. Bean, L.: *Anal. Chem.*, **29**, 987 (1957).
23. Gevantman, L. H., R. K. Main, and L. M. Bryant: *Anal. Chem.*, **29**, 170 (1957).
24. Graf, M. M., and E. L. Skau: *Ind. Eng. Chem., Anal. Ed.*, **15**, 340 (1943).
25. LeRosen, A. L., R. T. Moravek, and J. K. Carlton: *Anal. Chem.*, **24**, 1335 (1952).
26. LeRosen, A. L., et al.: *Anal. Chem.*, **22**, 809 (1950).
27. Fillinger, H. H.: "Chromatographic Analysis for the Metal Ions of a First Course in Qualitative Analysis," Hollins College, Virginia, 1952.
28. Ovenston, T. C. J.: *Nature*, **169**, 924 (1952).
29. Karagunis, G., and G. Coumoulos: *Nature*, **142**, 162 (1938).
30. Weil, H.: *Petroleum, London*, **16**, 95 (1953).
31. Schwab, G. M., and K. Jockers: *Naturwissenschaften*, **25**, 44 (1937).
32. Koschara, W.: *Ber. deut. chem. Ges.*, **67**, 761 (1934); *Z. physiol. Chem.*, **232**, 101 (1935).
33. Wohlleben, G.: *Angew. Chem.*, **68**, 752 (1956).
34. Hesse, G., and H. Schildknecht: *Angew. Chem.*, **67**, 737 (1955).
35. Oshchapovskii, V. V.: *Zhur. Anal. Khim.*, **11**, 170 (1956).
36. Sauer, R. W., T. A. Washall, and F. W. Melpolder: *Anal. Chem.*, **29**, 1327 (1957).
37. Bhargava, P. M., and C. Heidelberger: *J. Am. Chem. Soc.*, **77**, 166 (1955).
38. Synge, R. L. M.: *Biochem. J.*, **48**, 429 (1951).
39. Pollard, F. H., and J. F. W. McOmie: "Chromatographic Methods of Inorganic Analysis," Academic Press, Inc., New York, 1953.
40. Moore, S., and W. H. Stein: *Ann. N.Y. Acad. Sci.*, **49**, 265 (1948).
41. Bumpus, F. M., W. R. Taylor, and F. M. Strong: *J. Am. Chem. Soc.*, **72**, 2116 (1950).
42. Haenni, E. O., J. Carol, and D. Banes: *J. Am. Pharm. Assoc.*, **42**, 167 (1953).
43. Vandenheuvel, F. A., and E. R. Hayes: *Anal. Chem.*, **24**, 960 (1952).
44. Partridge, S. M., and T. Swain: *Nature*, **166**, 272 (1950).
45. Wittenberg, J. B.: *Biochem. J.*, **65**, 42 (1957).

CHAPTER 5

GAS CHROMATOGRAPHY

BUDDHADEV SEN

Department of Chemistry, Louisiana State University, Baton Rouge, La.

5.1. Introduction. From the definition of chromatography given in the preceding chapter, it is immediately apparent that chromatography consists in percolating a phase containing the sample mixture through another phase which is stationary and has a very large surface area. The word *percolation* is deliberately used to emphasize the fact that there is only one moving phase in chromatography in contrast to two moving phases in countercurrent distillation and extraction and similar processes. The percolating phase can be a liquid or a gas, and the stationary phase in turn can be a solid or a liquid immobilized by being adsorbed on a suitable adsorbent. Liquid-solid (adsorption) and liquid-liquid (partition) chromatography have been described, which brings up the discussion of chromatography involving a mobile gas phase. Obviously such a technique can be broadly classified into two distinct types: gas-solid chromatography (GSC) having a solid as the immobile phase and gas-liquid chromatography (GLC) or gas-liquid partition chromatography (GLPC) having a liquid as the immobile phase. The liquid is immobilized by adsorbing it on a suitable solid such as crushed firebrick or Celite.

By the foregoing definition, gas chromatography has long been used by industry for cleaning gas streams and analyzing hydrocarbons and esters,[1-4] but the real recognition for the discovery of gas chromatography belongs to the British biochemist A. J. P. Martin, who also invented liquid-liquid partition chromatography. After being vexed by the problem of separating and identifying amino acids,[5] Martin, in his now famous and always referred-to paper,[6] developed the brilliant and simple theory and described the experimental practice of partition chromatography. In the same paper he predicted the possibility of developing gas-liquid partition chromatography and emphatically expressed the potentialities of such a method. He even predicted the possibility of separating isotopes by means of this still unknown procedure. Nevertheless, this brilliant idea had to hibernate for a full decade until Martin[7] returned to pick up the lead he had left. Since then instrumentation as well as theorization and application in this new field has developed at a phenomenal rate. In fact, Muller[8] contends that the invention and the development of gas chromatography (which won Martin a Nobel prize in chemistry) is one of the greatest analytical achievements of all times and that chromatographic (gas) homogeneity is the most infallible criterion of purity. Such is the status of gas chromatography only 10 years after its invention.

Gas-liquid chromatography enjoys a number of advantages[8,9] over gas-solid chromatography. In GLC the elution bands are narrower and quite frequently symmetrical in contrast to the tailed bands in GSC. In GLC one has a wide choice of the stationary phases, and by suitable selection of the liquid stationary phase almost any separation can be achieved. Besides, GLC is more amenable to theoretical treatment because the gas-liquid partitioning phenomenon is better understood than the physical adsorption process occurring in GSC. As a result, the theoretical and experimental advances in gas chromatography since 1951 have been almost exclusively in the field of GLC. Henceforth, in this chapter only occasional mention will be made of GSC. The interested reader is referred to the writings by Keulemans,[10] Claesson,[11] and James and Phillips[12] and also the very interesting paper by Young.[13] It is worth noting, though, that there is very little difference in instrumentation between the two types of gas chromatography.

5.2. Theory. Martin's[6] line of argument in developing the plate theory for liquid-liquid partition chromatography is closely analogous to that used by Craig[14] in explaining the distribution of naphthoic acid in his novel extraction machine. In fact, Craig's machine is a wonderful nonchromatographic model of a chromatographic column. In his machine one set of tubes containing one phase was stationary just like the stationary phase of the chromatographic column, while the other set of tubes containing the other immiscible phase was moving in one direction just like the mobile phase in a chromatographic column. As Craig's theory has been presented in Chap. 3, it will not be discussed further here.

Martin imagined the chromatographic column to be composed of a number of theoretical plates. The height equivalent of a theoretical plate (HETP) was defined by him as the thickness of the layer such that the solution issuing from it was in equilibrium with the mean concentration of the solute in the immobile phase throughout the layer. Thus, when a unit mass of a single solute is placed onto the first of such plates and is followed by the addition of successive infinitesimal volumes ∂v of

the solvent (the mobile phase), the quantity of solute in each plate is a
term of the binomial expansion of $[(1 - \partial v/V) + \partial v/V]^n$.

h = HETP

A_s = area of cross section of stationary phase

A_m = area of cross section of mobile phase

v = volume of solvent used in development of chromatogram

α = the partition coefficient

$= \dfrac{\text{g of solute per ml of the immobile phase}}{\text{g of solute per ml of the mobile phase}}$

$V = h(A_m + \alpha A_s)$ = effective plate volume

r = serial number of plate numbered from inlet as 0

Q_r = total quantity of solute in plate r

When n successive volumes ∂v of the solvent have passed,

$$Q_r = \frac{n!\,(1 - \partial v/V)^{n-r}(\partial v/V)^r}{r!\,(n - r)!} \tag{5.1}$$

Now when n is large and $\partial v/V$ is very small, which condition is realized
in the chromatographic column, Eq. (5.1) becomes

$$Q_r = \frac{1}{r!}\left(\frac{n\,\partial v}{V}\right)^r e^{-n\,\partial v/V} \tag{5.2}$$

This is the expression for a Poisson distribution. Putting $n\,\partial v = v$,

$$Q_r = \frac{1}{r!}\left(\frac{v}{V}\right)^r e^{-v/V} \tag{5.3}$$

When r is large (say > 10), then by Stirling's approximation, the above
becomes a gaussian distribution and

$$Q_r = \frac{1}{(2\pi r)^{\frac{1}{2}}}\left(\frac{v}{V}\right)^r e^{-v/V} \tag{5.4}$$

The foregoing is a deduction of the plate theory in its most simple form
as developed by Martin.[6]   Van Deemter, Zuiderweg, and Klinkenberg[15]
have extended the plate theory to take into account the feed volume.
Recently de Wet and Pretonius[16] have discussed the factors affecting the
separation of large samples.

Keulemans[17] has also given an exceedingly simple and straightforward
derivation of the plate theory. In Eq. (5.3) the term v/V is in fact the
number of effective plate volumes of the mobile phase that has passed
through the column. With the help of this equation it is possible to
calculate the location of maximum concentration of the solute after a
certain number of "plate volumes" of the solvent has passed through the
column and also the spread of the distribution of the solute in the column.

In Fig. 5.1 the quantity Q_r has been plotted against v/V (number of plate volumes) for different values of r. Each of these curves has a maximum and two points of inflection except for the one for which $r = 0$. The peak maximum is at $v/V = r$, the points of inflection are at $v/V = r \pm (r)^{1/2}$, and the tangents at these points intersect the v/V axis at

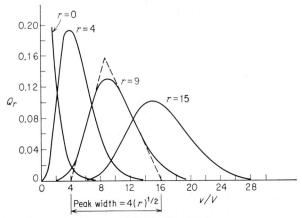

Fig. 5.1. Poisson distributions.

the points $v/V = r + 1 \pm 2(r)^{1/2}$. Therefore, the peak width w defined as the distance between these two points is given by

$$
\begin{aligned}
w &= [r + 1 + 2(r)^{1/2}] - [r + 1 - 2(r)^{1/2}] \\
&= 4(r)^{1/2}
\end{aligned}
\tag{5.5}
$$

The location of Q_{max} is given by

$$
Q_{max} = \frac{1}{r!} r^r e^{-r}
\tag{5.6}
$$

such that $v/V = r$.

A similar type of treatment is possible with the help of Eq. (5.4). From Eqs. (5.3) and (5.4) it is quite obvious that

$$
Q_n = \frac{1}{n!} \left(\frac{v}{V}\right)^n e^{-v/V}
\tag{5.7}
$$

and

$$
Q_n = \frac{1}{(2\pi n)^{1/2}} \left(\frac{v}{V}\right)^n e^{-v}
\tag{5.8}
$$

are the general equations of a chromatogram for a column of $n + 1$ plates. The peak maximum [cf. Eq. (5.6) and Fig. 5.1]

$$
Q_{max} = \frac{1}{n!} n^n e^{-n}
\tag{5.9}
$$

where $v/V = n$, will emerge from the column when n times the effective plate volume, $h(A_m + \alpha A_s)$, of the mobile phase has passed through the column. This volume is known as the retention volume and is usually symbolized as $V_R{}^0$. Therefore, the retention volume is

$$V_R{}^0 = n(hA_m + \alpha h A_s) \tag{5.10}$$

Now nhA_m and nhA_s are, respectively, the gas and liquid holdup volumes of the column. Putting $nhA_m = V_m$ and $nhA_s = V_s$,

$$V_R{}^0 = V_m + \alpha V_s \tag{5.11}$$

From this familiar relation, Porter, Deal, and Stross[18] concluded that the retention volume is an explicit function of the column geometry.

Before proceeding any further, it is desirable at this stage to summarize the simplifying assumptions of the plate theory. These are as follows:

1. Equilibrium conditions exist in each plate, and the partition coefficient is the same throughout the column.

2. The sample is charged onto the first plate and is contained in it.

3. The volume of the volume element of the carrier gas is unchanged as it passes through the column.

These assumptions are closely approximated in gas-liquid partition chromatography, but it should be kept in mind that the theory is developed on the basis of intermittent flow rate in contrast to the continuous flow rate taking place in gas-liquid chromatography. However, as has been already shown, Poisson and gaussian distributions, characteristic of a continuous-flow process,[19] are obtainable when n and r are large [cf. Eqs. (5.2) and (5.4)]. It is also possible to derive the equation for chromatographic distribution from purely statistical considerations without taking into account the mechanics of the distribution and the movement of the solute.[20] Recently Golay[21] has shown the mathematical relationship between a chromatographic column and an electrical transmission line by representing the column with an electrical analog.

5.3. Efficiency of a Column. The efficiency of the chromatographic column is expressed by the number of theoretical plates n. If d is the distance between the point of injection and the normal from the peak maximum on the volume axis (see Fig. 5.2) and the peak width is w, then

$$d = An \tag{5.12}$$
and
$$w = 4A(n)^{1/2} \tag{5.13}$$

[cf. Eq. (5.5)], where A is the proportionality constant. d and w must be expressed in the same but in any convenient unit. When the chromatogram is recorded on a strip-chart recorder, they can be expressed in centimeters or seconds or minutes.   Eliminating A between Eqs. (5.12) and (5.13) we get

$$\frac{d}{w} = \frac{1}{4}\,(n)^{\frac{1}{2}}$$

Therefore
$$n = \left(4\,\frac{d}{w}\right)^2 \tag{5.14}$$

The above relation is derived on the assumption that the entire sample is introduced as one single instantaneous plug and that all of it is contained in the first plate.   In practice, this is not true, and a number of single plate chromatograms start simultaneously from adjacent plates and overlap each other, causing a broadening of the chromatogram.   However, Van Deemter et al.[15] have shown that for a feed volume less than

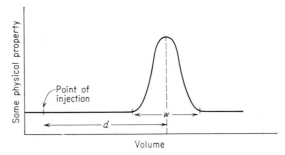

FIG. 5.2. Graphic description of elution peak along the volume axis.

$0.5(n)^{\frac{1}{2}}$ times the effective plate volume, the bandwidth is independent of the feed volume.   This means that under such conditions Eq. (5.14) can still be used to calculate the column efficiency.   It should also be remembered that the number of plates is dependent on the solute.

A general solution of the problem of calculating the number of plates needed for a chromatographic separation has been given by Glueckauf[22] and has been discussed at length by Kuelemans,[23] but a simpler treatment is possible in the special case when the feed volume is less than $0.5(n)^{\frac{1}{2}}$ times the effective plate volume and when the tangents of the elution curves of the subsequent solutes just touch at the base of the chromatogram.[15] If V_1 and V_2 are the effective plate volumes of the solutes 1 and 2, then the distance between the maxima of the bands is [see Fig. 5.1 and Eqs. (5.4) to (5.6)]

$$nV_2 - nV_1 = 2V_2(n)^{\frac{1}{2}} - 2V_1(n)^{\frac{1}{2}}$$

or
$$n_{\min} = 4\left(\frac{\eta + 1}{\eta - 1}\right)^2 \tag{5.15}$$

where
$$\eta = \frac{V_2}{V_1} \approx \frac{\alpha_1}{\alpha_2} \tag{5.16}$$

that is, η is the ratio of partition coefficients.

We have discussed the plate theory in fair detail because it has been so useful to the practicing chromatographer. It is now quite obvious that the whole purpose of the theory was to explain the mechanism of the band broadening when a slug of the solute is introduced at the first plate of the column and passed through the successive plates of the chromatographic column. Van Deemter, Zuiderweg, and Klinkenberg[15] developed a rate theory of chromatography in which they attributed band broadening to longitudinal diffusion and finiteness of transfer coefficient, that is, the resistance to mass transfer. By combining the results of the rate theory and the plate theory, these authors derived an expression for the HETP which reads

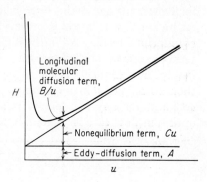

FIG. 5.3. Schematic representation of the van Deemter equation

$$H = A + B/u + Cu$$

$$H = 2\lambda d_p + 2\frac{\nu D_g}{u} + \frac{8}{\pi^2}\frac{K'}{(1+K')^2}\frac{d_f^2}{D_l}u \qquad (5.17)$$

where H = HETP

λ = measure of packing irregularity

d_p = particle diameter

ν = correction for tortuosity of channels

u = linear gas velocity

D_g = diffusion coefficient of solute molecules in gas phase

D_l = diffusion coefficient of solute molecules in liquid phase

d_f = effective film thickness

K' = $K(F_l/F_g)$, where K is partition coefficient and F_l and F_g are volume fractions of liquid and gas in column

For a particular column packing Eq. (5.17) reduces to

$$H = A + \frac{B}{u} + Cu \qquad (5.18)$$

The first and second terms of the equation represent the so-called "eddy diffusion" and the molecular diffusion, and these together constitute the diffusion term. For a comprehensive understanding of these two terms the interested reader should refer to the original paper. The third term of this equation represents the nonequilibrium effect. Figure 5.3 is a schematic plot of Van Deemter's equation with arbitrary values of the parameters.

The plot shows that there is an optimum gas velocity for the minimum value of H or the maximum number of plates. For small values of u the value of H is mainly determined by the second term of Eq. (5.17) or (5.18) and H becomes very large. Consequently, the column becomes inefficient owing to the large value of the longitudinal-diffusion term. At higher flow rates, H is primarily determined by the value of the non-equilibrium term. At fairly high flow rates, the longitudinal-diffusion term becomes negligible and constant. Sen[20] has shown that the longitudinal diffusion becomes negligible for volumetric flow rates greater then 20 ml per min for columns of 5 to 6 mm ID and is practically a constant for any solute. It is also quite obvious that a higher than optimum flow rate is preferable to a lower rate for efficient separations.

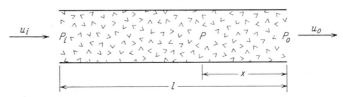

FIG. 5.4. A schematic presentation of distribution pressures and gas velocities in a packed column.

5.4. Mobile Phase. James and Martin[7] in their original paper pointed out that gas-liquid chromatography differs from liquid-liquid chromatography only by virtue of the fact that the mobile phase is compressible and thus produces a gradient of velocity along the column length. Following is James and Martin's derivation of the relation between retention volume and the pressure differential of the column assuming that the partial pressure of the solute is negligible.

p_i = gas pressure at column inlet
p_o = gas pressure at column outlet
p = gas pressure at distance x from outlet
u = linear gas velocity at point x
l = column length
t_R = time which elapses before center of zone emerges from column = retention time
V_f = volumetric flow rate of mobile phase
$V_R = V_f t_R$ = retention volume of center of zone
a = gas-phase cross section of column
$V_R{}^0$ = limiting value of V_R as p_i/p_o approaches unity
K = column constant, function of viscosity of gas and density of column packing. Some writers express this constant as a ratio of two constants, k/η, where k stands for the tightness of column packing and η for the viscosity of the gas phase

A schematic presentation of distribution of pressures and gas velocities in a packed column is given in Fig. 5.4. The volumetric throughput au

at the point x is given by

$$K \frac{dp}{dx} = \frac{V_f p_o}{p} = au \qquad (5.19)$$

Integrating to give the pressure along the column results in

$$K \frac{p^2}{p_o} = 2V_f x + K p_o$$

or

$$K = \frac{2V_f x p_o}{p^2 - p_o^2}$$

or

$$V_f = \frac{p_o K}{2x} \left[\left(\frac{p}{p_o} \right)^2 - 1 \right] \qquad (5.20)$$

Consden, Gordon, and Martin[24] defined a retardation factor R_f as

$$R_f = \frac{\text{rate of movement of solute}}{\text{rate of movement of mobile phase}}$$

This means that the average retention time of the solute molecule is $1/R_f$ times the average residence time of the carrier gas molecule. Therefore, the time dt required by the solute molecule to move distance dx is given by $dt = dx/uR_f$. Therefore,

$$t_R = \int_0^l \frac{dx}{uR_f} = \int_0^l \frac{ap\,dx}{R_f p_o V_f} \qquad (5.21)$$

because $u = V_f p_o / ap$ [cf. Eq. (5.19)].

Substituting for dx from Eq. (5.19) in Eq. (5.21) and rewriting Eq. (5.21) in terms of pressure we have

$$t_R = \int_{p_o}^{p_i} \frac{Kap^2\,dp}{R_f V_f^2 p_o^2}$$

$$= \frac{Ka(p_i^3 - p_o^3)}{3 R_f p_o^2 V_f^2} \qquad (5.22)$$

By definition, retention volume $V_R = V_f t_R$; therefore

$$V_R = Kap_o \frac{[(p_i/p_o)^3 - 1]}{3 R_f V_f} \qquad (5.23)$$

Substituting from Eq. (5.20) and making $x = l$

$$V_R = \frac{2al}{3R_f} \left[\frac{(p_i/p_o)^3 - 1}{(p_i/p_o)^2 - 1} \right] \qquad (5.24)$$

When p_i/p_o approaches unity, V_R approaches the limiting value V_R^0 which equals al/R_f by definition. V_R^0 is also known as the limiting retention volume. Therefore,

$$\frac{V_R}{V_R^0} = \frac{2}{3}\left[\frac{(p_i/p_o)^3 - 1}{(p_i/p_o)^2 - 1}\right] \qquad (5.25)$$

The above equations derived by James and Martin show the relation between actual retention volume and limiting retention volume and pressure differential. These relations also show explicitly the difference between liquid-liquid chromatography and gas-liquid chromatography.

5.5. Presentation of Data. From the very inception there has been a considerable amount of confusion in presenting chromatographic data. For qualitative purposes the data can be presented in any convenient form, but such data are very often completely useless to other investigators. A special panel discussed this matter at the request of the Committee of the Gas Chromatography Discussion Group under the auspices of the Hydrocarbon Research Group of the Institute of Petroleum of Great Britain. The recommendations of this special committee are embodied in an article by Ambrose, Keulemans, and Purnell.[25] These recommendations are very briefly described below.

One of the most useful ways of presenting the data is in the form of "specific retention volume," designated by the symbol V_g and first introduced by Littlewood, Phillips, and Price.[26] We have seen that

$$V_R^0 = fV_R \qquad (5.26)$$

[cf. Eq. (5.25)], where

$$f = \frac{3}{2}\left[\frac{(p_i/p_o)^2 - 1}{(p_i/p_o)^3 - 1}\right]$$

and the corrected retention volume is related to the partition coefficient by

$$V_R^0 = V_m + \alpha V_s$$

[cf. Eq. (5.11)], where V_m is the volume of the column occupied by the gaseous phase, V_s is the volume of the solvent at the column temperature, and

$$\alpha = \frac{\text{weight of the solute per ml of solvent}}{\text{weight of the solute per ml of gas}}$$

and is assumed to be constant at low concentrations prevailing in gas chromatography. The volume V_m can be readily determined for any column by the elution of some material for which $\alpha \to 0$. Gases such as nitrogen, hydrogen, air, or the rare gases are normally employed for this purpose. When all retention volumes or times are measured from the peak maximum for one of these gases, the above relation reduces to

$$V_R^0 = \alpha V_s = \frac{\alpha w}{\rho_c} = tV_f f \qquad (5.27)$$

where w = weight of solvent in column

$\quad\quad \rho_c$ = density of solvent at column temperature

$\quad\quad t$ = time elapsed between air peak and solute peak

$\quad\quad V_f$ = volumetric flow rate

Equation (5.27) can be readily expressed in terms of recorder chart speed. If d is the distance between the air peak and the solute peak on the chart, and if U_c is the chart speed, then $t = d/U_c$ and

$$\alpha = \frac{V_f f d}{V_s U_c} = \frac{V_f f \rho_c d}{w U_c} \tag{5.28}$$

and

$$V_R{}^0 = \frac{V_f f d}{U_c} \tag{5.29}$$

The above relations immediately show the explicit relation between $V_R{}^0$ and the weight of the solvent and the independence of α of the column dimensions and the solvent weight.

Littlewood et al.[26] converted $V_R{}^0$ to a standard value by calculation of the value at standard temperature and pressure per unit weight of the solvent and designated this by the symbol V_g, so that

$$V_g = \frac{273 V_R{}^0}{T_c w} = \frac{273 \alpha}{T_c \rho_c} \tag{5.30}$$

where T_c is the column temperature. It is experimentally more convenient to put

$$V_g = \frac{273 V_m{}^0}{T_m w} = \frac{V_{f,m} f d}{U_c} \frac{273}{T_m w} \tag{5.31}$$

where subscript m refers to the measurement at the temperature T_m of the flowmeter. The suggested method of presenting data is to tabulate the values of V_g or plot V_g versus $1/T$ for different solutes. These plots are normally straight lines. The most popular method of presenting data, however, is to plot log of relative retention volumes against $1/T$.[26,27] In the latter case data should be given for at least two temperatures and the partition coefficient and V_g for the standard should be given.

5.6. Instrumentation. Instrumentation in the field of gas chromatography has literally mushroomed over the last few years. In fact, it is difficult to say offhand how many instrument manufacturers are at the moment marketing gas chromatographs. This fact signifies that in spite of all sorts of apparent sophistication the basic instrumentation of gas chromatography is simple and inexpensive. Only the barest outlines of the instrumentation will be discussed here. Figure 5.5 is a simple schematic diagram of a gas chromatograph showing its basic components. The discussion that follows will consider the functions of the different components.

The Carrier Gas. The carrier gas almost universally used in this country is helium. However, other gases like hydrogen, nitrogen, argon, carbon dioxide, and even air are usable where an integral type of detection system is employed as in James and Martin's[6] pioneering experiment on the separation of volatile fatty acids. Any of the above gases can be used provided they do not react chemically with the detection system. This latter consideration would exclude the use of carbon dioxide in the setup used by James and Martin. However, most of the gas chro-

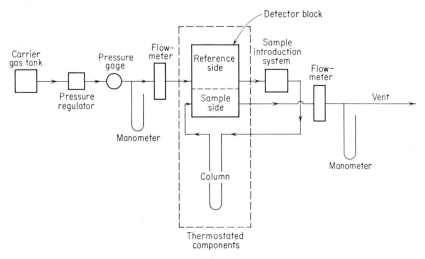

FIG. 5.5. Block diagram of a typical gas-chromatography unit.

matographs employ a differential detection technique, and the physical property almost exclusively exploited is the thermal conductivity. In such cases greater discretion is desirable in the selection of the carrier gas. Hydrogen would be the best carrier gas when a thermal-conductivity cell is used as detector but for the hazards involved in its use. The next best choice is helium. Thermal conductivity of helium is about twelve times as great as the thermal conductivity of average organic vapors.[28] Thermal conductivity of air is approximately only twice as much as that of the average organic vapors. This indicates that the detector's sensitivity would increase almost sixfold by using helium instead of air (nitrogen). Besides improving the sensitivity, the use of helium renders the empirical calibration for quantitative purposes more convenient owing to the large difference in thermal conductivity between helium and the organic vapors.[29]

At present any of the above-mentioned carrier gases can be obtained commercially in a very high state of purity and can be used without any further purification.

Gas Flow Rate and Pressure Differential. Contrary to popular belief, separation of the components in a mixture by gas chromatography does not intrinsically require a precise control of the flow rate. When identification and quantitative estimation of the separated components are also the objectives, a better control of the flow rate is imperative. It is quite obvious that there must be a pressure differential between the inlet and the outlet of the system in order for the carrier gas to flow. This can be achieved by controlling the pressure at both ends of the column or only at one end of the column, allowing the other end to ride at atmospheric pressure. Most of the commercial instruments control the pressure at the inlet. It should be emphasized at this point that it is not immaterial how the pressure differential is established, that is, whether by increasing the inlet pressure or by decreasing the outlet pressure. Equation (5.25) can be readily converted to the following form:

$$t_R = \frac{2}{3} \frac{V^0}{V_f} \left[\frac{(p_i/p_o)^3 - 1}{(p_i/p_o)^2 - 1} \right] \tag{5.32}$$

For two sets of pressure differentials, Eq. (5.32) becomes

$$\frac{t_{R,1}}{t_{R,2}} = \frac{V_{f,1}}{V_{f,2}} \left[\frac{(p_{i,1}/p_{o,1})^3 - 1}{(p_{i,1}/p_{o,1})^2 - 1} \right] \left[\frac{(p_{i,2}/p_{o,2})^2 - 1}{(p_{i,2}/p_{o,2})^3 - 1} \right] \tag{5.33}$$

The substitution of numerical values for p's in Eq. (5.33) will immediately prove that an increase in inlet pressure is more desirable than reducing the outlet pressure as far as the shortening of the elution time is concerned. The ratio U_i/U_o is also adversely affected by the reduction of inlet pressure. As a result, except in certain specific cases, arrangement for reduced pressure at the outlet is an unnecessary accessory. Most of the commercial instruments employ only one flowmeter either before the column inlet or after the column outlet. Both rotameter and orifice flowmeters are employed. Flow rates ranging from 10 to 400 ml per min have been used. However, for normal packed columns (5 to 6 mm ID) flow rates between 50 and 100 ml per min are generally satisfactory. It should be quite obvious from Fig. 5.3 that a higher than optimum flow rate is less harmful than a lower than optimum flow rate. The commercial instruments are not provided with manometers because in routine analytical procedures they are not essential, as the retention data are recorded relative to the retention data of a standard solute under identical conditions. Hausdorff and Brenner[30] have reported that retention times obtained at flow rates of 50, 100, and 200 ml per min showed that the change in flow rates expanded and contracted the recordings without effecting relative separation. This observation might be true for the particular groups of compounds studied by them but may not be true for all systems. However, it has been observed that the optimum flow rate for a column at a definite temperature is the same for any solute.[20] The best way to determine the optimum flow rate is by calculating the numbers of plates with the aid of Eq. (5.14) and with respect to a suitable standard.

Column. The column is the heart of any chromatographic method. The gas-liquid partition chromatographic column consists of a tube packed with a solid material coated with a thin layer of an appropriate solvent. The column may be straight, bent, or coiled and has been made of glass, stainless steel, aluminum, and copper tubings. The analytical columns are usually 5 to 8 mm ID and packed uniformly with a solid adsorbent coated with the appropriate solvent. Powdered firebrick (Johns-Manville) or chromosorb (Johns-Manville) is almost universally used as the solid support for the solvent. As far as absorptive capacity is concerned, firebrick seems to be slightly superior to chromosorb, but it is exceedingly soft, and as a result, during the coating and packing process, a considerable amount of it is reduced to fine powder. In this respect, chromosorb is far superior. From all considerations, chromosorb seems to be a better support material. The mesh fractions most commonly used are $^{30}/_{50}$ or $^{30}/_{60}$. The column packing is usually prepared by first dissolving the substrate material (immobile liquid-phase material) in a suitable volatile solvent such as acetone, petroleum ether, or benzene. Enough solvent is used so that, when the solution is poured over the solid support, the solid will be completely immersed. After thorough mixing, the volatile solvent is removed by evaporation. Most frequently 20 to 30 per cent by weight of substrate material is used, but much lower and higher proportions have been reported in the literature. Table 5.1 gives a list of substrate material, but this list is by no means complete.

In most of the commercial instruments, the column and the detector are placed in an air oven whose temperature may be varied between room temperature and 200°C. In some instruments the column is heated by a heating coil and is well insulated. The latter type has the advantage that with slight modification the column can be immersed in cooling baths, thus enabling one to operate the column below the room temperature. Many laboratory-built instruments use vapor jackets for heating purposes.

Sample introduction is a very important aspect of gas-chromatographic technique. It may be recalled here that in developing the plate theory it was assumed that the entire sample was contained in the first plate and the maximum sample volume was equal to $0.5(n)^{1/2}$ times the effective plate volume. Therefore, an effort is made to keep the sample volume small and to introduce it in the form of a plug and as quickly as possible. Sample volumes of 0.1 to 10 μl are often used in analytical separations.

TABLE 5.1. SUBSTRATE MATERIALS USED IN GLC AND THE TYPES OF
SUBSTANCES REPORTED SEPARATED ON EACH

Substrate material	Separation
n-Dodecane	C_6 hydrocarbons
n-Hexadecane	C_5, C_6 hydrocarbons
n-Octadecane	C_7 to C_9 hydrocarbons
n-Decane	Low-boiling hydrocarbons
2,5-Hexanedione	C_4 hydrocarbons and low-boiling hydrocarbons
Acetonylacetone	C_3 to C_5 hydrocarbons and low-boiling hydrocarbons including olefins and diolefins
Dibutyl phthalate	General hydrocarbons
Di-2 ethylhexyl sebacate	General hydrocarbons, chlorinated hydrocarbons
Aircraft engine oil (bright stock)	High-boiling hydrocarbons and general separation of high boilers
Silicone 550	General hydrocarbons and organometallics
Quinoline + brucine (7:1)	Isomeric hexanes
Diethylformamide	Olefins and acetylenes
Dimethylformamide	Olefins and acetylenes
Dimethyl sulfolane	Olefins from paraffins, olefins, pentenes, and hexenes
Oxydipropionitrile	Olefins from paraffins, olefins, pentenes, and hexenes
Tri-isobutylene	C_2 and C_3 compounds including paraffins, olefins, and acetylenes
Diethylene glycol monoethyl ether	C_3 to C_5 compounds including paraffins, olefins, and acetylenes
Silicone 550 and stearic acid	Fatty acids
Apiezon L	High boiler, general purpose, esters of fatty acids
Apiezon M	Same as above
Paraffin wax	Amines
Carbowax 4000	Amines and water
Carbowax 6000	Higher boiling amines
Polyoxyethylene ⎫ Sorbitan monostearate⎭	Organics including moisture
Sorbitan monostearate	Same as above
Dioctyl phthalate ⎫ Dinonyl phthalate ⎪ Tricresyl phosphate⎬ Silicone 702 ⎪ Narcoil 40 ⎭	General purpose including ketones and esters, fluorinated hydrocarbons
Polypropylene glycol	Separation of polar and nonpolar compounds
High-vacuum silicone grease	High-boiling compounds
1-Chloronaphthalene	Isomeric xylenes
Silver nitrate in polyethylene glycol	Low-boiling olefins
Hydrogenated vegetable oil	N-acetyl butyl esters of amino acids

Various techniques of sample introduction have been developed during the last few years, but the most common technique for liquid samples is the rapid injection by means of a hypodermic syringe. Gaseous samples are usually swept out of some type of gas pipet by means of the carrier gas.

Martin[31] has stated that the most outstanding achievement in the field of gas chromatography in recent years is the invention of the capillary

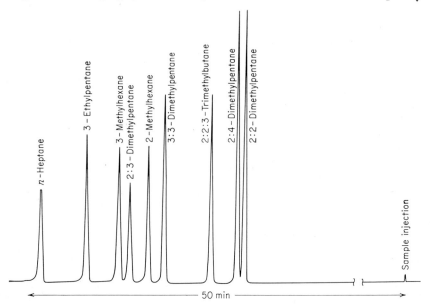

FIG. 5.6. Chromatogram obtained from a capillary column of a mixture of the isomeric heptanes. Column, 250 ft, 10 thou. ID copper capillary; stationary phase, Squalane; temperature, 72°C; carrier gas, nitrogen; inlet pressure, 15 psi; flow rate, 0.6 ml per min; sample size, approximately 2 μg; efficiency, 106,000 theoretical plates (3-ethylpentane); detector, flame ionization. [*From R. P. W. Scott, Mfg. Chemist,* **29**, 517 (1958).]

column by Golay.[21,32] Briefly, a capillary column consists of a capillary tube of approximately 0.01 in. ID 100 to 300 ft long with no packing material. This has led Martin to comment[31] that "he [Golay] has shown that nothing is an excellent packing. So, I would like to thank him for nothing." In contrast, the ordinary packed columns are about ¼ in. in diameter and hardly ever longer than 30 ft. The inside of the capillary tube is coated with a thin film of the appropriate stationary phase. Because of the high pneumatic resistance of the capillary, volumetric gas flow rates of 0.5 to 1 ml per min are used, but the linear gas velocity is very high due to the small capillary cross-sectional area. Consequently, analyses with capillary columns are much faster than with conventional packed columns, and columns with several hundred thousand plates have been reported.   A maximum sample charge of 1 to 2 mg is used with capillary columns, which necessitates the use of highly sensitive detectors. Flame ionization or radiological detectors are generally employed. The operating principles of capillary column gas chromatography have been described in fair detail by Condon[33] and Scott.[34]

Large numbers of papers describing the application of capillary columns are appearing, and it seems from the results that capillary columns may supersede the packed columns for routine analytical work. The following advantages of the capillary column must be acknowledged: The apparatus is compact, the preparation of the column is very simple, the thermostatic bath can be small and easily regulated, efficiency is high, analyses are fast, and minute quantities of sample are required. Most striking, though, is a comparison of elution curves for a complex sample obtained from a capillary column and a high-efficiency packed column (compare Figs. 5.6 and 5.7).

Detectors. If the column is the heart of a gas chromatograph, the detector or the sensing device is the brain of a gas chromatograph. The desirable properties of any kind of detector are the following: (1) It must be fast; that is, its response to any change in the composition of the effluent must be very fast. (2) It must be very sensitive; that is, it must detect a minute trace of any other material in the carrier gas. (3) It should be quantitative; that is, the intensity of its response should bear some quantitative relation to the amount of the solute in the carrier gas.

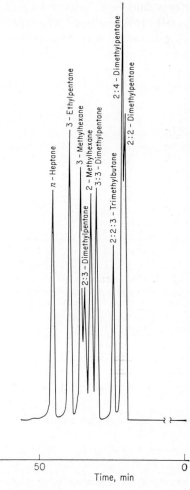

Fig. 5.7. Chromatogram obtained from a conventional packed high-efficiency column of a mixture of the isomeric heptanes. Column, 50 ft, 2.2 mm; stationary phase, 20 per cent w/w "apiezon" oil on 100-120 firebrick; temperature, 78°C; carrier gas, argon; inlet pressure, 180 psi; sample size, 15 μg; efficiency, 30,000 to 40,000 plates; detector, argon. [*From R. P. W. Scott, Mfg. Chemist,* **29,** 517 (1958).]

Although the success of the gas-chromatographic method depends upon the availability of the detectors which fulfill the foregoing requirements, a detailed discussion of the different types of detectors should form the subject matter of an entirely independent topic of discussion. The physical principles utilized in the detectors and in their instrumentation have no relation to the physical principles involved in gas chromatography and the instrumentation of the chromatographic assembly. Such a discussion is beyond the scope of this chapter. Therefore, only some of the more important types of detectors will be mentioned here.

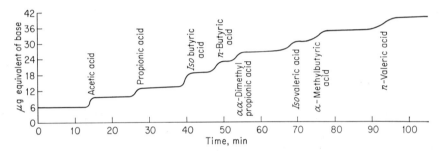

Fig. 5.8. The separation of acetic, propionic, n-butyric, and isobutyric acids and the isomers of valeric acid, showing the complete resolution of all bands and change in band shape in ascending the series. Column length, 11 ft; liquid phase, stearic acid (10 per cent w/w) in DC 550 silicone; nitrogen pressure, 74 cm Hg; flow rate, 18.2 ml per min; temperature, 137°C. [*From James and Martin, Biochem. J.*, **50**, 679 (1951).]

The chromatographic detectors can be broadly classified into two groups, the integral detectors and the differential detectors. The detector used by James and Martin[7] in their pioneering experiment was an integral detector which automatically performed the titration of the fatty acids in the effluent. It is quite obvious that the method is limited. When the integral detector is employed, the chromatogram is obtained in the form of steps, whereas when a differential detector is used, the chromatogram consists of a number of peaks. Figures 5.6 and 5.7 represent chromatograms obtained by using a differential detector, whereas Fig. 5.8 shows a typical chromatogram employing an integral detector.

By far the most common differential detector is the thermal-conductivity type, which is almost exclusively used in commercial instruments. This detector has been exhaustively studied[36] and is adequate for most analytical purposes. The other important types are the dielectric constant detector,[37] surface potential detector,[37,38] Martin's density comparator,[39] flame detector, flame ionization detector, and radiological detector.[35] The flame ionization and radiological detectors have great potentialities as far as sensitivity and high-temperature gas chromatography are concerned. With the flame ionization detector, the sample must be organic in nature.

In the instruments using differential detectors the signal due to any imbalance between reference and the measuring sides of the detector is fed into a strip-chart recorder after proper amplification. As a result, the arrival of the different solutes in the effluent is recorded in the form of

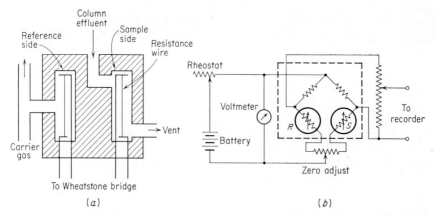

FIG. 5.9. (a) A schematic diagram of a differential thermal-conductivity detector. (b) The variation in resistivity of the wires is measured with a Wheatstone-bridge circuit.

peaks in contrast to steps obtained in integral methods. Figure 5.9 is a schematic diagram of a differential thermal-conductivity detector. The principle of the method is that heat is conducted away from a hot body in a gas at a rate depending on the nature of the gas if other factors are held constant. In practice, a resistance wire placed in the gas line is heated by a constant direct current. Thus, the temperature of the wire and its resistance is determined by the heat conductivity of the surrounding gas. Since absolute measurements of thermal conductivity are difficult to make, a differential procedure is adopted that places one resistance wire in the effluent-gas stream and one in the pure carrier-gas stream. The variation in resistivity of the wires, which is a function of the thermal conductivity of the gas, is measured with a Wheatstone-bridge circuit. If the bridge is first balanced with pure carrier gas about both wires, any change in the effluent-gas composition will unbalance the bridge and can be recorded.

5.7. Applications. There has been such a tremendous number of papers pertaining to the use of gas chromatography that it is impossible to summarize them here. It is possible only to classify the various applications into broad groups and give representative examples of the groups appropriate to this discussion.

Basically, the applications are either analytical or nonanalytical in nature. Nonanalytical applications include such things as the measurement of activity coefficients, heats of solution, partition coefficients, and the determination of structure and fall outside the realm of this discussion. The interested reader should consult the current chemical literature. Analytical applications are by far the most important and include the separation, identification, and quantitative estimation of the components of complex mixtures.

Since chromatography is essentially a separation technique, it is not surprising that literally thousands of separations of all conceivable mixtures have been reported. A careful check of the review literature[40-43] and bibliographies will reveal a wealth of information. Consequently, only a few separations will be discussed here that partially illustrate the selectivity, sensitivity, and versatility of gas chromatography.

The separation of the volatile fatty acids (see Fig. 5.8) by James and Martin[7] is of classic interest and shows what can be done with gas chromatography. Isovaleric acid (bp 176.7°C) can be completely separated from α-methyl butyric acid (bp 177°C) by a very simple procedure. Thus, for quite obvious reasons, the petroleum industry is tremendously interested in the development of gas chromatography. Petroleum mixtures containing 20 or more constituents in any boiling fraction have been successfully resolved. With the introduction of temperature programming, even more complex fractions boiling over a wide range have been analyzed in a single chromatogram. In the coal-tar fraction boiling up to 218°C, for example, 52 compounds have been separated and identified. Of these, 27 compounds were separated and identified for the first time by gas chromatography.[44] Figure 5.10 demonstrates well the results of temperature programming and suggests why a number of commercial instruments feature temperature programming up to 350°C. The difference between conventional chromatography and programmed temperature chromatography lies in the fact that in conventional chromatography separation takes place under isothermal column conditions whereas in programmed temperature chromatography the column temperature is raised during the course of analysis. Temperature can be raised at definite intervals or continually at a uniform rate. In the latter case it is known as linear programming. The chief advantage of temperature programming is that it makes possible the analysis of a mixture covering a wide range of boiling points within

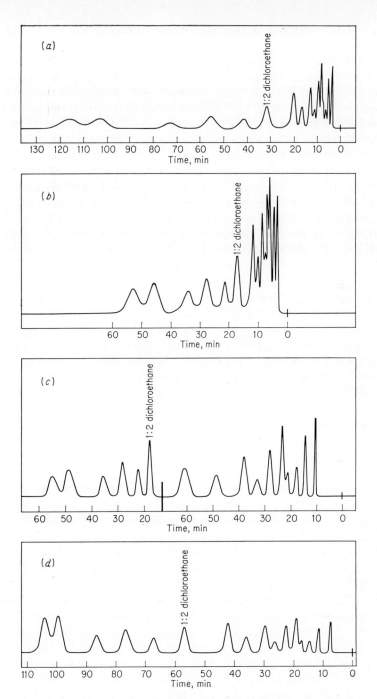

Fig. 5.10. Chromatograms of a complex chlorinated hydrocarbon mixture. (a) Analysis on one column at 75°C. (b) Analysis on one column at 100°C. (c) Two-stage analysis on two columns at 77 and 55°C. (d) Analysis on one column programmed from 25 to 100°C. [From R. P. W. Scott. Mfg. Chemist. **29,** 517 (1958).]

a reasonable time and still gives peaks with uniform shape and characteristics.

Gas chromatography has been just as effective in resolving isomers, products of aldol condensations, derivatives of amino acids, long-chain fatty acids, products in automobile exhausts, air pollutants, and volatile food products. A rather unusual and very interesting application is the identification and determination of alcoholic intoxication.[45]

Another area of potentiality is the separation of volatile inorganic compounds. Freiser[46] and Wachi[47] have reported the separation of some volatile metal chlorides, while Duswalt[48] and Biermann and Gesser[49] were able to resolve some metal acetylacetonates.

From the theoretical discussion, it should be apparent that under a definite set of experimental conditions, the retention volume or time is a characteristic property of a substance and can be used in its identification. In routine analyses, though, a suitable standard is added to the sample mixture and retention volumes or times are measured relative to the standards. Thus, any changes occurring in operating conditions during the analyses affect all solutes alike and relative retention times are unaffected. A direct comparison of relative retention times for a known and an unknown can serve as a criterion for identification of the unknown just as a comparison of R_f values for known and unknown is used for identification in other forms of chromatography.

A more sophisticated identification test for unknowns involves a plot of the logarithm of the relative retention volume of members of a homologous series versus the number of carbon atoms. Such plots and modifications of such plots yield straight lines.[7,50] Figure 5.11 is one such plot for a series of paraffin hydrocarbons, alcohols, esters, ethers, and methyl ketones. The results clearly indicate the feasibility of applying such data in the identification of unknown compounds in a given class. Pierotti et al.[51] went further and obtained sets of parallel lines for different homologous series by plotting the log of retention volumes in one solvent against the log of retention volumes in another solvent and showed that the slopes and intercepts of such straight lines are characteristic of the functional groups.

The principle of quantitative estimation is somewhat empirical when a thermal-conductivity differential detector is used, but it is possible to get accurate determinations if calibration curves are prepared by plotting areas under the elution curve of a pure compound versus the amount used. Less precise determinations can be achieved for a large number of substances simultaneously if helium is used as the carrier gas and the calibration curve is prepared from a suitable substance. This is possible because the thermal conductivity of helium is far greater than the compounds being analyzed. Still another technique is to isolate and

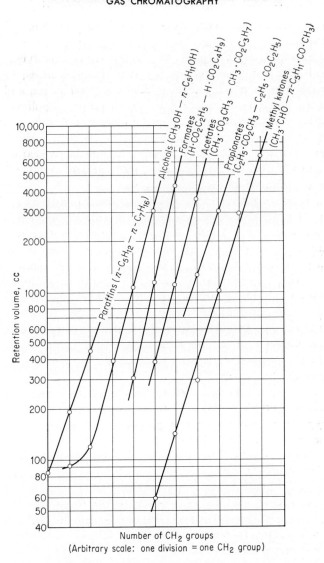

Fig. 5.11. Relationship between retention volume and chain length. [*From M. H. Ray, J. Appl. Chem. (London)*, **4**, 21 (1954).]

collect the pure substance with a fraction collector[52] and determine it by conventional means.   This, of course, is also a means of preparing small amounts of high-purity samples.

Automation has also dawned in the field of gas chromatography, but it is primarily confined to the analysis of gas samples, particularly hydrocarbon gas streams of petroleum refineries.

5.8. Limitations.   Gas chromatography has some distinct advantages over solution chromatography and other separation techniques.   It is rapid, efficient, extremely selective, easily adapted to automatic recording and control operations, and columns can be used over and over again without repacking.   Sample components are diluted very little with carrier gas and can be analyzed for directly by a number of methods. Detectors are extremely sensitive and reliable.

There are also some rather severe limitations to the use of gas chromatography.   Separations are restricted to readily volatile substances or to those which are stable at the temperatures required for volatilization, and only small quantities of sample can be used in the usual equipment. The latter is the main restriction in the use of the technique as a general preparative scheme for pure components.   In the commercially available preparative scale gas chromatographs these difficulties are overcome in the following ways: (1) using columns of larger diameters, from $\frac{3}{8}$ to $\frac{5}{8}$ in.; (2) using a number of parallel columns; and (3) using automatic sample injection and collection devices.   According to manufacturers' literature 9-ml samples can be introduced into the Beckman Megachrom, which employs eight $\frac{5}{8}$-in. parallel columns.   Another commercial model, the Aerograph Autoprep A-700, can repeat itself 200 times in approximately 60 hr using a 100-ml sample with 0.5-ml injection.   Some substrate materials show a great variation in capacity, selectivity, and reversibility of the sorptive process.

5.9. Selected Bibliography

Coates, V. J., H. J. Noebels, and I. S. Fagerson (eds.): "Gas Chromatography," Academic Press, Inc., New York, 1958.
Desty, D. H., and C. L. A. Harbourn: "Vapor Phase Chromatography," Academic Press, Inc., New York, 1957.
Keulemans, A. I. M.: "Gas Chromatography," 2d ed., Reinhold Publishing Corporation, New York, 1959.
Nogare, S. D.: Analytical Reviews, *Anal. Chem.*, **32**, 19R (1960).
Pecsok, R. L. (ed.): "Principles and Practice of Gas Chromatography," John Wiley & Sons, Inc., New York, 1959.
Phillips, C.: "Gas Chromatography," Academic Press, Inc., New York, 1956.

REFERENCES

1. Turner, N. C.: *Petrol. Refiner*, **22**, 98 (1943).
2. Claesson, S.: *Arkiv. Kemi, Mineral Geol.*, **23A**(1) (1946).
3. Glueckauf, E., K. H. Barker, and G. P. Kitt: *Discussions Faraday Soc.*, **7**, 199 (1949).
4. Phillips, C. S. G.: *Discussions Faraday Soc.*, **7**, 244 (1949).
5. Martin, A. J. P.: "Gas Chromatography," V. J. Coates (ed.), chap. XXIV, pp. 237–247, Academic Press, Inc., New York, 1958.
6. Martin, A. J. P., and R. L. M. Synge: *Biochem. J.*, **35**, 1358 (1941).

7. James, A. T., and A. J. P. Martin: *Biochem. J.*, **50**, 679 (1951).
8. Muller, R. H.: *Anal. Chem.*, **32**, 125A (1960).
9. Keulemans, A. I. M.: "Gas Chromatography," p. 14, Reinhold Publishing Corporation, New York, 1957.
10. Keulemans, A. I. M.: "Gas Chromatography," chap. 8, pp. 185–199, Reinhold Publishing Corporation, New York, 1957.
11. Claesson, S.: *Discussions Faraday Soc.*, **7**, 34 (1949).
12. James, D. H., and C. S. G. Phillips: *J. Chem. Soc.*, 1954, p. 1066.
13. Young, J. F.: "Gas Chromatography," V. J. Coates (ed.), chap. II, pp. 15–23, Academic Press, Inc., New York, 1958.
14. Craig, L. C.: *J. Biol. Chem.*, **155**, 519 (1944).
15. Van Deemter, J. J., F. J. Zuiderweg, and A. Klinkenberg: *Chem. Eng. Sci.*, **5**, 271 (1956).
16. de Wet, W. J., and V. Pretonius: *Anal. Chem.*, **32**, 169 (1960).
17. Keulemans, A. I. M.: "Gas Chromatography," chap. 4, pp. 110–111, Reinhold Publishing Corporation, New York, 1957.
18. Porter, P. E., C. H. Deal, and F. H. Stross: *J. Am. Chem. Soc.*, **78**, 2999 (1956).
19. Klinkenberg, A., and F. Sjentizer: *Chem. Eng. Sci.*, **5**, 258 (1956).
20. Sen, B.: *Anal. Chim. Acta*, **22**, 130 (1960).
21. Golay, M. J. E.: *Anal. Chem.*, **29**, 928 (1957).
22. Glueckauf, E.: *Trans. Faraday Soc.*, **51**, 34 (1955).
23. Keulemans, A. I. M.: "Gas Chromatography," chap. 4, pp. 116–119, Reinhold Publishing Corporation, New York, 1957.
24. Consden, R., A. H. Gordon, and A. J. P. Martin: *Biochem. J.*, **38**, 224 (1944).
25. Ambrose, D., A. I. M. Keulemans, and J. H. Purnell: *Anal. Chem.*, **30**, 1582 (1958).
26. Littlewood, A. B., C. S. G. Phillips, and D. T. Price: *J. Chem. Soc.*, 1955, p. 1480.
27. Tenny, H. M.: *Anal. Chem.*, **30**, 473 (1958).
28. Hausdorff, H. H., and N. Brenner: *Oil Gas J.*, July 14, 1958.
29. Rosie, D. M., and R. L. Grob: *Anal. Chem.*, **29**, 1263 (1957).
30. Hausdorff, H. H., and N. Brenner: *Oil Gas J.*, July 21, 1958.
31. Martin, A. J. P.: "Gas Chromatography," V. J. Coates, H. J. Noebels, and I. S. Fagerson (eds.), chap. XXIV, p. 237, Academic Press, Inc., New York, 1958.
32. Golay, M. J. E.: "Gas Chromatography," V. J. Coates, H. J. Noebels, and I. S. Fagerson (eds.), p. 1, Academic Press, Inc., New York, 1958.
33. Condon, R. D.: *Anal. Chem.*, **31**, 1717 (1959).
34. Scott, R. P. W.: *Mfg. Chemist*, **29**, 517 (1958).
35. Scott, R. P. W.: *Mfg. Chemist*, **29**, 411 (1958).
36. Dimbat, M., P. E. Porter, and F. H. Stross: *Anal. Chem.*, **28**, 290 (1956); also see the different manufacturers' bulletins including those distributed by Gow-Mac Instruments Company.
37. Griffiths, J. J., D. James, and C. Phillips: *Analyst*, **77**, 897 (1952).
38. Phillips, G.: *J. Sci. Instr.*, **28**, 342 (1951).
39. Martin, A. J. P., and A. T. James: *Biochem. J.*, **63**, 138 (1956).
40. Nogare, S. D.: Analytical Reviews, *Anal. Chem.*, **32**, 19R (1960).
41. Hardy, C. J., and F. H. Pollard: *J. Chromatog.*, **2**, 1 (1959).
42. Applied Reviews, *Anal. Chem.*, **31**, 631 (1959).
43. Strain, H. H.: Analytical Reviews, *Anal. Chem.*, **32**, 3R (1960).
44. Chang, T. L., and C. Karr, Jr.: Presented at the Symposium on Tars, Pitches and Asphalts at the ACS Meeting in Boston, April, 1959.
45. Cadman, W. J., and Theron Jhons: Presented at the Pittsburgh Conference on Analytical Chemistry and Applied Spectroscopy, March, 1958.

46. Freiser, H.: *Anal. Chem.*, **31**, 1440 (1959).
47. Wachi, F. M.: Ph.D. Dissertation, University of Illinois, 1959; *Dissertation Abstr.*, **20**, 53 (1959).
48. Duswalt, A. A.: Ph.D. Dissertation, Purdue University, 1959; *Dissertation Abstr.*, **20**, 52 (1959).
49. Biermann, W. J., and H. Gesser: *Anal. Chem.*, **32**, 1525 (1960).
50. Ray, N. H.: *J. Appl. Chem. (London)*, **4**, 21 (1954).
51. Pierotti, G. J., E. L. Deal, and P. E. Porter: *J. Am. Chem. Soc.*, **78**, 2989 (1956).
52. Weinstein, A.: *Anal. Chem.*, **29**, 1899 (1957).

CHAPTER 6

PAPER CHROMATOGRAPHY

6.1. Introduction. Capillary analysis, the precursor of modern-day paper chromatography and filter-paper spot-test procedures, was introduced in 1861 by Schönbein.[1] Schönbein showed that, when a solution was allowed to rise through paper by capillary action, the solvent migrated faster than the solute. He observed that materials dissolved in water were retained to different extents by filter paper and that the relative heights reached by different solutes were characteristic of the solute. Goppelsroeder made a thorough investigation of this phenomenon and collected much information on the heights and rates of ascent in filter paper of organic solvents and solutions. Although these early workers recognized that capillary analysis was potentially a powerful analytical tool, it was many years before the techniques were fully developed for qualitative analyses.

Capillary analysis suffered from some inherent difficulties that are now apparent. The technique was essentially that of present-day "frontal analysis" and, as a consequence, was incapable of completely resolving even a binary mixture. With only one solute in a solvent, two zones can be formed on paper. The outer zone will contain pure solvent, and the inner zone, solvent plus solute. For example, dilute sulfuric acid undergoes separation on paper to give a narrow zone of pure water and a zone of slightly more concentrated acid. A quantitative separation of sample components is never accomplished.

Capillary analysis revealed that filter paper exhibited selective adsorption toward solutes and that it was possible to accumulate solutes in zones when solutions migrated through filter paper. The heights and times of migration were very dependent on the temperature, nature, and concentration of the solute and on the capillary medium. It was predicted that the observed differences in heights of ascent for different solutes could be the basis for a new method of analysis.

In 1944, Consden, Gordon, and Martin[2] introduced a new kind of adsorption analysis on filter paper that did not have many of the disadvantages associated with capillary analysis. The new modification utilized filter paper as the adsorbing medium with a technique analogous to "elution analysis" used in adsorption chromatography. The development of a paper chromatogram is carried out roughly in the following manner: The solution to be analyzed is placed or spotted on the paper a short distance from one end, and the solvent is evaporated, leaving a restricted deposit of solutes. The end of the paper is then inserted in a solvent, and the solvent flows through the paper by capillary action. Under suitable conditions the deposited solutes will dissolve and migrate from their original position under the flow of the solvent. Just as in elution analysis, it is possible to effect a complete resolution of solutes owing to the selective adsorption of the filter paper.

The paper chromatography of Consden, Gordon, and Martin was a direct extension of the partition column developed by Martin and Synge.[3] The mechanism of zone development was believed the result of solute partitioning between a mobile solvent phase and a stationary phase composed of a cellulose-water complex. Inasmuch as cellulose will take up to 20 per cent its own weight of water when equilibrated in a moisture-laden atmosphere, this was not a wild conclusion. In fact, there is much evidence to support the view that under certain conditions the solutes are partitioned between the solvent and the cellulose unit. There are, however, other mechanisms by which the solutes can be taken up by the cellulose. Certainly physical adsorption of molecular species and the ion exchange of ionic species must be considered. To understand what the binding mechanism is, it is necessary to know something about the physical and chemical properties of cellulose.

6.2. Physical and Chemical Properties of Cellulose. Commercial grades of filter paper or filter-paper pulp are very high purity samples of cellulose. The cellulose molecule is a polymeric structure made up of several thousand anhydroglucose units linked through the oxygen. Theoretically, three hydroxyl groups are available on each glucose residue and there are potential aldehyde groups on the ends of the chain. There is also a very low mineral content that is not completely inactive chemically. Traces of metal salts are adsorbed or deposited on the paper during preparation, and some are held as exchangeable cations by carboxyl groups.

The cellulose contains hydroxyl, carboxyl, aldehyde, and ketone functional groups. Oxidation of the hydroxyl groups during manufacturing is responsible for most of the carboxyl, aldehyde, and ketone groups. Cellulose is electronegative in water and is highly polar. It has a great affinity for water and other polar solvents and holds them strongly through the formation of hydrogen bonds. The complex cellulose molecule can act as a reducing agent and upon prolonged contact will reduce permanganate, ferric salts, alkali ferricyanides, and dipicrylamines.

Mechanical and chemical treatment during manufacture shortens the naturally long glucose chains and contributes to the capillary adsorption properties of the cellulose. The diffusion of solutions through the filter paper is due to capillary and adsorption phenomena. Relatively large interstitial spaces between the cellulose fibers are responsible for the rates of diffusion. Smaller capillaries within the individual fibers expose a large surface area, which is favorable to increased adsorption of solutes.

Cassidy[4] has given an excellent review of the factors which influence the flow of a liquid through filter paper. The bulk-phase and molecular properties of the paper, the fluid, and the entire system are discussed. Some 92 references are listed.

6.3. Adsorption Mechanisms Involving Cellulose. Filter paper is used in several different ways as a chromatographic medium. It can provide the cellulose-water complex for the stationary phase in a partition mechanism. Although the exact composition of the complex is unknown, there is substantial evidence that it does exist and that under certain circumstances it is the dominant factor in the development of a chromatogram. A number of workers have shown that the R_f values of amino acids chromatographed on filter paper agree well with the values calculated from their respective partition coefficients. The evidence presently available suggests that the cellulose under certain circumstances may act as the stationary phase for a partitioning mechanism. It would be unrealistic, however, not to mention that many separations cannot be explained on the basis of the partitioning theory.

Filter paper may serve in a dual role as a medium for a true partitioning process. Besides being saturated with water prior to the use of a water-immiscible solvent, papers have been impregnated with rubber, high-molecular-weight alcohols, petroleum jelly, various fatty derivatives, and silicones. Most of these substances are good solvents for at least certain types of solutes. When supported on paper they serve as the immobile phase for the partitioning process. For example, rubber will absorb a large volume of petroleum ether and other organic solvents. With the solvent-impregnated rubber fixed to the paper as a support, an immobile organic solvent phase is established.

Cellulose must be classified as a weak adsorbent if compared in its adsorptive powers with a number of the more common solid adsorbents. Nevertheless, the adsorption characteristics of cellulose are sufficient to produce a differential migration of solutes in certain solvent media. Burma[5] briefly surveyed the suggested mechanisms by which paper may selectively retard the migration of solutes and offered experimental evidence to show that true adsorption of the solute by cellulose could occur. He reasoned that the water associated with the cellulose was of two distinct types: chemically bound water which could not be the immobile solvent in a partitioning process and free adsorbed water. Any partitioning of solute between the bulk phase and the adsorbed water would be a true liquid-liquid distribution, but any partitioning of solute between the adsorbed water and the chemically bound water would be adsorption. Evidence indicated that the adsorption process played a definite but minor role in the selective retardation of solute-migration rates in cellulose. Thus, it is mainly a matter of definition of terms whether the mechanism is pure adsorption or a true liquid-liquid partitioning.

In addition to its use as a solid adsorbent, cellulose has been widely used as a substrate or support for various adsorbents. Alumina[6] and silicic acid[7] have been precipitated in the pores of filter paper to produce a thin sheet of adsorbent with the flexibility of paper but the adsorbent characteristics of the precipitate. Similarly, papers have been saturated with solutions and dried to produce a paper impregnated with an adsorbent. Starch, 8-hydroxyquinoline,[8] dimethylglyoxime, sodium chloride, and many other solutes have produced papers with unusual adsorption characteristics. Procedures involving papers impregnated with common precipitants are sometimes referred to as precipitation chromatography and facilitate spot-test procedures.[9]

Spot-test and chromatographic procedures on filter-paper disks are very useful for the separation of two or three components, but they are not a satisfactory substitute for large-scale paper chromatography in the separation of more complex mixtures. Weisz[10] has introduced a "ring-oven" technique (see Chap. 8) that permits the concentration of solutes from a single drop in concentric rings on a disk of filter paper. His technique is suitable for the qualitative detection of at least 14 cations in a single drop. The method is not a chromatographic procedure because the separation of solutes is not achieved by differential migration in an equilibrium system.

Filter paper can also be used as an ion-exchange adsorption medium. Ordinary filter paper possesses only a limited number of ionic functional groups that are capable of exchanging ions with other electrolytes. The ion-exchange capacity of paper is attributed to the presence of about one carboxylic acid group per 100 glucose residues. When cellulose is treated with succinic anhydride, the gross structure is unchanged but a large number of free carboxyl groups are produced. The number is great enough to produce a paper with distinct cation-exchange characteristics. Papers have also been impregnated with powdered ion-exchange resins to produce a flexible ion-exchange medium.

6.4. Apparatus. The basic equipment needed for the development of paper chromatograms is usually available in all laboratories, even those with meager supplies. A reasonably airtight container which will not

absorb the solvent vapors is a necessity.   Reproducible solute-migration
rates are possible only if the chromatogram is developed in an atmosphere
saturated with the solvent and free of drafts.   Under these conditions the
maximum resolving power can be obtained because the solvent-solute-
adsorbent system can approach equilibrium.   Glass jars, bell jars, battery
jars, test tubes, biological-specimen tanks, large graduated cylinders,
hydrometer jars, aquariums, and earthenware crocks and pipes have all
been used and are adequate if they can be covered with a tight-fitting
lid.   The cumbersome sealed containers can be dispensed with and the

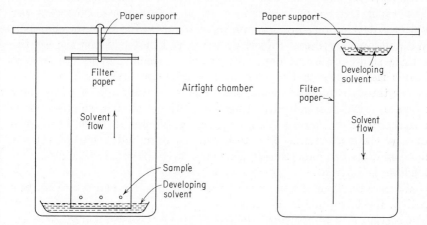

Fig. 6.1. Apparatus for ascending paper   Fig. 6.2. Apparatus for descending paper
chromatography.   chromatography.

equipment made more compact if the paper is sandwiched between two
glass plates.

A tray for the developing solvent must be provided, although the
solvent can be poured directly into the chromatographic chamber, thus
eliminating the need for a separate reservoir.   Some means of supporting
the paper in a vertical position with one end dipping into the developing
solvent completes the list of necessary equipment.   Figure 6.1 illustrates
a typical laboratory setup that provides an efficient and versatile means of
developing paper chromatograms.

Additional apparatus that will prove helpful is an atomizer for spraying reagents on the developed chromatogram and an ultraviolet lamp.
Both of these accessories are invaluable aids to the operator.

6.5. One-dimensional Chromatography.   Conventionally, paper chromatograms are developed in the following way.   Small volumes of the
sample solution are spotted near one end of the filter paper, and the excess
sample solvent evaporated.   Preferably the dimensions of the spots or

initial zones of deposited solute are kept to a minimum, usually less than 0.5 cm in diameter or width.

Attempts[11,12] have been made to restrict the spreading of drops on filter paper by surrounding the area with a ring of suitable material (paraffin waxes, naphthalene, etc.) that will contain the solvent. In this way, sample aliquots of 50 to 100 μl can be deposited in an area normally covered by 5 μl. To apply relatively large quantities of material to paper quickly and simply, fold the paper along a line parallel to and near the bottom of the sheet. Dip the edge of the fold into the solution and withdraw. A narrow to wide band of solute is deposited on the paper. The paper is then suspended in the sealed chromatographic chamber until the developing solvent vapors have saturated the air in the chamber. Without opening the chamber, drop the end of the paper nearest the sample solutes into the developing solvent. Immediately the solvent begins rising through the capillaries of the paper. When the solvent passes through the solute zone, some of the solutes are leached out and migrate with the solvent. The interactions of the solute-solvent-adsorbent system cause solutes to migrate at different rates and thus produce a chromatogram. The technique is essentially that of elution analysis described under adsorption chromatography; only the adsorption medium is different.

When the solvent flows upward through the filter paper by capillary action, the technique is referred to as *ascending* paper chromatography. The solvent is flowing against the pull of gravity; consequently, there is a practical, as well as theoretical, limit to the height the solvent will rise. If the migration rates of solutes are not greatly different, then the distance of migration or height of rise of solvent may limit the effectiveness of the method.

The difficulties associated with ascending methods are easily overcome by letting the solvent flow downward through the paper. The method is referred to as *descending* paper chromatography. Apparatus design is illustrated in Fig. 6.2. Usually the relative migration rates of solutes are the same regardless of whether the chromatogram is developed by ascending or descending techniques. Chromatograms developed in the preceding manner are referred to as one-dimensional because the solutes are free to migrate in only one direction.

6.6. Two-dimensional Chromatography. A simple means of increasing the effectiveness of chromatographic separations is to develop a two-dimensional chromatogram. Develop the chromatogram first in one direction. Remove the paper, and evaporate the solvent. Rotate the paper through 90°, immerse the lower edge in a second solvent, and develop the chromatogram. Two different solvents are employed in succession, and the solutes are caused to migrate first in one direction, and then at 90° to the original direction. Resolution efficiency is greatly enhanced by the use of two-dimensional chromatography. Table 6.1 lists the R_f values measured for some amino acids in different solvent systems. Obviously, the resolution of glutamic acid, serine, threonine, aspartic acid, and alanine would be almost impossible with collidine as solvent and incomplete if phenol were the solvent. If, however, the chromatogram were developed first in one direction with collidine and later with phenol in a direction normal to the flow of collidine, then a complete resolution of the mixture would be effected.

TABLE 6.1. R_f VALUES FOR A MIXTURE OF AMINO ACIDS MEASURED IN TWO DIFFERENT SOLVENT SYSTEMS

Amino acid	R_f values	
	Phenol	Collidine
Glutamic acid.............	0.13	0.25
Serine...................	0.33	0.28
Threonine................	0.41	0.32
Alanine..................	0.54	0.32
Aspartic acid.............	0.12	0.22

6.7. Detection of Zones. The positions of the various solute zones after the chromatogram is developed are measured relative to the position of the solvent front. Relative migration rates of the solutes are expressed as R_f values.

$$R_f = \frac{\text{distance solute moved}}{\text{distance solvent moved}}$$

Prior to the measurement of R_f values it is necessary to locate the solute zone on the paper. The following techniques are in common use for the qualitative location of solutes on the paper.

Solutes are easily detected if they are intensely colored or will absorb ultraviolet radiations. When exposed to ultraviolet radiation some solutes quench the natural fluorescence of filter paper while others fluoresce much more strongly than the paper. In either case, the solute will stand out against the cellulose background. Solutes can be made visible by the introduction of a sensitive color- or fluorescent-producing reagent. Test reagents are easily applied by spraying or immersing the paper or simply by placing it in a suitable atmosphere.

Biological "printing" tests locate zones of nutrients or growth inhibitors on paper. The developed chromatogram is placed in contact with a culture medium and left for a period of time. Relative growth rates of the bacteria along the paper strip are indicative of the position of different solutes.

The position in the final chromatogram of radioactive-labeled solutes or radioactive tracers added to the original sample is determined by photographic printing or by more direct measurement of the radioactivity of the paper strip.

Not to be overlooked is the simple procedure of cutting the chromatogram into narrow strips perpendicular to the flow of solvent. Each segment of the chromatogram can then be tested for solutes by various chemical and physical means.

6.8. Applications. Filter-paper chromatography is useful in analytical chemistry mainly for the qualitative and quantitative analysis of complex mixtures. Unknowns are identified by a comparison of their behavior with that of known substances on pilot strips or in mixed chromatograms. The known substance is chromatographed on a pilot or control strip side by side with the unknown or in admixture with the unknown. Identical chromatograms are the criteria for identification of the unknown. Identification of unknowns is also possible by the direct comparison of theoretical and measured R_f values. This has been used as a qualitative test for amino acids and other organic compounds that are members of a homologous series.

Specific test reagents applied in one of the zone-location methods is invaluable in identifying unknowns. The streak reagents referred to in Sec. 4.12 are useful in verifying the presence or absence of a given class of compounds on paper also.

Paper chromatography is one of the most effective means of resolving mixtures on a microscale. It is not at all unusual for the techniques to resolve 1 or 2 μg of solutes in less than 10 μl of sample solution. The determination of substances after they have been resolved by paper chromatography requires special methods. Some of the more common procedures applied to the quantitative analysis of resolved species on paper are listed below.

1. Visually.[13] Compare the resolved solute color with the color of a standard preparation chromatographed adjacent to the sample.

2. Planimetry.[14] Measure the area of the resolved solute spot, and compare it with the area of a standard sample chromatographed under identical conditions. To obtain quantitative results, the area of the unknown spot must be compared with spots obtained from the same volume of a standard solution and developed on the same sheet of paper. Filter paper is usually uniform enough that the spots can be cut out and the area compared by weight measurements.

3. Photometry.[15-18] After a substance has been separated by chromatography, the quantity present can be determined by measuring the

amount of monochromatic light adsorbed by the substance.   No separation or removal from the filter paper is necessary; the paper is brought between the light source and a photoelectric measuring device.   It is essential that the paper be translucent and that the substance be colored or quantitatively convertible to a colored substance or absorb light in the ultraviolet spectrum.   The absorbance or other optical property is plotted versus the distance along the paper strip.   The area under the absorption peak, above background absorption due to the filter paper itself, is proportional to the total absorbing material present.   An accuracy of ± 5 per cent is obtainable, and quantities as small as 10^{-6} g can be determined.

4. Chemical determination.   Elute the individual solutes separately, and determine by ordinary chemical means.

5. Physical properties.   Elute the resolved solutes, and measure some specific physical property of the eluate.

6. Biological assay.[19,20]

7. Radioautography or counting technique.[21]

6.9. Advantages and Disadvantages.   Paper-chromatographic procedures offer the following advantages over more conventional methods of resolving mixtures: The apparatus and techniques are simple, and analyses can be performed rapidly by experienced personnel.   Multiple samples can be run simultaneously under identical conditions.   Microgram-sized samples can be resolved at low temperatures in an inert atmosphere.   Perhaps its greatest advantage is its remarkable resolving power.   Particularly noteworthy is the enhancement of resolutions effected through the development of a two-dimensional chromatogram.

Paper chromatography has the following disadvantages: Procedures are generally arrived at in an empirical fashion, and a sound theoretical understanding of the adsorption mechanism is unknown.   The procedure is ineffective in most preparative work because a severe limitation is placed on the quantity of material to be resolved.   This disadvantage has been partially overcome by using special papers several millimeters thick[22] and powdered cellulose in columnar chromatography.

6.10. Selected Bibliography

Balston, J. N., and B. E. Talbot: "A Guide to Filter Paper and Cellulose Powder Chromatography," T. S. G. Jones (ed.), H. Reeve Angel & Co., London, 1952.

Block, R. J., R. LeStrange, and G. Zweig: "Paper Chromatography—A Laboratory Manual," Academic Press, Inc., New York, 1953.

Clegg, D. L., Anal. Chem., **22**, 48 (1950).

Forsyth, W G. C. Chem. & Ind., 1953, p. 315.

Lederer, E., and M. Lederer: "Chromatography," 2d ed., D. Van Nostrand Company, Inc., Princeton, N.J., 1957.

Pollard, F. H., and J. F. W. McOmie: "Chromatographic Methods of Inorganic Analysis," Academic Press, Inc., New York, 1953.

Strain, H. H., et al.: *Anal. Chem.*, **21**, 75 (1949); **22**, 41 (1950); **23**, 25 (1951); **24**, 50 (1952); **26**, 90 (1954); **28**, 687 (1956).

REFERENCES

1. Schönbein, F.: *Ann. Chem. Liebigs*, **114**, 275 (1861).
2. Consden, R., A. H. Gordon, and A. J. P. Martin: *Biochem. J.*, **38**, 224 (1944).
3. Martin, A. J. P., and R. L. M. Synge: *Biochem. J.*, **35**, 1358 (1941).
4. Cassidy, H. G.: *Anal. Chem.*, **24**, 1415 (1952).
5. Burma, D. P.: *Anal. Chem.*, **25**, 549 (1953).
6. Datta, S. P., B. G. Overell, and M. Stack-Dunne: *Nature*, **164**, 673 (1949).
7. Kirchner, J. G., and G. J. Keller: *J. Am. Chem. Soc.*, **72**, 1867 (1950).
8. Laskowski, D. E., and W. C. McCrone: *Anal. Chem.*, **23**, 1579 (1951).
9. Feigl, F.: "Qualitative Analysis by Spot Tests," Elsevier Press, Inc., New York, 1947.
10. Weisz, H.: *Mikrochim. Acta*, 1954, p. 376.
11. Ultee, A. J., Jr.: *Chem. Weekblad*, **48**, 82 (1952).
12. Wiegand, O. F., and A. R. Shrank: *Anal. Chem.*, **28**, 259 (1956).
13. Arden, T. U., F. H. Burstall, and R. P. Linstead: *J. Chem. Soc.*, **S**, 311 (1949).
14. Fisher, R. B., D. S. Parsons, and G. A. Morrison: *Nature*, **161**, 764 (1948).
15. Campbell, H., and J. A. Simpson: *Chem. & Ind.*, 1953, p. 342.
16. Drake, N. A., W. J. Haines, R. E. Knauff, and E. D. Nielson: *Anal. Chem.*, **28**, 2036 (1956).
17. Parke, T. V., and W. W. Davis: *Anal. Chem.*, **24**, 2019 (1952).
18. Hashimoto, Y., and I. Mori: *Nature*, **170**, 1024 (1952).
19. Winsten, W. A., and E. Eigen: *J. Biol. Chem.*, **181**, 109 (1949).
20. Winsten, W. A., and A. H. Spark: *Science*, **106**, 192 (1947).
21. Tomarelli, R., and K. Florey: *Science*, **107**, 630 (1948).
22. Brownell, H. H., J. G. Hamilton, and A. A. Casselman: *Anal. Chem.*, **29**, 550 (1957).

CHAPTER 7

ELECTROCHROMATOGRAPHY (ZONE ELECTROPHORESIS)

7.1. Introduction. If a foreign phase which is charged or about which an electrical double layer exists is subjected to a potential gradient, the foreign phase will migrate through the continuous medium to the cathode or anode according to the sign of the charge on the particle. This phenomenon is electrophoresis.

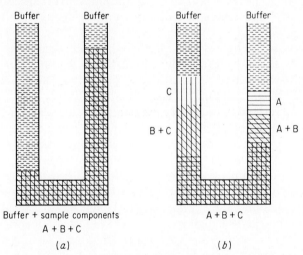

FIG. 7.1 Free electrophoresis of protein mixture.

Early in the development of electrochemical principles it was shown that the passage of an electric current through a homogeneous conducting solution cannot effect changes in the composition of the solution except in regions of discontinuity such as exist at the electrode-solution interface or at concentration gradients. Thus, the basis for electrophoresis is the initial establishment of an inhomogeneity or concentration gradient in the system prior to the application of a potential gradient across the system. Suppose, for example, that an aqueous buffer solution in a U tube (Fig. 7.1) is homogeneous except for the presence of low concentrations of proteins or other charged substances in a portion of the tube. When an electric current is passed through the tube, the charged sample particles will migrate toward the appropriate electrode and a partial separation is achieved. The separations can be followed because particles, such as proteins, do not contribute much to the conductivity of the solution but they generally increase appreciably the refractivity and density of the solution in which they are present. When optical methods are employed to detect the refractive index or its gradient as a function of the height of the U tube, the method is known as free electrophoresis by the boundary method or as the Tiselius method.

The information derived from electrophoretic investigations has been particularly reliable for the characterization of labile biochemically important substances because of the gentleness of the method. Colloids, proteins, enzymes, and the like show characteristic electrophoretic mobilities and isoelectric points which can be used for the identification of a specific substance. It is apparently most unusual for two proteins or enzymes to show the same mobility over the entire pH range studied, and since even small differences in mobility can be detected, the method is used for analysis.

Separations are achieved only if the separated components do not spontaneously remix by convective circulation. At each sample-buffer boundary after migration the least dense solution will lie above a denser one, etc. This stabilization of the boundary system with respect to gravity by the formation of density gradients is a characteristic feature of free electrophoresis, but it is not conducive to a complete separation of the sample components. Rather, in most instances, it means that complete separations are not possible by free electrophoresis. A quantitative resolution of the sample components would give rise to zones that are gravitationally unstable and spontaneously undergo mixing by convection in the electrophoresis tube. Therefore, although the Tiselius or moving-boundary method gives a high resolution of boundaries, it serves more as a guide for separation by other procedures than as a separation method per se. At the end of the experiment only the fastest and slowest moving components can be removed from the migration medium with a fair degree of purity, but not quantitatively. To a certain extent the method is directly comparable to a frontal-analysis chromatographic technique. Because of this very restrictive applicability of free or moving-boundary electrophoresis to separation procedures, the technique will not be discussed in detail.

Fortunately, a variety of techniques has been developed which circumvents the limitations of free electrophoresis and permits a complete separation of sample components. One method involves the development, prior to electrophoresis, of a gravitationally stable density gradient in a vertical electrophoresis tube by the appropriate mixing of the buffer solution and varying amounts of a soluble nonelectrolyte. The density gradients produced by the separated solutes, though less important than in a homogeneous medium, are still undesirable, and the solute relative concentrations must be such that positive density gradients do not arise during the separation process. In the relatively large tubes used for free electrophoresis any density gradient having a component other than vertical or negative tends to set up convection currents which destroy the usefulness of the method.

On the other hand, if electrophoretic migration is allowed to proceed within a porous or stabilized medium, the migrating zones are not affected by convection currents produced by temperature and density gradients as in free electrophoresis. Convection currents are greatly reduced in porous media because the flow of a liquid in a tube is inversely proportional to the square of the radius and the cross-sectional area of the tube is proportional to the square of the radius. Thus, as capillary tubes are substituted for the larger conventional electrophoretic tubes, convection currents resulting from density gradients are practically eliminated. Consequently, quantitative separations of sample components by electrophoresis are possible in a porous medium. Quantitative separations are subject, of course, to the conditions that sample components begin their migration from a narrow zone and are selectively attracted by the established electrical potential and/or selectively retarded by the conducting medium itself.

A variety of materials has been used to provide the necessary capillary interstices as a stabilizing factor in electrophoresis. The more common stabilizers are filter paper, gelatin, agar, starch, foam rubber, and glass spheres, but filter paper is the most versatile and by far the most widely employed medium. Electrophoresis on paper has a number of advantages over electrophoresis in free solutions and other media: Complete separations are possible on a batch or continuous basis, small samples are easily handled, the apparatus is simple and inexpensive, separations can be achieved horizontally as well as vertically, and boundary anomalies interfere less. These advantages are gained at the expense of lowered accuracy in measuring mobilities and isoelectric points, but these limitations are far outweighed by the possibility of achieving a quantitative resolution of sample components. In view of this, the discussion will be centered about electrophoresis on paper.

Electrophoresis on paper was introduced[1] in 1939 and is several years older than the corresponding form of paper chromatography which utilizes an electrical potential, rather than a flowing solvent, as the driving force for solutes. Although the two processes were developed independently, they have through modifications evolved into what is essentially a single technique. To appreciate this, it is necessary to consider only the basic difference between chromatography and electrophoresis. There is a sorptive factor in chromatography, not present in free electrophoresis, which tends to retard selectively the flow of solutes through the migration medium and enhances the separation of sample components. But as soon as paper is substituted as the migration medium in electrophoresis, it is virtually impossible to rule out a sorptive factor as an effective resistive force to the flow of solutes. It is at this point then that electrophoresis on paper and electrochromatography on paper become indistinguishable. Distinguishing features are more the concern of semanticists than of technical personnel interested in the technique as a separation tool. For convenience, then, the single term electrochromatography will be used to refer to the physical transport of charged solutes through paper under the influence of a potential gradient.

7.2. Theory. The migration of charged particles in paper depends on the magnitude and sign of the net charge on the solute, surface charges, the applied voltage, electrolyte concentration, ionic strength, pH, temperature, viscosity, solute adsorptivity, and other physicochemical properties of the migration medium. Ions migrating in one direction also affect the mobility of other ions moving in the opposite direction. The net result is that the system is too complicated to be treated mathematically. Additional complications arise owing to the adsorption of the solutes on the cellulose, a process which depends as much on the properties of the cellulose (discussed in Sec. 6.2) as it does on the properties of the solutes. Inasmuch as there is no comprehensive theory for the prediction of sorptive effects, the prediction of separations and migration rates in electrochromatography remains on an empirical basis.

From what has been said, it is apparent that a comprehensive theoretical treatment of electromigration in cellulose is difficult or next to impossible at the present time, but it is possible to draw some corollaries between electromigration in free or homogeneous media and in cellulose. In free electrophoresis the path traversed by a charged particle is given by the expression

$$d = \frac{uti}{qk} = \frac{utV}{l}$$

where V = volts
l = length of channel
i = current, amp
q = cross-sectional area of migration tube, sq cm
k = conductivity, ohms^{-1} cm^{-1}
d = path traversed by solute particle
u = mobility of ion
t = time

The expression for electromigration in cellulose as derived by Kunkel and Tiselius[2] is

$$d' = \frac{uti}{q_a k} = d\frac{l'}{l}$$

where q_a is the cross-sectional area of the paper strip. The difference in the two expressions is attributed to the particularly sinuous path of solute particle in the cellulose; the path does not correspond to the shortest distance d but is related to it by the factor l'/l, which is a function of the cellulose and which assumes the character of a material constant in experimental measurements. For example, it has been demonstrated

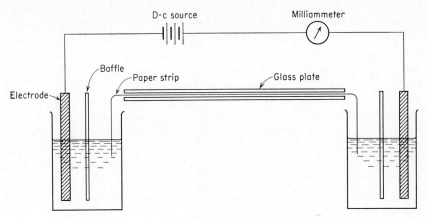

Fig. 7.2. Simple paper electrochromatographic apparatus.

that the measured mobilities of certain solutes are different for different papers but that all values for the same solute become approximately identical when each is multiplied by the appropriate correction factor l/l'.

7.3. Apparatus. The simplest experimental technique for electrochromatography (zone electrophoresis) employs sheets of filter paper moistened with an electrolyte and stretched horizontally between two electrode vessels (see Fig. 7.2) to which a potential difference is applied. The sample is placed in the center of the strip in much the same manner that samples are applied to paper strips for paper chromatography. Since the paper tends to warm up during the passage of current, it is customary to sandwich the paper strip between glass or plastic plates to help conduct the heat away and also to prevent rapid evaporation of the solvent. Capillary flow from the electrolyte vessels will make up any loss of liquid by evaporation, but this movement of solvent can and frequently does interfere with the separation of components. The glass plates have been dispensed with by many workers who simply maintain the paper strip in an atmosphere saturated with the appropriate solvent.

A direct current can be supplied with a rectifier or batteries which will deliver between 100 and 300 volts d-c, although voltages up to 1000 volts are not unusual, particularly for applications to continuous separations. The electric circuit usually contains a milliammeter to measure current flow through the system and a voltmeter to measure the voltage drop across the paper.

In practically all cases the electrodes are either carbon or platinum. If carbon electrodes are used, it is wise to make the electrical contact with platinum wire to prevent corrosion and resultant contamination of the electrode vessel. If platinum electrodes are used, they should have sufficient surface area to prevent an undue amount of polarization.

The combination of electrochromatography with the simultaneous flow of solvent to separate ionic substances has been developed by a number of workers using slightly different techniques. Among the leaders in such work have been Strain and coworkers,[3] who used a modification of the sandwich technique. A thick sheet of filter paper moistened with an electrolyte solution is clamped between two glass plates and held in a vertical position with the electrodes along the side edges. In principle, the current flows horizontally across the paper while the developing solvent moves downward through the paper. The cell is outlined in Fig. 7.3 and is designed for both continuous and discontinuous separations. The vertical edges of the paper are waxed to seal the sides of the cell and contain the supporting electrolyte.

For continuous separations, the sample solution is introduced continuously to the top of the paper in a narrow stream through a wick or waxed channel. As the sample solution flows downward through the paper, the mixture is not resolved because this is a frontal-analysis technique. If it were not for the diversion of charged particles toward the oppositely charged electrodes simultaneously with the chromatographic development, resolutions would be impossible. As it turns out, though, each sample component travels a characteristic path, which is the resultant of the chromatographic and electromigration factors, to the bottom of the paper. The individual components emerge from the paper on various points of the serrated lower edge of the paper and are collected as individual fractions. A continuous separation of positive and negative components is illustrated in Fig. 7.3.

If discontinuous separation is employed, a space is left without paper filler along the top edge of the plates to accommodate the chromatographic developing solvent. A small quantity of the sample mixture is applied as a spot on the top edge of the paper and washed downward through the paper with the developing solvent. As the solution travels downward, an elution chromatographic separation of the sample components occurs simultaneously with the diversion of charged species toward the oppositely charged electrode.   The migration path of the solutes is the resultant of the chromatographic and electromigration factors, and sample components can be completely resolved as replicas of the initial sample spot. This technique is illustrated in Fig. 7.4 with the separation of mercurous, lead, and silver ions in lactic acid.[3]

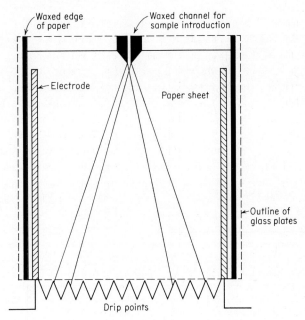

FIG. 7.3. Paper electrochromatographic cell after Strain.

Both the continuous and discontinuous electrochromatographic techniques on large sheets of paper are a special case of two-dimensional paper chromatography.   The only differences are that the driving force of the second developing solvent in conventional two-dimensional paper chromatography has been replaced with a potential gradient and the two driving forces acting normal to each other are applied simultaneously.

All instruments with electrodes contacting the filter paper directly along an entire edge suffer from the diffusion of electrode products into the region of the paper used for the separation.   Strain and Sullivan[3] point out, for example, that, if ammonium acetate were used as the supporting electrolyte, the region about the cathode would become basic and the region about the anode would become acidic during the course of the electrolysis, as is illustrated in Fig. 7.5.   The diffusion of foreign ions from the electrode compartment into paper strips suspended in the electrode compartment is also a distinct possibility unless precautions are taken to separate the electrode compartment from the paper strip with baffles that will retard the migration of electrode products to the vicinity of the paper strip.

The detection of solute zones on paper after an electrochromatographic development is not significantly different from that in paper chromatography to warrant discussion here.

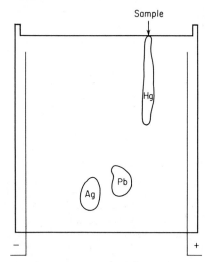

FIG. 7.4. Discontinuous electrochromatographic separation of mercurous, lead, and silver ions with 60 ml of 0.1 M lactic acid as supporting electrolyte.

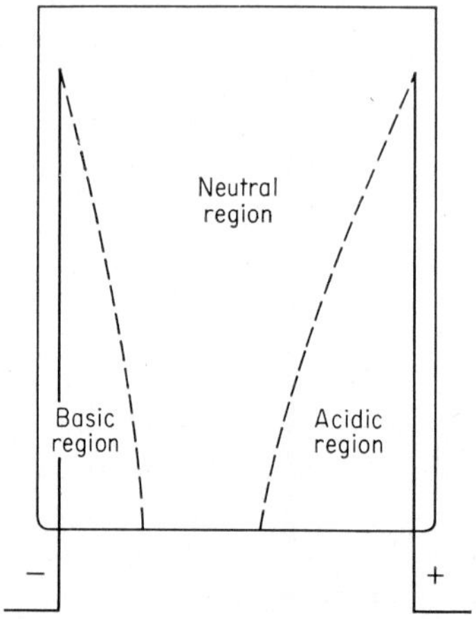

FIG. 7.5. Acidic and basic regions formed in an electrochromatogram using 0.1 M ammonium acetate as the supporting electrolyte.

7.4. Applications. Electrochromatographic sequences serve for the description, comparison, and identification of substances in much the same manner that R_f values are used in conventional chromatography, and electrochromatographic homogeneity of zones is an important criterion in the establishment of purity, but these are not necessarily the most important applications. Foremost in the field of analysis is the resolving power of the technique which makes the subsequent identification and determination of the sample components possible.

Electrochromatographic techniques on paper have been applied to the separation of a rather large number of systems, and it is impossible to cover all the applications here. Bibliographies and reviews[4,5] of the technique are available in the literature and should be consulted for a comprehensive treatment of what has been accomplished with the technique. For these reasons the versatility of the technique will be exemplified with a very limited number of separations selected from the chemical literature in two main areas—inorganic separations and separations of complex organic substances, particularly amino acids. These few examples should be sufficient to orient one as to the chances of success when applying the technique to yet untried systems.

Numerous publications dealing with the separation of groups of inorganic cations have appeared in the literature, principally from the laboratories of M. Lederer and H. H. Strain. A special feature of these inorganic separations is the fact that separations are achieved most readily in the presence of complexing agents, since the simple ions have a strong adsorption affinity for cellulose. The introduction of a complex-forming reagent to the electrolyte affects the rate of both chromatographic development and electromigration, since the complexes formed can have different adsorption affinities for the migration medium and different charges than the simple ions. Thus, even the direction of electromigration can be reversed for a given solute

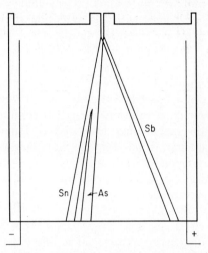

FIG. 7.6. Continuous electrochromatographic separation of stannous, arsenious, and antimonious chlorides. The supporting electrolyte is a mixture of 0.02 M lactic acid, 0.02 M tartaric acid, and 0.04 M DL-alanine. [*H. H. Strain and J. C. Sullivan, Anal. Chem.*, **23**, 816 (1951).]

if it becomes complexed. Silver and nickel ions in a simple electrolyte migrate toward the cathode, but in the presence of ethylenediaminetetraacetic acid the nickel complex moves toward the anode, making a continuous separation of the two ions possible.

Strain and coworkers[3,4] have separated various cations on paper using a combination of solvent flow in one direction and electromigration normal to the flow of solvent. Using either a continuous or discontinuous technique, they effected separations of arsenic, antimony, and tin; silver, mercury, and lead; and iron, cobalt, nickel, and aluminum. The continuous separation of Sn(II), As(III), and Sb(III) chlorides is illustrated in Fig. 7.6.

Harasawa and Sakamoto[6] applied the technique of electrochromatography on paper strips to the separation of alkali metals and magnesium. The sample material was placed in the center of the paper saturated with ammonium hydroxide and subjected to a potential of 225 or 500 volts. They effected complete separations of mixtures of lithium, sodium, rubidium, and magnesium or potassium, sodium, lithium, and magnesium. Separations of potassium and rubidium were incomplete. The migration rates of the alkali ions were reported to be in the order of their ionic mobility and radius. Gross[7] effectively separated the alkali and alkaline-earth ions, with the exception of rubidium and cesium, in 0.1 M ammonium carbonate solution (pH 8.9) with a 100 volts per cm voltage gradient.

Tuckerman and Strain[8] have determined the mobilities of the cations of sodium, potassium, rubidium, and cesium by an electrochromatographic technique on paper using various organic solvents and a potential gradient of 15 volts per cm. Useful separations were obtained in nitromethane solutions using ammonium formate and trichloroacetic acid as the supporting electrolyte. Ionic mobilities decreased in the order cesium, rubidium, potassium, and sodium.

Good separations of quaternary mixtures of lead, platinum, rhodium, iridium, osmium, ruthenium, and gold were obtained on paper strips by electrochromatography in different electrolyte solutions.[9]

Strain et al.[10] have considered the separation of fission products by electrochromatography and reported the separations of various parent-daughter mixtures, including Nd-Pm, Ce-Pr, Ba-La, and Sr-Y. They also reported continuous separations of Y from Ce and of the rare earths from anions such as phosphate.

Continuous separations have been reported also for mixtures of copper and silver; copper and nickel; silver, copper, nickel, and iron; aluminum and iron; and yttrium and cerium.

Lederer and coworkers[11,12] have reported on the electromigration in paper of a number of inorganic cations using various concentrations of hydrochloric and hydrobromic acid as the electrolyte.

Electrochromatographic studies of silver, mercury, lead, and thallium in about 30 different electrolyte media are reported by Majumdar and Singh.[13] The four ions are completely separated in 0.1 M sodium chloride, potassium chloride, and potassium cyanide solutions in about 3 hr. Pučar[14] reports that best results are obtained on the separation of the halogen complexes of mercury, bismuth, cadmium, lead, and copper in 0.5 N potassium bromide or hydrogen bromide solutions.

Organic substances separated by electrochromatography include aliphatic amines,[15] dyes,[16] hydrolysis products of nucleic acids,[17,18] organic acids,[19] monosaccharides,[20] amino acids,[21-23] and proteins.

Typical electrochromatograms obtained in amino acid separations are illustrated in Fig. 7.7. By the proper selection of pH the amino acids can be readily fractionated into three groups: acidic, neutral, and basic. Separations within these groups are then more easily effected by a further control of pH and operational variables.

The application of paper electrochromatography to protein analyses is so extensive that the reader is referred to the monographs and reviews on electrochromatography for a discussion.

An interesting modification[24] of the electromigration procedure in paper is the combination of a centrifugal force with a high-voltage d-c electric field to produce a rapid planar electrochromatographic separation on filter-paper disks. The apparatus is simple and effective.

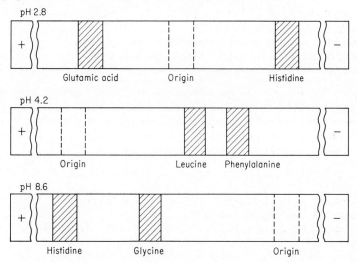

FIG. 7.7. Typical electrochromatograms obtained in amino acid separations. The pH listed is that of the buffer system used. The uppermost electrochromatogram illustrates a case where the pH of the buffer falls between the isoelectric points of the two amino acids and they migrate in opposite directions.

Next to paper, the most promising stabilized medium for electromigration experiments is starch. Starch columns and blocks have been used successfully for the separation of a number of components and are credited with having some definite advantages over paper. The proponents of the starch migration medium argue that proteins and other complex biological materials are adsorbed to a lesser extent on starch than on cellulose and larger quantities can be resolved on starch. The latter argument is not a valid one because it is a comparison of capacities of starch blocks with sheet filter paper and not blocks or columns of cellulose. The reader interested in the applications of starch, gels, agar, etc., as the migration medium in electrochromatography is referred to the monographs in the selected bibliography.

7.5. Selected Bibliography

Bier, M. (ed.): "Electrophoresis," Academic Press, Inc., New York, 1959.
Lederer, M.: "An Introduction to Paper Electrophoresis and Related Methods," Elsevier Press, Inc., New York, 1955.

McDonald, H. J.: "Ionography," Year Book Publishers, Inc., Chicago, 1955.
Pollard, F. H., and J. F. W. McOmie: "Chromatographic Methods of Inorganic Analysis," Butterworths Scientific Publications, London, 1953.
Strain, H. H.: *Anal. Chem.*, **32**, 3R (1960).

REFERENCES

1. von Klobusitsky, D., and P. König: *Arch. exptl. Pathol. Pharmakol. Naunym-Schmiedeberg's*, **192**, 271 (1939).
2. Kunkel, H., and A. Tiselius: *J. Gen. Physiol.*, **35**, 89 (1951).
3. Strain, H. H., and J. C. Sullivan: *Anal. Chem.*, **23**, 816 (1951).
4. Strain, H. H.: *Anal. Chem.*, **32**, 3R (1960); **24**, 356 (1952); T. R. Sato, W. P. Norris, and H. H. Strain, *Anal. Chem.*, **26**, 267 (1954).
5. Lederer, M.: "An Introduction to Paper Electrophoresis and Related Methods," Elsevier Publishing Company, Amsterdam, 1955.
6. Harasawa, S., and T. Sakamoto: *J. Chem. Soc. Japan*, **74**, 862 (1953).
7. Gross, D.: *Nature*, **180**, 596 (1957).
8. Tuckerman, M. M., and H. H. Strain: *Anal. Chem.*, **32**, 695 (1960).
9. Majumdar, A. K., and M. M. Chakrabartty: *Naturwissenschaften*, **44**, 9 (1957).
10. Sato, T. R., H. Diamond, W. P. Norris, and H. H. Strain: *J. Am. Chem. Soc.*, **74**, 6154 (1952).
11. Lederer, M., and F. L. Ward: *Anal. Chim. Acta*, **6**, 355 (1952).
12. Lederer, M.: *Nature*, **167**, 864 (1951).
13. Majumdar, A. K., and B. R. Singh: *Anal. Chim. Acta*, **17**, 541 (1957).
14. Pučar, Z.: *Anal. Chim. Acta*, **18**, 290 (1958).
15. Edward, J. T., and R. Crawford: *J. Chromatog.*, **1**, 449 (1958).
16. Durrum, E. L.: *J. Am. Chem. Soc.*, **73**, 4877 (1951).
17. Davidson, J. N., and R. M. S. Smellie: *Biochem. J.*, **49**, XV (1951).
18. Turba, F., and H. J. Enenkel: *Naturwissenschaften*, **38**, 189 (1951).
19. Barnett, A. J. G., and D. K. Smith: *Nature*, **174**, 659 (1954).
20. Consden, R., and W. M. Stanier: *Nature*, **169**, 783 (1952).
21. Durrum, E. L.: *J. Am. Chem. Soc.*, **72**, 2943 (1950); **73**, 4875 (1951); *J. Colloid Sci.*, **6**, 274 (1951).
22. Katz, A. M., W. J. Dreyer, and C. B. Anfinsen: *J. Biol. Chem.*, **234**, 2897 (1959).
23. Matthias, W.: *J. Chromatog.*, **2**, 434 (1959).
24. McDonald, H. J., L. P. Ribeiro, and L. J. Banaszak: *Anal. Chem.*, **31**, 825 (1959).

CHAPTER 8

THE RING-OVEN TECHNIQUE

8.1. Introduction. With the exception of a few physical techniques such as distillation, solvent extraction, etc., the classic methods of analytical separations depend on the conversion of one part of the sample into an insoluble compound and isolation by filtration. This requires a number of steps, among which are the actual precipitation, filtration, washing, and dissolution of the precipitate and concentration of the filtrate. The decision as to which reagents and techniques are employed is determined by which substances can be collected and determined in groups and the desired purity of each fraction. Ordinarily, none of these procedural steps causes the analyst any undue concern unless the sample is very small and several separations and tests must be employed. Granted that the present knowledge of highly selective and even specific reagents and the use of masking agents permit the analyst to carry out identification reactions for several ions in the presence of one another, the task is a difficult one if only a single drop of solution is available for analysis. It is here in the realm of microchemical analysis that the ring oven presents an almost unparalleled separation efficiency.

The ring oven evolved from a proved analytical technique of testing single drops of solution on filter paper for several components. A single drop of test solution is applied to filter paper and one of the components fixed (precipitated) locally with a particular reagent. The soluble or unreacted components are then washed to the outer portions of the paper with an appropriate solvent by capillary action. At this point difficulties begin to arise. If too little solvent, say one or two drops, is used, the separation is incomplete; if the original spot is washed thoroughly with solvent, the soluble components are greatly diluted in an irregular circular area. In spite of such difficulties, the technique is widely employed in spot-test analyses. For example, barium and strontium can be resolved on potassium chromate-impregnated paper because the strontium salt is more soluble than the barium salt and can be washed free of the initial precipitation zone.

Weisz* reasoned that the filter-paper spot-test procedure would be generally applicable for analytical separations on a microscale if the soluble components were *collected* and *concentrated* at a previously determined place on the filter paper. The technique devised for this purpose is described in the following section.

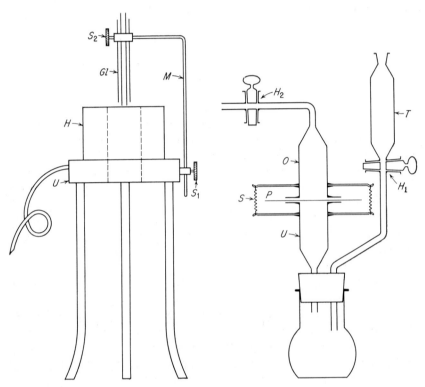

FIG. 8.1. Weisz ring oven. (*From H. Weisz, Die Ringofenmethode, Mikrochim. Acta, 1956, p. 667.*)

FIG. 8.2. Gas generator for use with the ring oven. (*From H. Weisz, Die Ringofenmethode, Mikrochim. Acta, 1956, p. 667.*)

8.2. Apparatus. The ring oven serves as an ingenious device for washing out the soluble components from a precipitate zone on filter paper with any quantity of solvent without the dilution of the soluble components. The ring oven as devised by Weisz[1] is illustrated in Fig. 8.1. It consists of a cylindrical block of aluminum 35 mm high and 55 mm in diameter with a bore hole 22 mm in diameter. The block is fitted with an electrical heating element for controlling the temperature and sup-

* Much of the material in this chapter was obtained by private communication with Professor Herbert Weisz and used with his permission.

ported on a stand.   A piece of tubing 60 mm long serves as a guide for a capillary pipet and is adjustable in height and position with the support M.

Auxiliary equipments used in conjunction with the ring oven are a capillary pipet (1.5 μl capacity) for transferring samples to the test paper, a larger capacity capillary pipet for adding solvent to the sample spot, and a gas generator for applying appropriate reagents.

If separations are to be achieved, part of the sample must be fixed in the original sample spot on the paper.   Gaseous reagents are used advantageously for this precipitation because there is no danger of enlarging and diluting the original sample spot as is the case with liquid reagents.   A convenient gas generator is illustrated in Fig. 8.2.   It consists of a wide-necked flask fitted with dropping funnel T and a 20-mm glass tube U, joined with plane ground flanges.   The flanged joint is held together with springs S, and the generator is connected to an aspirator by the stopcock H_2.   The filter paper P with test drop applied is placed in the flanged joint of the gas generator.   The gas is generated in the flask or added as a volatile liquid through the dropping funnel.   When the stopcock is opened, the gaseous reagent is sucked through the filter paper impregnated with sample.   It should be mentioned that simply holding the sample spot over an open bottle of volatile reagent can be satisfactory but it does not ensure a quantitative reaction.

The following example will serve to show the operation of the ring oven.   A drop (1.5 μl) of an iron(III) chloride solution (1:10,000 dilution) is placed in the center of a filter-paper disk, and the paper is placed on the hot (several degrees above the boiling point of the solvent) ring oven with the sample spot centered in the middle of the bore.   The paper is kept in place with a porcelain or glass ring having an inner diameter of about 25 mm.   The iron chloride is then washed out of the original spot with 0.05 N hydrochloric acid from the larger capillary pipet.   The pipet is filled by simply dipping it into the reagent and then placed on the sample spot through the guide tube.   The solvent is removed from the pipet by capillary action, and the iron salt is dissolved and spread concentrically through the paper.   The pipet is repeatedly filled and placed on the spot until all the iron has been dissolved and carried toward the extremities of the filter-paper disk.   The migration of the soluble solute is limited to the diameter of the bore of the ring oven because as the solvent approaches the edge of the heating block, it is vaporized and deposits the nonvolatile solute in a ring approximating the dimensions of the bore of the ring oven.   In practice, the ring zone of solute is very sharply defined and does not exceed the width of a thin pencil line. Weisz has shown that the area of the ring is considerably less than the area of the original sample spot and that the soluble solutes are actually concentrated as much as three to five times their concentration in the original sample spot.   Thus, if the concentration of an ion in the original test drop is sufficient for normal spot tests, the practical identification limit in ring tests is improved several-fold.   The paper disk is then dried and sprayed with or bathed in an appropriate reagent to develop a characteristic test color for the solute.   Figure 8.3 illustrates a typical test ring obtained with microgram quantities of solute.

A distinct advantage accrues at this point in the ring-oven procedure if several substances are to be tested for in the ring.   Since the circumference of the ring is about 70 mm, it can be divided into at least ten

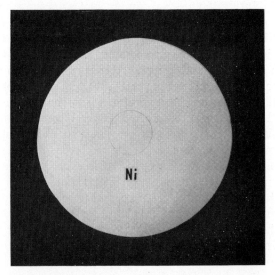

FIG. 8.3. A typical test ring obtained with microgram quantities of solute.

sectors showing a circular arc of solute about 7 mm long.   Identification reactions can be carried out on as many of these sectors as needed for the complete analysis.   Provided the identification reactions do not diffuse the solute zones, and this is why gaseous reactants or sprays are desired, the following statement can be made regarding the sensitivity of spot reactions carried out in this manner: If the concentration of the solute in the test drop is great enough for a normal spot reaction, the solute can be identified in any aliquot part of the ring zone.   This means that instead of *one* reaction in one test drop, there can be several reactions with a higher sensitivity.   Moreover, the unused parts of the ring can be kept as a record or for additional test purposes.

8.3. Separations for Qualitative Analysis.   In most cases it is advantageous to carry out separations before applying different identification reactions.   The following four-component system will illustrate the procedure. One drop of a mixture containing lead, antimony, iron, and nickel is placed on the filter paper, and the lead and antimony are fixed with hydrogen sulfide. All the iron and nickel are washed into a ring zone with 0.05 N hydrochloric acid. The inner spot bearing the sulfide precipitate is punched out with a paper punch and placed in the center of a second filter-paper disk on the ring oven for further separation. Antimony is washed into a ring with yellow ammonium sulfide; the separation of the lead and antimony is complete. Iron and nickel are tested for on sectors of the first ring, antimony on the second ring formed, and lead in the punched-out disk.

In most analyses, there is no need for further separation of solutes collected in a ring provided the appropriate group precipitants and solvents are used. In other words, a judicious choice of conditions and reagents will bring only solutes into the ring which do not interfere with individual identification reactions. Nevertheless, there are several techniques[2,3] for separating components previously concentrated in the ring. This makes the ring-oven method more flexible and versatile for practical applications.

TABLE 8.1. SCHEMATIC SEPARATION OF FOURTEEN IONS
BY RING-OVEN TECHNIQUE*
Sample drop + H_2S
Wash out with 0.05 N HCl

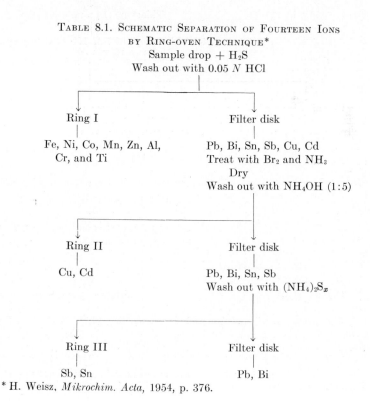

Ring I

Fe, Ni, Co, Mn, Zn, Al,
Cr, and Ti

Filter disk

Pb, Bi, Sn, Sb, Cu, Cd
Treat with Br_2 and NH_3
Dry
Wash out with NH_4OH (1:5)

Ring II

Cu, Cd

Filter disk

Pb, Bi, Sn, Sb
Wash out with $(NH_4)_2S_x$

Ring III

Sb, Sn

Filter disk

Pb, Bi

* H. Weisz, *Mikrochim. Acta*, 1954, p. 376.

Weisz[4] has demonstrated the ring-oven technique for the analysis of complex mixtures containing as many as 14 ions, namely, lead, bismuth, copper, cadmium, tin, antimony, iron, nickel, cobalt, manganese, chromium, aluminum, zinc, and titanium. The scheme is outlined in Table 8.1. Keep in mind that the separations and multiple analyses are

TABLE 8.2. SCHEMATIC SEPARATION OF THIRTY-FIVE IONS BY THE
RING-OVEN TECHNIQUE EMPLOYING SOLVENT EXTRACTION*

Chloride group separation
|

Test solution + 2 drops concd. HCl + 2 ml methyl isobutyl
ketone and n-amyl acetate (2:1 mixture)
Extract with an extraction pipet
|

Organic phase 1
Sb^{+5}, Au^{+3}, Fe^{+3}, V^{+5}, Mo^{+6}, Ga^{+3}, As^{+3}, Ge^{+4}, and Te^{+4}
(Extract collected in ring for individual ion-identification tests)

Aqueous phase 1
Co^{+2}, Zn^{+2}, Be^{+2}, Sn^{+4}, Al^{+3}, Cr^{+3}, Cu^{+2}, U^{+6}, Zr^{+4}, Ti^{+4}, Ni^{+2}, Cd^{+2}, Bi^{+3}, Pb^{+2}, Hg^{+2}, Tl^{+1}, W^{+6}, Mn^{+2}, Se^{+4}, In^{+3}, Ba^{+2}, Sr^{+2}, Ca^{+2}, Mg^{+2}, Ce^{+3}, and Th^{+4}

Thiocyanate group separation
|
Add 3 drops of 7 M NH$_4$CNS. Extract with 2 ml of diethyl ether

Organic phase 2
Co^{+2}, Zn^{+2}, Be^{+2}, and Sn^{+4}
(Extract collected in ring for individual ion-identification tests)

Aqueous phase 2
Al^{+3}, Cr^{+3}, Cu^{+2}, U^{+6}, Zr^{+4}, Ti^{+4}, Ni^{+2}, Cd^{+2}, Bi^{+3}, Pb^{+2}, Hg^{+2}, Tl^{+1}, W^{+6}, Mn^{+2}, Se^{+4}, In^{+3}, Ba^{+2}, Sr^{+2}, Ca^{+2}, Mg^{+2}, Ce^{+3}, and Th^{+4}

Acetylacetonate group separation
|
Add 2 ml acetylacetone, wait for a few minutes, and extract

Organic phase 3
Al^{+3}, Cr^{+3}, Cu^{+2}, U^{+6}, Zr^{+4}, and Ti^{+4}
(Extract collected in ring for individual-ion identification tests)

Aqueous phase 3
Ni^{+2}, Cd^{+2}, Bi^{+3}, Pb^{+2}, Hg^{+2}, Tl^{+1}, W^{+6}, Mn^{+2}, Se^{+4}, In^{+3}, Ba^{+2}, Sr^{+2}, Ca^{+2}, Mg^{+2}, Ce^{+3}, and Th^{+4}

Diethyldithiocarbamate group separation
|

TABLE 8.2. SCHEMATIC SEPARATION OF THIRTY-FIVE IONS BY THE
RING-OVEN TECHNIQUE EMPLOYING SOLVENT EXTRACTION (*Continued*)

Add 2 ml of diethyldithiocarbamate solution. Extract immediately with diethyl ether

Organic phase 4	Aqueous phase 4
Ni^{+2}, Cd^{+2}, Bi^{+3}, Pb^{+2}, Hg^{+2}, Tl^{+1}, W^{+6}, Mn^{+2}, Se^{+4}, and In^{+3} (Extract collected in ring for individual-ion identification tests)	Ba^{+2}, Sr^{+2}, Ca^{+2}, Mg^{+2}, Ce^{+3}, and Th^{+4} (Collected in ring for identification reactions)

* After P. W. West and A. K. Mukherji, *Anal. Chem.*, **31**, 947 (1959).

accomplished on a single small drop (1.5 μl) of test solution and the entire procedure requires less than 15 min.

Qualitative analysis with the ring-oven method has been used in investigations on art objects where no visible attack on the objects can be tolerated. This is possible because only microgram quantities of sample are needed and these amounts can be collected by etching or electrolysis without defacing the objects. In this way, the composition of ancient Egyptian bronzes has been determined.[5]

Semiquantitative determinations[6] can be achieved by the ring-oven method using a single standard solution. Standard solute rings are prepared using different numbers of drops of the standard solution. The intensity of color developed in the unknown ring is then compared with the series of standard rings. Estimates of the amount of unknown ranging from ±5 to 10 per cent are readily achieved. One disadvantage of the procedure is the requirement that a series of standards must be prepared for each component of the unknown.

Weisz et al.[7] have prepared a universal standard scale for comparing a number of different elements. It is based upon the conversion of both standard and sample rings to the corresponding metal sulfide, which is then transformed into an equivalent amount of silver sulfide. Treating standard and sample alike makes a comparison of silver sulfide rings with silver sulfide rings possible. Thus, since silver sulfide can be formed in the same way from quite a number of metals, it is possible to apply a single standard scale in the determination of several elements.

West and Mukherji[8] have adopted the ring-oven technique for the separation of some 35 metallic ions in a single drop by employing liquid-liquid extraction methods rather than the classic methods of precipitation and filtration described in the several applications above. The general outline of this scheme is given in Table 8.2. Individual ions are then identified in each subgroup.

The application of the ring-oven technique in trace analysis has been discussed by West[9,10] and used as a tool for the transfer, concentration, and analysis of air-borne particulates in air-pollution studies.[11]

There are some obvious advantages associated with the technique in forensic chemistry, in the investigation of paints in old paintings, in radiochemical work, and in corrosion studies, all characterized by minute samples on occasion. It is expected that the ring-oven method will become a common technique in microanalytical work.

8.4. Selected Bibliography

Weisz, H.: Die Ringofenmethode, *Mikrochim. Acta*, 1956, p. 667.

Weisz, H.: "Microanalysis by the Ring Oven Technique," Pergamon Press, London, 1960.

REFERENCES

1. Weisz, H.: *Mikrochim. Acta*, 1956, p. 667.
2. Ballczo, H.: *Mikrochim. Acta*, 1959, p. 314.
3. Weisz, H.: "Microanalysis by the Ring Oven Technique," Pergamon Press, London, 1960.
4. Weisz, H.: *Mikrochim. Acta*, 1954, p. 376.
5. Weisz, H.: *J. Chem. Educ.*, **32**, 70 (1955).
6. Stephen, W. I.: *Mikrochim. Acta*, 1956, p. 1540.
7. Weisz, H., M. B. Celap, and V. Almazan: *Mikrochim. Acta*, 1959, p. 36.
8. West, P. W., and A. K. Mukherji: *Anal. Chem.*, **31**, 947 (1959).
9. Yoe, J. H., and H. J. Koch, Jr.: "Trace Analysis," chap. V, John Wiley & Sons, Inc., New York, 1957.
10. West, P. W.: *Anal. Chem.*, **28**, 758 (1956).
11. West, P. W., H. Weisz, G. C. Gaeke, Jr., and G. Lyles: *Anal. Chem.*, **32**, 943 (1960).

CHAPTER 9

ZONE MELTING

9.1. Introduction. Zone melting is so closely allied to the phenomena occurring at a freezing interface that it is advantageous to look first at a relatively simple solid-liquid system. A portion of the phase diagram for a binary system is given in Fig. 9.1. This phase diagram is typical of one in which the solute lowers the freezing point of the solid. If the solute distributes itself selectively between the two phases at equilibrium, the following would be observed upon cooling a solution of composition C_l at temperature T to its freezing point T_f. The first solid to appear will have the composition $C_s = kC_l$, where k is the distribution coefficient of the solute as defined by the ratio C_s/C_l. Since the freezing action rejects solute, the solute concentration in the liquid and the freezing solid will rise as further crystallization occurs. If the entire solution is frozen, no separation of components or purification is achieved. Purification of the solvent occurs only if the frozen solid

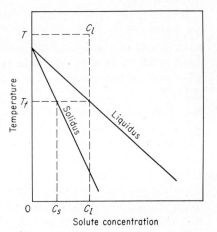

Fig. 9.1. A portion of the phase diagram for a binary system in which the solute lowers the freezing point of the solid.

is removed at some early stage of the crystallization process. The maximum purification factor will be k, and this will be applicable to only a small part of the solid formed at the beginning of the crystallization process. If the freezing rate is large relative to the diffusion rate of solute in the solid and the solution is stirred to give a uniform composition at all times, the distribution of solute in the system can be given by the equation

$$C = kC_0(1 - g)^{k-1} \qquad (9.1)$$

where C is the solute concentration in the solid when a fraction g of the original solution has frozen and C_0 is the mean solute concentration in the original solution. It is assumed that the distribution coefficient k remains constant during the course of the crystallization. This equation describing the distribution of solute in a normal freezing process is only an approximation and will not hold for the entire range of g. In a real system, either k changes with the composition of the system or a eutectic or peritectic composition is reached. In either case the equation is invalid.

If the solute raises the melting point of the solid, the same considerations will hold except that solute is now concentrated in the solid phase and k is greater than unity.

These facts about the nonhomogeneous distribution of solutes between the solid and melt in freezing solutions are well known and are the basis for separations by fractional crystallization. After all, normal freezing of a portion of the solution is the elemental step in a fractional crystallization.

What, then, is the relation between normal freezing or fractional crystallization and zone melting? The general term *zone melting* denotes a number of similar techniques used for controlling the concentration and distribution of soluble solutes in crystalline materials. In each method a narrow cross-sectional molten zone is produced in the crystalline material and slowly moved through the entire length of the solid. The molten zone has two liquid-solid interfaces, a melting interface and a freezing interface. At the melting interface the solid material is merely melted with no segregation of solute or impurity possible. It is at the freezing interface that the solute distribution varies, just as in normal freezing. If the solute lowers the melting point of the solvent, it will be concentrated in the molten phase. That is, the solute will be rejected by the freezing solid and it will accumulate in the liquid. If the solute raises the melting point of the solvent, it will be concentrated in the newly frozen solid. The freezing interface can thus reject or attract certain solutes.

The net result is that solutes or impurities travel through the sample charge either with or opposite to the motion of the zone, depending on whether they lower or raise the melting point of the sample. They thus become concentrated in one end of the charge, leaving the other end relatively purer. The degree of purification attained approaches a limiting value which depends on the inherent distribution of the solute between the two phases, the number of molten zones passed through the charge, and numerous system variables, such as the degree of mixing within the molten zone and the relative dimensions of the molten zone.

The first paper on zone melting was reported in 1952.[1]

9.2. Theory.   Zone melting and fractional crystallization work as a method of purification because the concentration of solute in the freezing solid differs from that in the bulk of the solution.   A system parameter very useful in describing such matters is the distribution coefficient k, defined as the ratio of the solute concentration in the freezing solid to that in the liquid phase.   The value of k depends on a number of factors such as the rate of zone travel, degree of mixing within the zone, and freezing conditions.   The constant is not a true equilibrium constant.

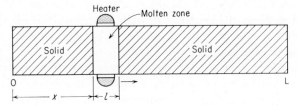

Fig. 9.2. Movement of a molten zone of length l through a sample charge of length L.

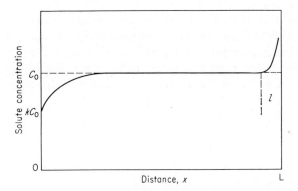

Fig. 9.3. Solute distribution as a function of the length of the charge after one pass of the molten zone. C_0 is the mean concentration of the original charge.

Let us first consider the solute distribution after a single molten zone has passed through an ingot.   For simplicity, idealized conditions are assumed; namely, the distribution coefficient k is constant and less than unity, the ingot has a uniform composition, and the molten zone is of constant length and cross-sectional area.   Pass a molten zone of length l through the ingot slowly, as shown in Fig. 9.2.   The consequences of a single pass of the molten zone through the ingot are illustrated in Fig. 9.3. Note that the composition of the ingot now varies along its length and can be broken into three distinct parts: In the first part the solute concentration has been reduced, in the central part the solute concentration is unchanged, and in the final part the solute concentration has been increased.

The qualitative interpretation of solute distribution after a single pass is as follows: The concentration of the solute in the molten zone at the very beginning of the pass will be C_0, the concentration of solute in the unmelted ingot, because no segregation of solute occurs at the melting interface. After the zone has advanced a short distance, a freezing interface forms at $x = 0$. The solute concentration in the newly frozen solid will be kC_0. Simultaneous with the deposition of solute in the freezing melt, the melting interface at $x = l$ is taking in a solute concentration of C_0. Thus, as the zone advances through the ingot, the concentration of solute in the zone builds up, resulting in the freezing out of higher concentrations of solute. This enrichment of the zone continues at a decreasing rate until the concentration of solute in the zone is equivalent to C_0/k. From this point on, the amount of solute entering and leaving the molten zone at the two interfaces is equal and the concentration of solute in the newly frozen ingot remains constant until the melting interface reaches the end of the ingot. Further movement of the zone merely decreases the length of the zone, causing the solute concentration to rise sharply in the melt and the solid. This latter stage is completely analogous to a normal freezing technique.

The variation of solute concentration with ingot length for a single pass of the molten zone can be described by a single equation up to $x = L - l$, where L is the length of the ingot. The equation as presented by Pfann[1] is

$$\frac{C}{C_0} = 1 - (1 - k)e^{-kx/l} \qquad (9.2)$$

where C is the concentration of the solute in the newly frozen solid and x is the distance the zone has traveled.

Curves of C/C_0 versus the distance the molten zone has traveled are given in Fig. 9.4 for k's ranging between 0.01 and 5. Only the first 9 zone lengths of a 10-zone-length ingot are given, since the equation is invalid in the final zone length. This final region is described by the normal freezing equation

$$C = kC_0(1 - g)^{k-1}$$

where g is the fraction of the melt that has solidified and C_0 is the mean concentration of the solute in the melt. At $x = L - l$ the two equations give the same value for C/C_0 but have different slopes.

A comparison of normal freezing curves ($k < 1$) with these curves shows that less purification is achieved (up to $x = L - l$) with the passage of one molten zone through an ingot than if the entire ingot were molten and slowly frozen from one end. Thus, zone refining has merits as a purification process only if a number of molten zones can be passed through the ingot.

Now, without going into a mathematical treatment, let us picture what general form the distribution curves will assume on multiple passes

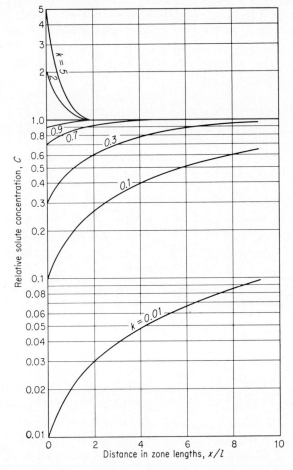

Fig. 9.4. Relative solute concentration as a function of the length of the charge after one pass of the molten zone through a charge 10 zone lengths long for various values of k.

of the molten zone through the ingot. Consider the advance of a second molten zone through an ingot with solute distribution like that shown in Fig. 9.3 after one pass. As the zone advances through the ingot the second time, it again accumulates solute and leaves behind it a region of lower solute concentration that is appreciably longer than the initial region. When the melting interface of the zone reaches the beginning of the normal freezing region, namely, when $x = L - 2l$, the curve will rise sharply. The accumulation of solute at the end of the ingot on the first pass of the zone is reflected backward one zone length during the second pass. For each succeeding pass the initial region becomes lower and longer (see Fig. 9.5) and the effect of accumulated solute in the final region is reflected back one additional zone, but with diminishing intensity. Finally, all three regions blend into a relatively smooth curve. In comparing the curves, keep in mind that the value of k and the coordinates are arbitrary and that these curves only approximate the shapes obtained in multiple passes.

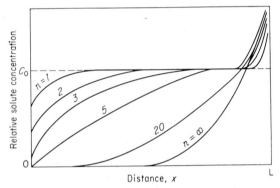

FIG. 9.5. Relative solute concentration as a function of the length of the charge after n passes of the molten zone.

It has not been possible to express with a single equation the solute concentration as a function of distance along the ingot for any number of passes of the molten zone. However, several mathematical formulations approach a general equation. The equations are complicated, though, and of limited practical value in predicting distributions. The basic equation as derived by Lord[2] and Reiss[3] relates the change in solute concentration in the moving zone to the difference between the solute concentration at the melting and freezing interface. The derivation is based on the following assumptions: k is constant; zone length and cross section are constant; there is no diffusion in solid; there is complete mixing in liquid; no volume change accompanies change in state. Let $C_n(x)$ be the solute concentration, in units of solute per unit volume of solution, freezing out at distance x in the nth pass. The amount of solute in the zone is then $lC_n(x)/k$. As the zone advances a distance dx, it freezes out a quantity of solute $C_n\,dx$ and takes in at the melting interface a quantity of solute $C_{n-1}(x + l)\,dx$. Therefore,

$$\frac{l}{k}\,dC_n(x) = C_{n-1}(x + l)\,dx - C_n(x)\,dx \qquad (9.3)$$

When the melting interface reaches $x = L - l$, the zone length is no longer constant, being $l = L - x$, and solute is no longer taken in. Equation (9.3) then reduces to

$$dC_n(x) = \frac{1 - k}{L - x} C_n(x) \, dx \qquad (9.4)$$

The solution of Eq. (9.3) for $n = 1$ and $C_{n-1} = C_0$ is Eq. (9.2). The solution for Eq. (9.4) is

$$C_n(x) = C_n(L - l) \frac{L - x}{l} \qquad (9.5)$$

which is one form of the normal freezing equation.

Lord's expression for solute concentration as a function of distance along the ingot and n number of zone passes is in effect a formula for repeated integration of Eq. (9.3). Lord's equation is

$$\frac{C_n(a)}{C_0} = 1 - (1 - k)e^{-ka}Z \qquad (9.6)$$

where a is the distance in zone lengths x/l measured from the beginning of the ingot and Z is a complicated triple summation term. Reiss arrived at the same formula independently. Solutions to this equation are possible, but they are beyond the scope of this treatment; the interested reader should consult the original literature. The results of the detailed calculations necessary to show the solute concentration versus the length of the charge for different values of k and n have been published by Burris et al.[4] and Pfann[5] as a convenient collection of curves. Thus, if k is known for a relatively simple binary mixture, one can determine from the appropriate curve the number of passes required to attain the desired purity.

Finally, consider the steady-state distribution of solute that is achieved after an infinite number of zone passes through the ingot. When this state is reached, the rate at which solute is deposited at the freezing interface will be the same as the rate at which the zone takes up solute at the melting interface through the entire length of the ingot. The equation for the steady-state condition, namely, for the ultimate refinement of the ingot, is rather easily derived. Let the ultimate concentration of solute be $C(x)$. Now, if a zone passes through the ingot without changing the distribution of the solute, the concentration of solute at the freezing interface x must be $C(x)$ and the concentration in the zone must be $C(x)/k$. But the concentration in the zone can also be given by the expression

$$\frac{C(x)}{k} = \frac{1}{l} \int_x^{x+l} C(x) \, dx \qquad (9.7)$$

if it is assumed that the cross-sectional area is unity.   Therefore

$$C(x) = \frac{k}{l} \int_x^{x+l} C(x) \, dx \tag{9.8}$$

The solution of Eq. (9.8) is a simple exponential

$$C(x) = Ae^{Bx} \tag{9.9}$$

The constants A and B are obtainable from the expressions

$$k = \frac{Bl}{e^{Bl} - 1} \tag{9.10}$$

and

$$A = \frac{C_0 BL}{e^{BL} - 1} \tag{9.11}$$

C_0 is the mean solute concentration in units of solute per unit volume of solution, and L is the length of the ingot.

Ultimate solute concentrations relative to the initial concentration can thus be calculated for various values of k to show that at least theoretically very large separations are possible.   Thus, for $k = 0.1$, the ultimate solute concentration is approximately 10^{-14} its original value.

It is not, however, necessary to pass an infinite number of zones through the charge to effect a very high degree of purity.   Calculations show that 20 passes will bring about a separation approximating the ultimate if k is as small as 0.1 and if the ratio of charge length to zone length is 10. Solute concentrations of the order of 10^{-6} their original concentrations are readily obtainable provided the distribution coefficients are favorable. It is only in the case where k approaches unity that large numbers of passes are required for purification.   Hundreds of passes may be needed for purification if k is greater than 0.5.

9.3. Apparatus.   The problem of equipment design for zone refining exhibits many facets in terms of simplicity, economy, efficiency, and basic techniques, but all equipment components are designed to achieve the primary objective, the passage of a molten zone or zones through a sample charge.   For convenience of discussion, zone-refining apparatus can be broken down into a group of essential components, namely, heaters, travel mechanisms, stirrers, and sample containers.

The most common heating devices are short resistance coils wound about the sample or sample tube.   The device is simple and inexpensive, but it means that the sample container will be hotter than the zone, which increases the possibility of contamination.   Induction heating eliminates this difficulty by generating the heat within the charge itself, but the equipment is bulky and expensive.   Other techniques used in heating include direct contacts of sample or container with flames, passage of an electric current through the charge, electron bombardment, radiant heating, and heat transfer with fluids.

The number of molten zones passed through a given charge can be controlled by n passes of the sample charge through a single heater or by one pass through n heaters. The complication of involving an unusually large number of heaters in the latter case is overcome by using short reciprocating strokes which carry the charge through a number of heaters and then quickly return it to the starting position to begin a new stroke, thus simulating the passage of the charge through any desired number of heaters.

The choice of which should move, the sample charge or the heaters, is a matter left for the individual to decide. In certain cases it may be more desirable to move one than the other. The chief requirement is that the motion be fairly steady and of the order of inches per hour. The movement of the zone must be relatively slow to allow crystal formation without the occlusion of liquid. Many kinds of drive mechanisms have been employed, lead-screw drive, cord and drum drive, cam drive, direct motor drive, etc. Generally speaking, though, fairly crude mechanisms give satisfactory results.

The efficiency of zone refining is greatly increased if the molten zone is vigorously stirred. Convection currents within the zone are usually adequate for stirring purposes, particularly with organic materials, but forced convection is sometimes desirable. Induction heating produces convection currents, and so do supersonic vibrations. Magnetic stirring can be achieved in ingots if an electrical current is passed through the charge axially and a magnetic field is impressed near one end of the molten zone, normal to the sample axis. If the change in magnetic strength over the length of the zone is large, the liquid will be stirred, since a force proportional to the product of field strength and current is exerted on the liquid.

The selection of a container for the charge in zone refining is largely a matter for the individual researcher to decide. It is essential only that the container not contaminate the sample and that the longitudinal thermal conductance of the container be less than or comparable to that of the sample material. The latter property is highly desirable to prevent the uneven heating and broadening of the molten zone. Materials that have found widespread applications are Pyrex glass, Vycor, fused silica, graphite, alumina, and magnesia.

The most common shape for the container or ingot is a straight cylinder, but numerous other designs have been employed. Cross-sectional shapes have been circular, ring shaped, and rectangular. Lengthwise, the charges have been formed into circular, spiral, and helical forms. The helical form (Fig. 9.6) has a distinct advantage in that a long charge can be compressed into a small space and a single heater can produce all the zones. As the helical coil is slowly rotated, the molten zone at the

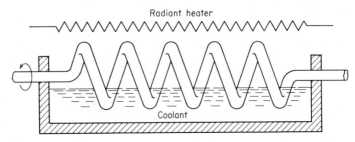

FIG. 9.6. Helical tube container for zone refining.

top of each turn moves along the length of the tubing, passing through the solid phase in each turn.

Methods of zone refining without a sample container have been widely employed, and the technique is responsible for producing exceedingly pure materials. The most popular form of the containerless procedure is the floating-zone technique. The molten zone is held in place by its own surface tension as indicated in Fig. 9.7. The method is generally limited to charges held in a vertical position, but additional support can be given the floating zone which makes horizontal operations feasible. For example, if the center of the floating zone can be made to lie above the induction coil used for heating the zone, the levitating action that arises from the repulsion between induced and inducing currents will help to support the zone. Pfann et al.[6] have reported on several magnetic suspension methods which can effectively counterbalance the force of gravity on a zone moving horizontally.

A thorough discussion of equipment and techniques can be found in the chemical literature and the monograph on zone refining by Pfann.[5]

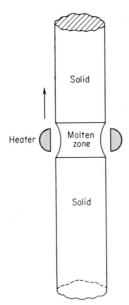

FIG. 9.7. Floating-zone technique which produces a molten zone held in place by surface tension.

9.4. Applications. The basic principles involved in zone melting suggest that the technique can be used in a variety of fields for the purification of substances, but the method has come into prominence primarily because of its applicability to the purification of germanium and silicon for the transistor industry. Six zone passes[7] through the purest commercially available germanium reduced the conductivity-producing impurities to less than 1 in 10^{10} atoms of germanium.

Silicon is more difficult to purify because the distribution of impurities is not favorable for rapid purification, it is extremely reactive, and it has a high melting point. Nevertheless, horizontal zone refining in containers has been effective,[8] as has the floating-zone technique[9,10] in reducing impurities greatly.

Aluminum, copper, gallium, iron, lead, nickel, tin, silver, uranium, and many other metals have been extensively studied by zone refining. In many cases the properties of the highly purified metals have been significantly different from the properties generally attributed to the commercially available products.

It is interesting to note that several years before Pfann reported on the purification of germanium by zone refining, Schwab and Wichers[11] of the National Bureau of Standards applied the principle to the purification of benzoic acid and acetanilide. The technique involved the slow lowering of a cylindrical cell of the fused compound through a heating coil in such a way that freezing began at the bottom and progressed upward through the cell. Three passages of benzoic acid through the heated ring raised the purity from 99.91 to 99.997 mole per cent. Two passages of the cell through the heated ring were comparable to the purity achieved by 11 recrystallizations from benzene or 25 recrystallizations from water.

Owing to the great difference in density, thermal conductivity, heat of fusion, surface tension, rate of crystallization, and tendency to form supercooled melts between metals and organic substances, there are a number of problems that arise in zone refining of organics. Contrary to the practice of purifying metals in a horizontal tube, organics must usually be treated in a vertical tube, and the method is suitable only for those substances which are stable at their melting point for long periods. Because of the poor heat conductivity of organic materials, it appears probable that the use of radiofrequency dielectric heating is most promising for generating uniform temperatures throughout the narrow molten zone in a matter of seconds.

Handley[12] and others[13] have discussed the problems of purification of organics by zone refining and indicate some probable trends in the field.

An outstanding example of purification of organics by zone melting is the treatment of naphthalene. Wolf and Deutsch[14] claim that the main impurity, anthracene, in naphthalene was reduced to less than 1 part in 10^6 by lowering a test tube of the substance through a narrow ring-shaped furnace at the rate of 1 cm per hr.

Several applications of zone melting to organic substances that normally exist in the solid state have been discussed, but the technique is equally applicable to the purification of low-melting substances, such as benzene and bromotoluene.   Herington et al.[15] place the entire apparatus in a refrigerator at $-25°$, whereas Rock[16] provides a cooling jacket to solidify all the material and then raises a molten zone through it.   On the other hand, progressive freezing, in which a solid boundary advances into a liquid, is superior in principle to zone melting because it involves a single solid-liquid interface, i.e., normal freezing.   Dickinson and Eaborn[17] have used this technique successfully to purify liquids and low-melting solids.   Chromatographically homogeneous benzene was prepared in six passages in which the top 10 per cent of the liquid was left unfrozen and discarded each pass.   For liquids of much lower melting points the liquid sample is lowered slowly from a warm tube into a constant-level dry-ice–acetone mixture.

Smith and Thomas[18] have attempted the separation of mixtures of ordinary and heavy water by zone refining in a 40-turn helical charge. The lower portion of the turns were submerged in brine at $-10°C$, and the exposed segments were kept at 35 to 40°C.   They were able to confirm that heavy water with a melting point 3.8° higher than that of normal water was concentrated in the solid phase, but the separation was so slow that it may be limited to theoretical studies or to the procurement of small quantities of ultrapure samples of D_2O or H_2O.   The equilibrium separation factor of 1.0211 was used in matrix calculations to explore the feasibility of separating the isotopic forms of water, but the experimental results fell far short of what was predicted.   Separation factors obtained under nonequilibrium conditions were as low as 1.0007, which certainly is not conducive to a rapid purification of the two forms of water.

Herington[19] and Pfann and Theuerer[20] give a good review of zone melting with pertinent comments on its analytical applicability.

Zone melting has important uses other than purification.   It can be used for zone leveling, namely, the uniform distribution of impurities through the charge.   It can make precisely controlled discontinuities in impurity concentration such as is needed in p-n or n-p-n junctions in semiconductors, and it can be used in special cases for concentrating impurities unobservable by conventional procedures prior to their analysis.   Concentrations of the order of 10^{13} atoms per cubic centimeter or 10^{-9} atom fraction have been determined in this manner.

There seems to be little reason to doubt that zone refining will eventually be applied to the purification of metal ingots weighing several tons.

The main advantages of zone melting are the simplicity of the method, its adaptability to automatic operation, the complete recovery of starting materials, purification without the introduction of extraneous reagents, and no need for a physical separation of pure and impure fractions after each pass through the furnace.

The main disadvantages are the inability to purify all the starting material, material transport when melting is accompanied by a volume change, and the necessity for working with small quantities of material. Contraction on melting causes a material transport of the solution in the direction of the zone movement.   The consequences are the enlargement of one end of the charge at the expense of the other end.   In open horizontal containers, material transfer can be avoided by tilting the container to produce a gravitational flow opposite and equal to the material transport.   In a vertical tube the heater must start at the top if the solid expands on melting.

Continuous zone refining appears to be a practical technique which will overcome many of the problems involved in handling small batches of material individually.

9.5. Selected Bibliography

Pfann, W. G.: "Zone Melting," John Wiley & Sons, Inc., New York, 1958.
Rock, H.: "Ausgewahlte moderne Trennverfahren zur Reinigung organischer Stoffe," Verlag Dr. Dietrich Steinkopff, Darmstadt, 1957.

REFERENCES

1. Pfann, W. G.: *Trans. AIME*, **194,** 747 (1952).
2. Lord, N. W.: *Trans. AIME*, **197,** 1531 (1953).
3. Reiss, H.: *Trans. AIME*, **200,** 1053 (1954).
4. Burris, L., C. H. Stockman, and I. G. Dillon: *Trans. AIME*, **203,** 1017 (1955).
5. Pfann, W. G.: "Zone Melting," John Wiley & Sons, Inc., New York, 1958.
6. Pfann, W. G., and D. W. Hagelbarger: *J. Appl. Phys.*, **27,** 12 (1956); W. G. Pfann, K. E. Benson, and D. W. Hagelbarger: *J. Appl. Phys.*, **30,** 454 (1959).
7. Pfann, W. G., and K. M. Olsen: *Phys. Rev.*, **89,** 322 (1953).
8. Hartmann, D. H., and P. L. Ostapkovich: *Metal Progr.*, **70,** 100 (1956).
9. Theuerer, H. C.: *Trans. AIME*, **206,** 1316 (1956).
10. Kaiser, W., P. H. Keck, and C. F. Lange: *Phys. Rev.*, **101,** 1264 (1956).
11. Schwab, F. W., and E. Wichers: *Natl. Bur. Standards J. Research*, **32,** 253 (1944).
12. Handley, R.: *Mfg. Chemist*, **27,** 451 (1956).
13. Ball, J. S., R. V. Helm, and C. R. Ferrin: *Petrol. Engr.*, **30,** C36 (1958).
14. Wolf, C., and H. P. Deutsch: *Naturwissenschaften*, **41,** 425 (1954).
15. Herington, E. F. G., R. Handley, and A. J. Cook: *Chem. & Ind.*, 1956, p. 292.
16. Rock, H.: *Naturwissenschaften*, **43,** 81 (1956).
17. Dickinson, J. D., and C. Eaborn: *Chem. & Ind.*, 1956, p. 959.
18. Smith, H. A., and C. O. Thomas: *J. Phys. Chem.*, **63,** 445 (1959).
19. Herington, E. F. G.: *Analyst*, **84,** 680 (1959).
20. Pfann, W. G., and H. C. Theverer, *Anal. Chem.*, **32,** 1574 (1960).

CHAPTER 10

ION EXCHANGE

10.1. Introduction. Two English agricultural chemists, Thompson[1] and Way,[2] are credited with the discovery of ion exchange in 1850. They reported and verified the exchange of calcium and ammonium ions in soils. The exchange involved equivalent quantities of ions and differed from true physical adsorption. The extent of exchange was dependent on ionic concentrations, and the exchange characteristics were traced to the aluminum silicates present in the soil. These observations stimulated work in related areas, and it was only a short time before specific minerals were studied for exchange behavior. As an example, leucite ($K_2O \cdot Al_2O_3 \cdot 4SiO_2$) was transformed into analcite ($Na_2O \cdot Al_2O_3 \cdot 4SiO_2$) by percolating a solution of sodium chloride through a bed of the granulated leucite. The leucite then was regenerated by treating the analcite with a potassium chloride solution.

The modern concept of the nature of an ionic solid proposes that the constituent particles of the crystalline lattice are ions and not molecules. Each ion of the crystal is surrounded by a fixed number of ions of opposite charge and is subject to coulombic attractive forces that are dependent on the distance between ions and their relative charges. Thus, ions in the surface of the crystal are subject to less attractive forces than ions in the interior of the crystal. When the crystal is placed in a highly polar solvent such as water, the net attractive forces holding the ion to the crystal are lessened sufficiently so that this ion can exchange with another ion in solution. The ease with which replacement or exchange occurs is dependent on the nature of forces binding the ion to the crystal, the size and charge of the two ions, the concentration of the exchanging ion, solubility factors, and the accessibility of the exchangeable ion. Since the zeolites are highly insoluble, porous, chainlike silicate structures, the sodium or potassium and calcium ions are accessible to other small ions in solution and exchange can proceed without destruction of the crystalline network. Hence, the exchange reaction can be represented as the simple replacement or exchange of ions of like sign between a pervious insoluble electrolyte and an electrolyte solution in contact with the solid.

$$Na_2O \cdot Al_2O_3 \cdot 4SiO_2 \cdot 2H_2O + 2K^+Cl^-$$
$$\rightleftharpoons K_2O \cdot Al_2O_3 \cdot 4SiO_2 \cdot 2H_2O + 2Na^+Cl^-$$
$$CaO \cdot Al_2O_3 \cdot 6SiO_2 \cdot 5H_2O + 2K^+Cl^-$$
$$\rightleftharpoons K_2O \cdot Al_2O_3 \cdot 6SiO_2 \cdot 5H_2O + Ca^{++}2Cl^-$$

A number of common clays, soils, minerals (particularly zeolites), and synthetic zeolites are known to exhibit ion-exchange characteristics, but their practical utilization is beset with many difficulties. The exchangers have low exchange capacities and generally must be finely divided. Consequently, large volumes of mineral are required for the exchange of small quantities of ions, and beds of the finely divided minerals offer high resistance to the flow of solutions, which makes it difficult to contact efficiently the exchanger with the sample or regenerant solution. The natural exchangers have been used commercially primarily for the softening of water.

Many other natural products such as humus, lignin, proteins, cellulose, wool, carbon, living cells, resins, phosphates, alumina, barium sulfate (see Sec. 14.12), silver halides, sulfides, and colloidal suspensions are also known to possess ion-exchange characteristics. None of the above exchangers is widely used for its exchange properties, but an explanation of the properties of these substances is often dependent upon the acknowledgment of their ability to exchange ions either from an adsorbed electrical double layer or directly from their crystalline or amorphous structure.

The explanation for the behavior of some of the above exchangers is not so clear cut as for zeolites, and there is much to be desired in the development of a theory that will be effective in all cases. Essentially all the exchange theories are quite similar in that they require that the exchange proceed by equivalents to satisfy the law of electrical neutrality. The prime difference in the various theories is in the location and origin of the exchange site.

Since the earlier work on ion exchange is primarily of historical interest and the natural exchangers have very limited applicability, the reader is referred to the works of Boyd,[3] Schubert,[4] and Kunin[5] for review.

Modern ion-exchange technology begins in 1935 with the discovery by Adams and Holmes[6] that certain synthetic resins are capable of exchanging ions. The synthetic resin exchangers proposed by Adams and Holmes are very pervious, reasonably stable, and exhibit high exchange capacities. They can be used as relatively large (1 to 2 mm diameter) particles and can be synthesized with specific ionic functional groups capable of exchanging with almost all anions or cations, as the case may be. The resins are widely used for the demineralization of water and produce a water comparable in conductivity to triply distilled water. For these and other reasons the synthetic resins have been enthusiastically accepted and further developed by researchers. Concurrent with the development of better exchangers was the widespread industrial and laboratory acceptance of ion exchange as another versatile separation technique. Within a 10-year period dating from the discovery of Adams and Holmes ion exchange was being used for separations, recoveries, demineralization, water softening, and catalysis both in the laboratory and on an industrial scale. This certainly attests to the enthusiasm with which the exchange resins were received and to their versatility. As a result, ion exchange is now another unit process for industry comparable to distillation, filtration, evaporation, precipitation, recrystallization, and dialysis. For the analytical chemist, it is another valuable tool to be used for the resolution of complex ionic mixtures, recovery of metals, removal of impurities or interfering electrolytes, and the dissolution of refractory ionics.

Since a basic knowledge of exchanger structure and the mechanism and kinetics of exchange is necessary for one to understand and appreciate the applications and limitations of the ion-exchange process, these topics will be discussed in turn at some length.

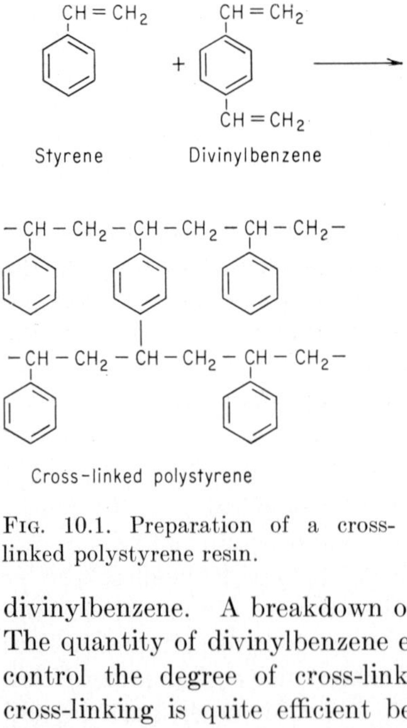

10.2. Ion-exchange Resins (Structure). Ion-exchange resins are highly polymerized cross-linked hydrocarbons containing ionized or ionizable groups. In essence, one part is a large, permeable, insoluble, nondiffusible ion consisting mainly of the basic resin structure. Its counterpart is an ion of equal but opposite charge, smaller size, and almost unlimited ability to migrate within the resin structure under exchange conditions.

A typical resin is prepared by the copolymerization of styrene and divinylbenzene. A breakdown of the preparation is shown in Fig. 10.1. The quantity of divinylbenzene employed is varied over a wide range to control the degree of cross-linking in the polymer. Apparently the cross-linking is quite efficient because monomer-free polymers contain little or no unsaturation. If the proportion of divinylbenzene is reduced as low as 0.1 per cent, a soluble polymer is formed. Increased cross-linking decreases the solubility of the polymer, increases rigidity, and reduces swelling and porosity. In general, 8 to 12 per cent divinyl-

Styrene   Divinylbenzene

Cross-linked polystyrene

FIG. 10.1. Preparation of a cross-linked polystyrene resin.

benzene is used in the commercial resins, but both higher and lower percentages are available, since the degree of cross-linking has such a profound effect on the physical characteristics of the resin.

Chemical stability is limited by the strength of the carbon-carbon bond of the hydrocarbon. As a result, the resins are exceptionally stable and can be used at temperatures slightly above 100°. They are highly resistant to attack by concentrated acids and alkalies and most common oxidizing and reducing agents. Even prolonged digestion of some of these resins in hot aqua regia has failed to destroy their character appreciably. The resins are quite insoluble in most common solvents, but they have a tendency to swell in organic solvents. The extent of swelling is inversely proportional to the degree of cross-linking.

The particle size and particle-size distribution of the product depend on the extent of mechanical agitation and reaction conditions during polymerization. Exchange resins in homogeneous bead or irregular form with diameters of the order of 1 μ to 2 mm are commercially available.

The ionic group attached to the skeleton of the resin determines the nature of the exchange characteristics. Cation exchangers are produced when acidic functional groups are introduced into the resin structure. The bulk resin takes on a negative charge with the acidic hydrogen available for exchange with other cations. Anion exchangers are produced when basic functional groups are introduced. The bulk of the resin takes on a positive charge, but the establishment of an anion for exchange is more complicated than the simple ionization of the acidic functional group. The more common exchange groups affixed to the skeletal resin structure are listed in Table 10.1. With functional groups of strong electrolytes the resin is completely ionized but highly insoluble. The resin exhibits the properties of a strong electrolyte. With functional groups of a weak electrolyte, the resin behaves as a weakly ionized substance. As long as a single ionizable group is introduced, the resin is monofunctional in behavior.

TABLE 10.1. COMMON EXCHANGE FUNCTIONAL GROUPS*

Cation exchangers	Anion exchangers
—SO_3H	—NH_2
—$COOH$	—NHR
—OH	—NR_2
—SH	—NR_3^+
—PO_3H_2	

* From R. Kunin and R. E. Barry, *Ind. Eng. Chem.*, **41**, 1269 (1949).

A typical strongly acidic cation exchanger (Fig. 10.2) is prepared by the sulfonation of the cross-linked polystyrene. Under controlled conditions one sulfonic acid group is introduced into each aromatic nucleus. The total number of functional groups per unit of resin volume determines the theoretical exchange capacity. Since no other functional groups are present, the exchanger is monofunctional.

The condensation of phenol or phenolsulfonic acids and formaldehyde also leads to stable cation exchangers. Unfortunately, the latter condensation produces polyfunctional resins with an acidic hydrogen available from the phenol and the sulfonic acid. In actual usage, though, the more highly ionized group is dominant.

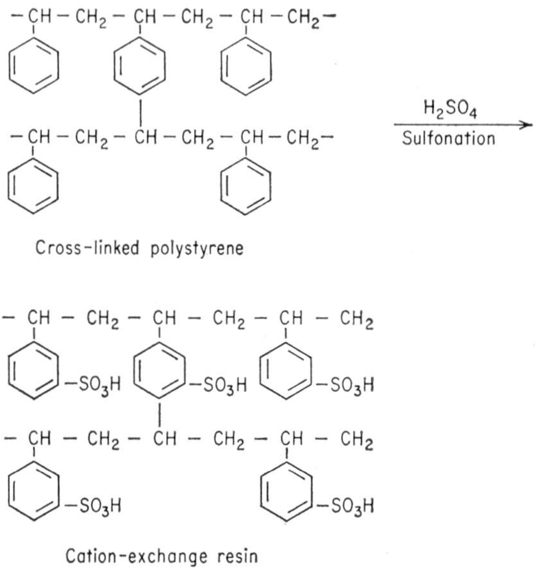

FIG. 10.2. Preparation of a sulfonic acid cross-linked polystyrene cation-exchange resin.

A typical weakly acidic cation exchanger can be prepared by copolymerization of divinylbenzene and methacrylic acid or resorcilic acid and formaldehyde.

Strongly basic anion-exchange resins are prepared by first chloromethylating the cross-linked polystyrene and then treating the product with a tertiary amine, such as trimethylamine. The resulting functional group is a strongly basic quaternary ammonium group. If the chloromethylated polystyrene is treated with a secondary amine instead of with a tertiary amine, the exchanger produced is a weakly basic tertiary amine. Treatment with ammonia or primary amines results in the formation of polyfunctional anion-exchange resins. Figure 10.3 outlines the preparation of strongly basic and weakly basic anion exchangers. Anion exchangers can be prepared also by the polymerization of monomeric amines in a fashion similar to that described for cation exchangers.

The chemical stability of the anion exchangers is much less than that of the cation exchangers.   Although the basic polymer network is the same, the chemical stability is limited by the strength of the carbon-nitrogen amine linkage.   At elevated temperatures the amines are easily hydrolyzed, resulting in a reduction of the exchanger capacity and the contamination of the solution with soluble organic fragments.

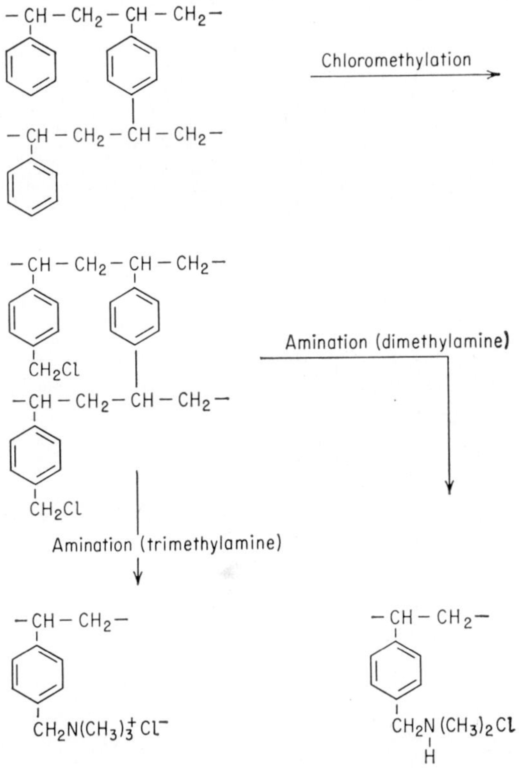

FIG. 10.3. Preparation of anion-exchange resins.

Because of the high proportion of polar groups in exchangers, the resins are strongly hydrophilic and behave as hygroscopic gels that swell and shrink reversibly with the absorption and desorption of water.   As much as 0.5 to 1 g of water can be absorbed per gram of dry resin.   Consequently, the ionic group fixed to the resin has the same characteristics that it would have in an aqueous solution.   More specifically, the functional group in the resin behaves in the same manner as if it were in solution in the free monomeric form.   There is convincing evidence that the ionic group does not change its characteristics upon joining the polymeric network, namely, the great similarity between the titration curves (Figs. 10.4 and 10.5) of a strong and weak acid exchanger and their analogous soluble monomeric forms.[7]   Although the curves are grossly similar, it is evident when the ionic strength of the solution or the base is

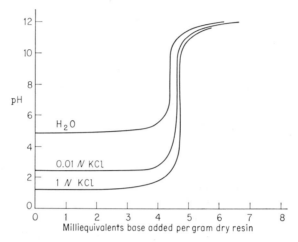

FIG. 10.4. Titration of a sulfonic acid cation exchanger.   [*From R. Kunin and R. E. Barry, Ind. Eng. Chem.*, **41**, 1269 (1949), *fig. 2.*]

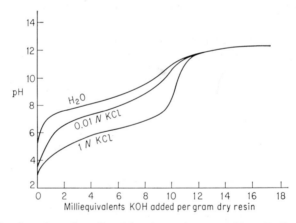

FIG. 10.5. Titration of a carboxylic acid cation exchanger.   [*From R. Kunin and R. E. Barry, Ind. Eng. Chem.*, **41**, 1269 (1949), *fig. 1.*]

changed that the titration of the resin involves more than the simple neutralization reaction

$$H^+ + OH^- \rightleftharpoons H_2O$$

which is characteristic of the titration of the monomeric acid.   The titration of the resin must be considered as a combination of two reactions, namely, the exchange or displacement of hydrogen ions in the resin for the cation of the base

$$R^-H^+ + M^+ \rightleftharpoons R^-M^+ + H^+$$

and the subsequent neutralization of the displaced hydrogen ions:

$$H^+ + OH^- \rightleftharpoons H_2O$$

The equilibrium of the exchange reaction affects the titration slightly and accounts for the difference between the titration curves of resin and monomer. Further evidence for the gel structure is the fact that x-ray studies and electron micrographs of resins show nothing more than a transient crystallinity. This is not surprising because the tendency to swell and contract greatly is far more characteristic of an amorphous or gel structure than of a crystalline structure. In addition to this, all functional groups within the resin are accessible as exchange sites. The total exchange capacity in milliequivalents per gram of dry resin is the same for all small ions and agrees very closely with the theoretical value determined from the synthesis. It is possible, though, to observe a much reduced exchange capacity if large organic ions are involved. The dimensions of these ions prevent their passage into the polymer network, and exchange occurs only on or near the resin surface.

The exchange behavior of the resin depends more on the nature of the functional group present than any other single factor. A strongly acidic resin (sulfonic acid type) appears to be more or less completely ionized under all conditions. On the other hand, carboxylic acid resins and phenolic resins behave as weak electrolytes, and their theoretical capacity can be achieved only in alkaline solution. Weakly basic resins cannot be used for the absorption of weak acids because of the unfavorable ionization factor, but strongly basic resins such as the quaternary amines readily exchange with the weak acids of silica and carbon dioxide. Salts of the strong resins do not hydrolyze on washing, only small changes in resin volume are observed with the exchange of different ions, and in all cases the rates of exchange are quite rapid. Contrary to this, the salts of the weak resins are slowly hydrolyzed and exchange rates are rapid only if the resins remain in a salt form. The conversion to the salt form of either the weak-acid or weak-base resins is accompanied by a volume increase because increased ionic character of the salt form requires an influx of water to accommodate the greater hydration of the salt.

10.3. Ion-exchange Equilibria. A comprehensive knowledge of the natural laws governing the distribution of ions between an aqueous phase and the resin phase would be extremely useful in designing ion-exchange experiments and predicting their outcome. Numerous attempts have been made to relate the ion-exchange phenomenon to certain physical and chemical characteristics of the system, but a real solution has not been offered for correlating facts and theory. Part of the difficulty stems from the inability of present solution theories to explain interionic forces in concentrated electrolyte solutions. Since the resin phase can be considered as a concentrated aqueous electrolyte solution, the resultant of long-range coulombic forces within the resin will be much the same as if the charges were homogeneously dispersed in solution. If only simple inorganic ions are involved in the exchange process, the exchange is governed primarily by electrostatic forces. The situation is complicated, though, if a nonelectrolyte is added to the resin phase because interfacial effects occur that are analogous to adsorption. In equilibria involving organic ions the two effects are superimposed and the affinity of the resin for the ion will depend on both electrostatic and van der Waals' forces.

Strangely enough, one of the more acceptable theories which predicts an exchange phenomenon has been known since 1911. This is the Donnan membrane equilibrium theory. The Donnan theory predicts the unequal distribution of a diffusible electrolyte in two aqueous phases separated by a semipermeable membrane if one phase contains an electrolyte with one nondiffusible ionic species. If solutions of NaCl and NaR are separated by a membrane permeable to sodium and chloride ions but not to the anion R^- of the other sodium salt, it is possible to derive an exchange expression. When equilibrium has been established, a certain amount of sodium and chloride will have diffused through the membrane and the chemical potential of the substances on both sides of the membrane must be equal; i.e.,

$$\mu NaCl_I = \mu NaCl_{II}$$

where I and II refer to the two solutions. But since the chemical potential of an electrolyte can be taken as the sum of the potentials of the ions,

$$\mu^0_{Na^+} + RT \ln a_{Na^+,I} + \mu^0_{Cl^-} + RT \ln a_{Cl^-,I}$$
$$= \mu^0_{Na^+} + RT \ln a_{Na^+,II} + \mu^0_{Cl^-} + RT \ln a_{Cl^-,II}$$

and
$$a_{Na^+,I}a_{Cl^-,I} = a_{Na^+,II}a_{Cl^-,II}$$

where a represents the activity of the indicated ions. If it is assumed that the solutions are dilute, activities can be replaced with concentrations and

$$[Na^+]_I[Cl^-]_I = [Cl^-]_I{}^2 = [Na^+]_{II}[Cl^-]_{II} = \{[Cl^-]_{II} + [R^-]_{II}\}[Cl^-]_{II} \quad (10.1)$$

provided the conditions of electroneutrality apply.

and
$$[Cl^-]_I{}^2 = [Cl^-]_{II}{}^2 + [Cl^-]_{II}[R^-]_{II}$$
$$[Cl^-]_I > [Cl^-]_{II}$$

The implication is that at equilibrium the concentration of diffusible electrolyte is greater in the solution free of the nondiffusible ion.

If a second diffusible cation, H^+, is added to the system, then

$$[Na^+]_I[Cl^-]_I = [Na^+]_{II}[Cl^-]_{II}$$

and

$$[H^+]_I[Cl^-]_I = [H^+]_{II}[Cl^-]_{II}$$

Dividing one equation by the other results in

$$\frac{[Na^+]_I}{[H^+]_I} = \frac{[Na^+]_{II}}{[H^+]_{II}} \tag{10.2}$$

According to this equation an exchange of ions must take place until the concentration ratios are equal on both sides of the membrane.

For pairs of ions of unequal valence such as Na^+ and Ca^{++}, the equation becomes

$$\frac{[Na^+]_I}{[Ca^{++}]_I{}^{1/2}} = \frac{[Na^+]_{II}}{[Ca^{++}]_{II}{}^{1/2}} \tag{10.3}$$

Although no membrane exists in the conventional ion-exchange procedure, the surface of the resin particle can be considered as a membrane and the fixed exchange sites of the resin as the nondiffusible ion. This is a realistic assumption because the resin behaves as an electrolyte solution and almost all the exchange sites are in the interior of the resin. The high fixed ionic concentration of a high-capacity resin excludes the diffusion of free electrolytes into the resin phase from solutions having considerably lower ionic concentrations than that found within the resin. It is this phenomenon which forms the basis for the ion-exclusion principle discussed in Chap. 11 and the selectiveness of ion-exchange membranes for the diffusion of either anions or cations.

It should be noted, though, that the Donnan treatment is for an ideal system and would hold only for dilute solutions and low-capacity resins. Even so, the Donnan theory predicts the inability of free electrolytes to diffuse into resins of high exchange capacity and the effects of electrolyte concentration and valency on the exchange.

The equilibria associated with ion-exchange resins and various ions are considerably more complicated than Donnan membrane equilibria because the system is heterogeneous with one phase essentially a nonideal solid solution having a high electrolyte concentration. With the resin electrolyte concentration ranging as high as 5 to 6 N, it is almost impossible to determine the activity of ions within the resin phase, and this makes it impossible to apply a quantitative thermodynamic treatment to the system. It is worth mentioning that these difficulties are inherent in almost all ionic reactions in concentrated media, including homogeneous media, and are not just a problem associated with ion exchange. There are, however, several other equilibrium relationships that can be applied qualitatively and even semiquantitatively to ion-exchange equilibria.

The simplest approach is to apply the mass-action law to the ion-exchange equilibrium. Thus, for the reaction

$$A^+ + B^+R^- \rightleftharpoons B^+ + A^+R^-$$

the equilibrium constant is given by the expression

$$\frac{a_B a_{AR}}{a_A a_{BR}} = K$$

if a_A and a_B represent the activities of the ions in solution and a_{AR} and a_{BR} represent the activities in the resin phase. This expression can be rewritten as

$$\frac{a_B}{a_A} \frac{x_{AR}}{x_{BR}} = K \frac{\gamma_{BR}}{\gamma_{AR}} = K' \tag{10.4}$$

where x_{AR} and x_{BR} are the mole fractions and γ_{BR} and γ_{AR} the activity coefficients in the resin phase. Attempts have been made to evaluate activity coefficients in the resin phase, but there are no direct experimental approaches for determining γ_{BR}/γ_{AR}, and the true equilibrium constant remains indeterminable. K', however, is an "apparent equilibrium constant" which can be evaluated experimentally, since all the terms on the left side of the equation are determinable. K' does not generally remain constant when the ratio x_{AR}/x_{BR} is varied. This is ascribed to the nonideality of the resin phase and the variation of the ratio γ_{BR}/γ_{AR} with a change in x_{BR}/x_{AR}.

The value K' expresses the practical relative affinity of the resin for the two ions and is sometimes referred to as the selectivity coefficient. The same function is obtained from the Donnan membrane equilibrium, but in that case the selectivity coefficient is unity.

Many workers have shown that the selectivity coefficient is a useful measure of ion affinities for the exchanger and can be helpful in predicting the separability of a pair of ions by an ion-exchange chromatographic technique. For ions of equal valency there is a wide spread of relative exchange affinities which show no exact correlation with any simple physical property of the ions such as atomic weight or crystal radii. There is, however, a crude inverse proportionality between exchange affinities of similarly charged ions and their hydrated ionic radii.

Boyd, Schubert, and Adamson[8] determined K' for various cation-exchange reactions involving the hydrogen ion. By arbitrarily assigning a value of unity to the apparent equilibrium constant for the half-reaction

$$H^+ + R^- \rightleftharpoons H^+R^-$$

they showed a linear correlation between the values of log K' for the alkali metals and the reciprocal of the parameter a^0 in the Debye-Hückel equation for mean activity coefficients.

$$\log \gamma^{\pm} = \frac{-A\mu^{\frac{1}{2}}}{1 + Ba^0\mu^{\frac{1}{2}}}$$

where $\gamma^{\pm}$ = mean activity coefficient
  A = constant
  B = constant
  μ = ionic strength
  a^0 = Debye-Hückel parameter

a^0 can be considered as the distance of closest approach of two ions in solution and can thus be related to the hydrated-ion radius.

According to present-day theory, it is assumed that ions in aqueous solutions are hydrated and that the degree of hydration is directly proportional to the ionic charge or valence and inversely proportional to the ionic radius. Ions having a high charge-radius ratio are therefore more highly hydrated than those with a low ratio. This will explain the fact that the exchange affinity of Cs^+ is greater than that of Na^+ because the hydrated ionic radius of Cs is actually smaller than that of Na. In general, the hydrated-ionic radii are not well defined, and this seriously limits any comparison of exchange affinity and hydrated-ionic radii. Since ion exchange is presumably controlled by coulombic forces, the exchange affinity should be directly proportional to ionic charge and inversely proportional to the hydrated-ionic radius. Therefore, $1/a^0$, as well as K', can be regarded as a practical measure of the relative affinity two ions have for an exchanger. It must be kept in mind, though, that K' can be regarded as a constant only over a limited concentration range. If the exchanging ions differ considerably in their physical and/or chemical properties, the variation of K' with concentration can be quite large.[9]

Other equilibrium data for ion-exchange reactions are given by Ketelle and Boyd;[10] Bauman and Eichhorn;[11] Gregor, Belle, and Marcus;[12] Kressman and Kitchener;[13] and Diamond.[14] Kressman and Kitchener have shown that the selectivity coefficients of a number of univalent cations are in the order

$$Li^+ < H^+ < Na^+ < K^+ = NH_4^+ < Rb^+ < Cs^+ < Ag^+$$

and the divalent cations in the order

$$Be^{++} < Mn^{++} < Mg^{++} = Zn^{++} < Cu^{++} = Ni^{++}$$
$$< Co^{++} < Ca^{++} < Sr^{++} < Pb^{++} < Ba^{++}$$

Appropriate mass-action expressions can be formulated and selectivity coefficients determined for exchange reactions involving ions of the same but higher valency, but nothing really precise can be obtained regarding the relative affinities of ions of different valence, such as the uni- and divalent ions. The mathematical treatment of exchange reactions involving ions of different valence is more difficult because of the differences in the powers of the activities of the two ions and the marked concentration dependency of the equilibrium. But in general for concentrations less than 0.1 N, the higher the valence of an ion, the greater its affinity for the resin.

In addition to the stoichiometric interchange of equivalent amounts of anions or cations in an exchange reaction there are several minor changes which should be considered, namely, the swelling of the resin and the penetration of free electrolytes into the resin. With the highly cross-linked high-capacity resins, the amount of free electrolyte which diffuses into the resin is small and can be neglected. The diffusion of free electrolyte into the resin becomes a disturbing influence only for those resins with a low degree of cross-linking and a low capacity.

Bauman[11] has shown that the degree of swelling of sulfonic acid exchangers markedly influences the exchange equilibrium. Further complications arise in establishing relative exchange affinities because the degree of cross-linking of the resin has a marked influence on selectivity— the greater the degree of cross-linking, the greater the selectivity. Resins which are cross-linked to a low degree swell readily and show little preference for similar small ions.[15] These effects must be considered in any precise theoretical treatment of ion exchange.

Gregor[16] advanced a theory to account for the selectivity of resins based primarily upon the measurable change in volume of the resin that occurs during the exchange of ions. The basic premise is that the exchange of ions that cause expansion of the resin is less favored than that of those that do not, since the cross-linked structure resists expansion. Consequently it is expected that selectivity would be determined entirely by the dimensions of the hydrated ion. This is consistent with a portion of the observed affinity series of the univalent cations in which the smallest hydrated ions have the greatest exchange affinity. It does not account for the position of the silver and thallium ions. Gregor's thermodynamic expression for the exchange can be given as

$$RT \ln \frac{a_B \, a_{AR}}{a_A \, a_{BR}} = p(\bar{V}_{BR} - \bar{V}_{AR}) \qquad (10.5)$$

where p is the swelling pressure and $\bar{V}$ is the specific ionic volume. Rearranging, the selectivity coefficient is given by

$$\ln K' = -\ln \frac{\gamma_{AR}}{\gamma_{BR}} + p \frac{\bar{V}_{BR} - \bar{V}_{AR}}{RT} \qquad (10.6)$$

which is essentially the equation derived by Glueckauf.[17]   The selectivity is, therefore, dependent on both the ordinary electrolyte activity in the resin phase and the swelling energy.   Experiments conducted on the osmotic properties of resins indicate that the swelling of resins is a function of the concentration of ions within the resin and not of the size of the ions themselves.   The more strongly the ions are held, the less the swelling.   This is in line with the fact that the salt forms of a given resin are often more swollen than the hydrogen form.   This is particularly true with the hydrogen form of weakly acidic resins.   The results seem to indicate that for small ions in ordinary exchange systems, the swelling pressure has little effect on K', meaning, of course, that the ratio γ_{BR}/γ_{AR} is determinative.   Essentially equivalent conclusions have been reached by Boyd and Soldano[18] and Davies and Yeoman.[19]

   Still another approach is the empirical equation of Rothmund and Kornfeld,[20] which can be expressed as

$$\frac{X_{AR}}{X_{BR}}\left(\frac{C_B}{C_A}\right)^p = k \qquad (10.7)$$

where k, p = empirical parameters
   X_{BR} = equivalent fraction of B in the resin
   X_{AR} = equivalent fraction of A in the resin
   C_A = concentration of A in the solution phase
   C_B = concentration of B in the solution phase
Many of the data in the literature seem to fit this equation.   It is evidenced by the fact that a plot of log (X_{BR}/X_{AR}) versus log (C_B/C_A) gives a straight line.   There are certainly similarities between this empirical equation and the ones arrived at in a more theoretical manner.

   Considerable work has been done by others toward the formulation of quantitative ion-exchange theory, but there is still much to be desired in the resulting equations.[21]

   Based on typical exchange reactions, the following generalizations can be made.   The reactions are stoichiometric and reversible and exhibit no exchange hysteresis.   All functional groups are accessible as exchange sites, and the total exchange capacity is the same for all small ions.

   Because of the inability of the present theories to predict fully ion-exchange behavior, it is common practice to apply empirical rules derived from experimental findings to predict relative exchange potentials. These rules are enumerated below for dilute aqueous solutions at room temperature.   The exchange potential:

   1. Increases with an increase in valence of the exchanging ion.   For example, $Na^+ < Ca^{++} < La^{3+} < Th^{4+}$.

   2. Increases with atomic number for ions of the same periodic group; i.e., $Li^+ < Na^+ < K^+ < Rb^+ < Cs^+$; $Mg^{++} < Ca^{++} < Sr^{++} < Ba^{++}$: $F^- < Cl^- < Br^- < I^-$.

3. Of ions of the same valence but different periodic groups can be approximated from their activity coefficients—the greater the activity coefficient, the greater the exchange potential.

4. Of the hydrogen and hydroxyl ions depends on the strength of the acid or base formed with the functional group of the resin—the weaker the acid or base formed, the greater the exchange potential.

5. Of high-molecular-weight organic ions and some anionic complexes of the metals is unusually high.

6. Of various ions becomes more alike as the degree of cross-linking and the capacity of the resin are lowered.

7. Decreases with increased degree of hydration of ions of the same valence.

Exceptions to the above exchange-potential series take place at high temperatures and high concentrations and in nonaqueous or partial nonaqueous media. Under such conditions the differences in exchange potentials of different ions usually decrease.

The exchange potentials for the anions do not appear in any well-defined order, but Kunin and Myers[22] have found the order for the exchange potential on a weak-base anion exchanger to be approximately: hydroxide > sulfate > chromate > citrate > tartrate > nitrate > arsenate > phosphate > molybdate > acetate = iodide = bromide > chloride > fluoride. The order varies with relative concentrations of ions, pH, and basicity of the functional exchange group. Hydroxyl ion is the weakest replacing ion on a strong-base exchanger.

Many ion-exchange materials show some degree of selectivity above that ascribed to valence, ionic size, degree of cross-linking, and physical adsorption. The carboxylic resins are particularly selective to hydrogen ions and the bivalent copper and calcium ions. The sulfonic acid resins are unusually selective to univalent silver and thallium ions. The anionic complexes of the transition metals, such as copper, nickel, cobalt, and the platinum-group metals, are held very strongly by the amine anion exchangers. The affinity is completely out of proportion to ionic charges and can be attributed to the formation of the metal-amine complexes which are known to be quite stable.

Still greater selectivity can be achieved through a chemical modification of the nature of the exchange site. Functional groups possessing chelating or complexing properties increase the selectivity of the exchange process.

McBurney[23] has prepared an exchanger containing a 1,3-diketone functional group which has an unusually great affinity for the cupric ion. Gregor et al.[24] have investigated various complex-forming resins containing such groups as o-aminophenol, formaldehyde, and m-phenylene diglycine. These resins show some selectivity for the transition metal ions. Blasius and Olbrich[25] have prepared resins from m-phenylene-diaminetetra-acetic acid, resorcinol, and formaldehyde and used them for the separation of copper and nickel.

10.4. Ion-exchange Kinetics. Generally the size (surface area) of commercially available exchange resins and their capacity rule out the possibility of exchange occurring entirely on the surface of the resin. The exchange capacity (2 to 10 milliequivalents per gram) is such that exchange must occur almost entirely in the interior of the resin because of the very limited surface area. Since it has been shown that the resins are gel-like substances whose exchange sites are dispersed randomly throughout each particle, the exchange process can be represented in five steps: (1) the diffusion of ions through the solution to the surface of the resin, (2) the diffusion of ions through the gel (resin) to the exchange site, (3) the exchange of ions, (4) the diffusion of exchanged ions through the gel to the surface, and (5) the diffusion of the exchanged ions from the resin surface into the bulk of the solution. It is now generally conceded that the actual exchange of ions in the gel phase (step 3) is instantaneous or nonexistent and that the rate of exchange reactions is determined by a diffusion mechanism governed by diffusion laws. It is apparent then that the net rate of exchange will depend on the concentration of the solution, particle size of the resin, diffusion coefficients of the ions in solution, and resin phase and consequently on the degree of cross-linking of the resin and temperature. In practice, all these factors influence the exchange rate as would be anticipated for a diffusion mechanism; thus, high rates of exchange are achieved in concentrated solutions at high temperatures with small resin particles, small hydrated ions, and lightly cross-linked resins.

The diffusion of ions to and away from the surface of the resin is eliminated as a rate-determining step if the solution is agitated or if sufficient turbulence is produced by the flow of solution over the resin particle. There remains, though, a more or less stagnant layer of solution near the surface of the resin through which diffusion is the only form of ion transport. Once inside the resin the ion must travel by diffusion through the charge-studded gel structure to the exchange site where exchange occurs. The exchanged ion must then go through the same diffusion process in reverse order.

Boyd et al.[26] have distinguished between the two possible rate-determining steps and shown that at concentrations below 0.001 M the diffusion of ions through the film of solution about the resin particle is rate determining. At concentrations greater than 0.1 M, the diffusion of ions through the resin particle is rate determining. For intermediate ion concentrations, 0.001 to 0.1 M, the rate of exchange is determined by a combination of the diffusional processes. The latter is of considerable practical importance because most ion-exchange applications involve concentrations within this range. A quantitative theoretical treatment of ion-exchange kinetics is further complicated because the compositions of the resin phase and solution phase are constantly changing as one ionic species is replaced by another.

Soldano[27] has demonstrated with radioactive tracers that diffusion rates in resins with normal degrees of cross-linking are five to ten times slower than those in free solution. Diffusion rates within the resin increase as the degree of cross-linking decreases. This, of course, is consistent with a diffusion-controlled rate mechanism. Further evidence for a diffusion-controlled rate mechanism is the fact that most measured rates of exchange increase with smaller resin particle size and increased temperatures.

Exceptions to these general diffusion characteristics can be encountered when the pores of the resin are too small to admit the exchanging ion. Under such conditions only the exchange sites in the resin surface are available for exchange, so the capacity of the resin increases with a decrease in resin particle dimensions. The rate-determining step then might be bulk solution diffusion.

Diffusion rates are dependent not only on the physical structure of the resin but also on the nature of the functional group and the exchanging ion. For sulfonic acid exchangers, the exchange rates are extremely rapid and there are only small differences in the rates of exchange of different ions. For carboxylic acid exchangers, the rates of exchange are quite rapid also (see Table 10.2) unless the hydrogen ion is involved.[28]

TABLE 10.2. A COMPARISON OF THE RATES OF EXCHANGE FOR STRONGLY AND WEAKLY ACIDIC CATION-EXCHANGE RESINS*

Equilibrium	90% equilibrium attainment time
$RSO_3H + KOH$	2 min
$RCOOH + KOH$	7 days
$RSO_3Na + CaCl_2$	2 min
$RCOONa + CaCl_2$	2 min

* From R. Kunin and R. E. Barry, *Ind. Eng. Chem.*, **41**, 1269 (1949).

The exchange of alkali with a weakly acidic cation exchanger in the hydrogen form is very slow compared with normal exchange reactions. This cannot be attributed to any difference in the resin structure because the exchange between different salt forms of the same resin is quite rapid. Clearly the slowness is associated with the formation of a weak electrolyte. Since soluble weak electrolytes ionize very rapidly, it is assumed that the exchange reaction itself has no bearing on the rate of exchange. According to diffusion laws, the rate of diffusion is dependent on the concentration gradient of the ionic species. Since only free ions can contribute to the concentration gradient, ions tied up as a weakly dissociated species cannot be considered.   Thus, in the exchange of alkali for hydrogen ions in a carboxylic acid exchanger, the hydrogen-ion concentration in the resin phase is very low and the rate of diffusion is very low.   The extremely low rates of exchange observed with phenolic resins in the hydrogen form are consistent with this approach.

10.5. Techniques of Ion Exchange.   There are two generally employed techniques for contacting solutions with ion-exchange resins: the batch method and the column method.   The batch method consists in mixing resin and solution in a vessel until equilibrium is obtained.   The solution is filtered off, and the resin is prepared for the next single-stage equilibrium process.   The extent to which ions are taken up by the resin depends upon the distribution coefficient of the solute under equilibrium conditions. Except in the most favorable cases, only a small portion of the exchange capacity of the resin will be utilized in a single or batch equilibrium. Obvious exceptions are exchange reactions that involve the formation of weak electrolytes, insoluble products, or stable complexes.   For example, the following exchanges are of practical significance because there are driving forces other than the exchange equilibrium that force the exchange to completion:

$$RSO_3H + K^+OH^- \rightleftharpoons RSO_3K + H_2O$$

The completeness of this reaction depends upon the neutralization of the base with the acidic resin and the forced quantitative takeup of the base cation to replace the consumed hydrogen ions.   The reaction is a practical means of neutralizing a base without the introduction of another soluble electrolyte.

In the following equation,

$$RSO_3Ag + Na^+Cl^- \rightleftharpoons RSO_3Na + AgCl$$

the great insolubility of the silver chloride causes the withdrawal of the silver ion from the resin to satisfy the solubility-product principle. There must be an equivalent amount of sodium ion absorbed by the resin to maintain electrical neutrality.   Survival kits employ such reactions for the small-scale desalting of sea water.   Both the anion and cation of the salt are effectively removed from solution, leaving a potable water.

Reasonably high-quality deionized water, suitable as a substitute for distilled water in lead storage batteries, steam irons, and other small volume users and in the laboratory, can be obtained from the batch treatment of tap water with a mixture of a strong-acid cation exchanger in the hydrogen form and a strong-base anion exchanger in the hydroxyl form.   The combination of displaced hydrogen and hydroxyl ions to form water shifts the equilibrium far to the right, giving a quantitative uptake of cations and anions from solution.   Although there are limited applications of single equilibrium processes, batch processes in general have proved of little value in separations work.

In column operation a vertical cylinder is filled with an exchange resin and the electrolyte solution is percolated through the column. Column operation can be considered as a large number of consecutive batch equilibria where fresh resin is contacted with the ion-depleted solution in each equilibrium step. While the extent to which the exchange takes place in each of the single equilibria is limited by the distribution coefficient of the solute, the overall effect is highly favorable, for as an electrolyte solution passes through a column of resin, the exchangeable ions

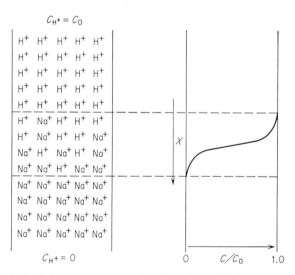

FIG. 10.6. Columnar exchange of sodium ions with hydrogen ions.

encounter millions of exchange sites every centimeter of column length. In this way multiple equilibria are established and solutes with even unfavorable distribution coefficients are quantitatively removed. In a sense this is a simple use of the mass-action principle to drive a reaction to completion. As the electrolyte solution passes through the adsorbent, the partially depleted solution is continually being brought into contact with fresh resin, where it is depleted still further until ultimately the uptake of the electrolyte is complete. This is, of course, analogous to the qualitative treatment given for the development of an adsorption chromatogram—the primary difference being the mechanism by which solute adheres to the adsorbent (in this case, the resin).

In a more practical vein, consider the uptake of hydrogen ions by a column of a sulfonic acid exchanger in the sodium form (Fig. 10.6).

After a small quantity of solution has been added, the upper part of the column is saturated with hydrogen ions and the lower part is still in the sodium form. The concentration of hydrogen ions in solution in the upper part of the column is the same as its concentration in the influent C_0, whereas in the lower part of the column the concentration of hydrogen ions is very low. In an intermediate zone of the column both hydrogen and sodium ions are present in solution as well as in the resin and the hydrogen-ion concentration of the solution varies along the length of this zone from C_0 to zero. The ratio of C/C_0 along the length of the column is given schematically. The effluent from the column is free of hydrogen ions but contains an equivalent concentration of sodium ions. Eventually the column will be saturated with hydrogen ions and hydrogen ions

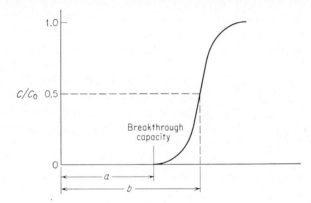

Fig. 10.7. Typical breakthrough curve for an ion-exchange column.

will appear in the effluent. This is the *breakthrough point* for the exchanged ion. The hydrogen-ion concentration in the effluent rapidly builds up to its concentration in the influent, and the sodium-ion concentration drops to zero.

A convenient way of illustrating the breakthrough point for a component and the capacity of an exchanger bed is to plot the volume of effluent versus the concentration of exchangeable ions as is done in Fig. 10.7. The volume a represents the breakthrough capacity of the column for an exchangeable ion under practical conditions. The volume b corresponds to the theoretical exchange capacity of the exchanger bed if the breakthrough curve is symmetrical. Usually the breakthrough curves are not symmetrical and the volume b is only an approximation of the total exchange capacity. When the breakthrough capacity is compared under different conditions, it is well to select an arbitrary concentration value, such as $C/C_0 = 0.001$, for the terminal concentration of the exchangeable solute in the effluent. This would mean that 99.9 per cent of the solute has been exchanged from that volume fraction and the exchange is considered quantitative.

In general, the breakthrough capacity of an exchanger bed is markedly influenced by the size of the exchanger particles, dimensions of the column, flow rate, temperature, and the composition of the solution.

Various studies[29,30] have indicated that the breakthrough capacity of a column is greatly increased as the size of the exchanger particles is decreased. Thus, where a quantitative uptake of solute is desirable, there is an obvious advantage in using relatively fine particles of exchanger. Equilibrium is more rapidly established with the smaller exchanger particles, and the breakthrough curves approach the ideal vertical form with diminished particle size.

For a given quantity of exchanger the breakthrough capacity increases with increased column length or decreased column diameter. Breakthrough curves are sharper for long columns than for short ones.

As the flow rate is decreased, the breakthrough capacity increases and the breakthrough curves become sharper. The effect is less pronounced with very porous exchangers than with strongly cross-linked resins, which is in keeping with an internal diffusion mechanism as the rate-determining step for the exchange of ions. An increase in temperature also speeds up the rate of exchange, sharpens the breakthrough curves, and increases the breakthrough capacity.

Various studies[31,32] indicate that the breakthrough capacity for cations decreases as the acidity of the solution increases. The effect of acidity on breakthrough capacity is much more pronounced for the ions with low exchanger affinity, such as lithium, sodium, and potassium, than for ions with high exchanger affinity, such as copper, iron, lead, and calcium. The reduced breakthrough capacity of the cations can be directly attributed to the increased competition for exchange sites exerted by the hydrogen ions. It is well to note, though, that there can be a quantitative uptake of metal cations from a strongly acidic solution but the breakthrough capacity will be less.

Although the presence of two exchangeable solutes in the solution complicates the exchange procedure, the uptake of the ions can be followed diagrammatically with breakthrough curves as easily as was done with single-component systems. Consider, for example, the uptake of a 60:40 (based on equivalents) solution of sodium and calcium ions on a cation exchanger in the hydrogen form. At first the two cations are quantitatively exchanged for hydrogen ions and the hydrogen-ion concentration of the effluent rapidly builds up until it equals the total electrolyte concentration of the influent (see Fig. 10.8). Because of the difference in exchangeability of the sodium and calcium ions, calcium ions preferentially displace the sodium ions, which in turn displace the

hydrogen ions.   As soon as the hydrogen ions are exhausted, sodium will
appear in the effluent, and its concentration will increase simultaneously
with the decrease in hydrogen-ion concentration.   For a while, then, the
effluent contains only sodium ions.   Later, the breakthrough point for
calcium ions is reached and the composition of the effluent is adjusted
until it is the same as that of the original solution.   Only a partial
resolution of the sample components is achieved because this is basically
a frontal-analysis technique and, just as in adsorption chromatography
(see Secs. 4.3 to 4.5), mixtures of similar solutes cannot be resolved by
frontal analysis.   Only the least adsorbable solute can be isolated in pure
form and even then only in nonquantitative yields.   Quantitative
resolutions of similar ionic species can be achieved only if the solutes are

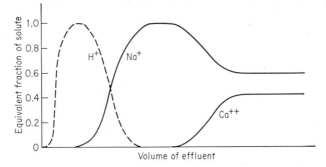

Fig. 10.8. Elution of sodium and calcium ions by frontal analysis from a cation
exchanger in the hydrogen form.

taken up on the topmost portion (generally the top 10 per cent or less)
of the column and eluted by either displacement or elution analysis.
    The most refined applications of ion exchangers are the separations of
similar ionic species by ion-exchange chromatography involving displacement or elution analysis where the common elutriants are acids, salts,
and complexing agents.
    Ion-exchange elution analysis can be demonstrated by the separation of
sodium and calcium ions on a sulfonic acid exchanger in the hydrogen
form.   Sodium and calcium are retained in a narrow zone at the top of
the column, and the displaced acid is removed by washing the column
with distilled water.   The metal ions can be eluted then by washing the
column with a dilute hydrochloric acid solution.   Sodium and calcium
ions will be partially replaced by hydrogen and carried downward
through the column.   The fresh acid contacting the sodium- and calcium-
depleted zone at the top replaces more metal ions until the displacement is
quantitative.   As the metal ions move down the column under the flow
of solvent, they are contacted with exchanger in the hydrogen form and

again exchanged.   Since the calcium ions have a greater exchange ability
than sodium ions, the composition of the solution will be continuously
changing, so that the Na^+/Ca^{++} will increase as the solution moves
downward.   Under the proper conditions the calcium and sodium ions
will be separated into two independent zones moving through the column
at different rates.   Sodium ions will appear in the effluent first.   If the
concentration of sodium and calcium in the effluent is plotted versus the
volume of effluent, a typical elution curve is obtained (Fig. 10.9).   The
effluent contains hydrogen ions during the whole course of the elution,
and the sum of hydrogen- and solute-ion concentrations, expressed as
equivalents, in the effluent equals the equivalent concentration of the
influent.   The elution curves are sharpest for the solute with the lowest
exchange ability.

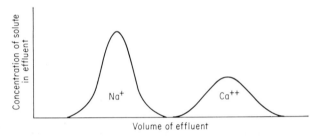

Fig. 10.9. Elution of sodium and calcium ions by elution analysis from a cation
exchanger in the hydrogen form.

Compared with frontal analysis, elution analysis has the distinct
advantage that mixtures of similar ionic species can be completely
resolved.   The contamination of all fractions with elutriant ions is the
chief disadvantage of the method.

Operational techniques and choice of elutriant determine the shape of
elution curves for a given solute-exchanger system and, therefore, determine the resolution efficiency.   The sharper the elution curves the shorter
the column needed for a complete resolution.   The factors that determine
the shape of elution curves also determine the shape of breakthrough
curves to a great extent.   Thus, as a generalization, resolution efficiency
should increase with a decrease in exchanger particle diameter and flow
rate and with an increase in temperature and column length.   With the
exception of elutriant composition these are the more important system
variables.   Separation efficiency can be improved in many analyses if a
stepwise elution is used.   First, elute the more easily displaced solutes
with a given elutriant, and then complete the elution of the remaining
solutes with an elutriant possessing a greater displacement ability than
the first.   By this procedure, the solutes with the greatest exchange ability

are eluted more rapidly in a smaller volume of effluent and the elution curves are not so broad as they would be with the first elutriant. An additional advantage is the saving of time.

Usually the exact mathematical treatment of an exchange column is too complex to be practical, but it is still very useful in obtaining qualitative information about the system and in guiding experimental work.

Mayer and Tompkins[33] described a theoretical approach to ion-exchange chromatography based on the analogy between the successive equilibria in an ion-exchange column and a distillation column. The similarity is quite great, and the height of theoretical plate concept can be applied to ion-exchange columns both mathematically and graphically. The column is considered as being made up of a number of theoretical exchange plates p holding a solution volume V. As the solvent percolates through the column, the finite volumes V progress from plate to plate. The distribution of solute in any plate can then be expressed as

$$\frac{S_{n,p}}{L_{n,p}} = C \tag{10.8}$$

where C = distribution of solute between solution and resin in plate p

$L_{n,p}$ = fraction of solute in solution which is in contact with plate p when nth V has equilibrated in that plate

$S_{n,p}$ = fraction of solute in resin phase in plate p when nth V has equilibrated in that plate

n = number of V's that have equilibrated with a given plate up to a given time

F = number of column volumes that have passed through a column = n/p

To maintain a material balance with the flow of solvent through the column

$$L_{n,p} + S_{n,p} = L_{n,p-1} + S_{n-1,p} \tag{10.9}$$

If the portion of the exchanger on which the solute is adsorbed is considered plate zero, then as the first increment V of developing solvent contacts this portion of the exchanger and equilibrates with it,

$$L_{1,0} + S_{1,0} = 0 + 1$$

Since

$$\frac{S_{1,0}}{L_{1,0}} = C$$

$$S_{1,0} = \frac{C}{1+C} \quad \text{and} \quad L_{1,0} = \frac{1}{1+C}$$

In turn

$$L_{2,0} + S_{2,0} = 0 + \frac{C}{1+C}$$

and

$$S_{2,0} = \frac{C^2}{(1+C)^2}$$

and

$$L_{2,0} = \frac{C}{(1+C)^2}$$

For plate zero, the general expressions for L and S become

$$S_{n,0} = \frac{C^n}{(1+C)^n} \quad \text{and} \quad L_{n,0} = \frac{C^{n-1}}{(1+C)^n} \tag{10.10}$$

For plate 1

$$L_{1,1} + S_{1,1} = L_{1,0} + S_{0,1} = \frac{C^0}{1+C} + 0$$

and

$$\frac{S_{1,1}}{L_{1,1}} = C$$

$$L_{1,1} = \frac{C^0}{(1+C)^2} \quad \text{and} \quad S_{1,1} = \frac{C}{(1+C)^2}$$

$$L_{2,1} + S_{2,1} = L_{2,0} + S_{1,1} = \frac{C}{(1+C)^2} + \frac{C}{(1+C)^2}$$

$$\frac{S_{2,1}}{L_{2,1}} = C$$

$$L_{2,1} = \frac{2C}{(1+C)^3} \quad \text{and} \quad S_{2,1} = \frac{2C^2}{(1+C)^3}$$

In general,

$$L_{n,1} = \frac{nC^{n-1}}{(1+C)^{n+p}} \quad \text{and} \quad S_{n,1} = \frac{nC^n}{(1+C)^{n+p}} \tag{10.11}$$

By extending the treatment to more theoretical plates it can be shown that

$$L_{n,p} = \frac{(n+p-1)!}{(n-1)!\,p!}\frac{C^{n-1}}{(1+C)^{n+p}} \tag{10.12}$$

and

$$S_{n,p} = \frac{(n+p-1)!}{(n-1)!\,p!}\frac{C^n}{(1+C)^{n+p}} \tag{10.13}$$

For large values of n and p Stirling's approximation can be used for $X!$, namely,

$$X! = e^{-x}n^x(2\pi x)^{\frac{1}{2}}$$

Therefore

$$L_{n,p} = \frac{1}{(2\pi)^{\frac{1}{2}}}\frac{(p+n-1)^{p+n-\frac{1}{2}}}{(n-1)^{n-\frac{1}{2}}p^{p+\frac{1}{2}}}\frac{C^{n-1}}{(1+C)^{p+n}}$$

and

$$S_{n,p} = \frac{1}{(2\pi)^{\frac{1}{2}}}\frac{(p+n-1)^{p+n-\frac{1}{2}}}{(n-1)^{n-\frac{1}{2}}p^{p+\frac{1}{2}}}\frac{C^n}{(1+C)^{p+n}}$$

The quantity of material in any plate of the column can be calculated from the equation

$$L_{n,p} + S_{n,p} = \frac{(1+C)(p+n-1)^{p+n-\frac{1}{2}}}{(2\pi)^{\frac{1}{2}}(n-1)^{n-\frac{1}{2}}p^{p+\frac{1}{2}}}\frac{C^{n-1}}{(1+C)^{n+p}} \tag{10.14}$$

From this equation the bandwidth of a solute zone can be calculated for the range of p's containing a given fraction of the solute.

The maximum in the equation for $L_{n,p}$ can be shown to occur at $n = pC$. Thus, the fraction of solute in solution at plate $n_{\max}$ corresponding to the elution peak is given by

$$L_{\max} = L_{pC\,p} = [2\pi pC(1 + C)]^{-\frac{1}{2}} \tag{10.15}$$

and the location of the elution peak in terms of free column volumes of eluate that have passed through the column is given by

$$F_{\max} = \frac{n_{\max}}{p}$$

Since

$$C = \frac{n_{\max}}{p}$$

$$F_{\max} = C \tag{10.16}$$

The usual elution curve is thus a plot of L for the last plate of the column versus n as n varies from zero to the terminal value. The value of p and C can be determined for a given system from an experimental elution curve, since F and C are numerically equal at any peak. Thus, the intervals between the peaks of an elution curve for several solutes are a measure of the differences in solute distribution coefficients. The material with the lowest C will move through the column most rapidly.

Since an elution curve is a plot of concentration versus volume which approximates the normal curve of error, the area under the elution curve is representative of the total material eluted. Tables are available relating the area under the curve to t, where t is the number of standard deviations σ that n is removed from the peak of the elution band. Thus, $t = n/\sigma$ with the peak of the curve at the origin. The ordinate of the normal curve at the peak equals $[\sigma(2\pi)^{\frac{1}{2}}]^{-1}$. The ordinate at the peak of an elution curve has been shown to be equal to

$$[2\pi pC(1 + C)]^{-\frac{1}{2}}$$

Therefore

$$\sigma = [pC(1 + C)]^{\frac{1}{2}}$$

and

$$t = \frac{n - n_{\max}}{[pC(1 + C)]^{\frac{1}{2}}} \tag{10.17}$$

when $n_{\max}$ is the value of n at the peak of the elution curve. But since $n_{\max} = pC$, the equation can be written as

$$t = \frac{p^{\frac{1}{2}}(F - C)}{C(1 + C)^{\frac{1}{2}}}$$

and when C is large, as

$$t = \frac{p^{\frac{1}{2}}(F - C)}{C} \tag{10.18}$$

If the equilibrium-distribution coefficients of two solutes and their individual elution patterns from short columns are known, it is possible to calculate the volume of elutriant required to remove them from any other size column. Elution curves and the degree of solute separation possible can then be calculated. It seems unnecessary to discuss the applicability of this concept to ion-exchange columns further, since the treatment is very similar to that for distillation and vapor-phase partition chromatography. Those interested in such treatment can refer to the works of Martin and Synge,[34] Mayer and Tompkins,[33] and others.[35,36]

Cornish[37] has provided a general approach to the selection of operating conditions for the separation of any pair of elements to any desired degree of purity for ion-exchange elution techniques.

Chromatographic separations can be improved sometimes if three or more columns of different diameter are connected in series in order of decreasing column diameters and a small mixing chamber is left between each pair of columns. Claesson[38] and Hagdahl[39,40] have shown that fronts achieved with this arrangement of columns are much sharper than those obtained with a single column. The improvement is based on the fact that a zone front with a high solute concentration moves faster than a front with a low concentration. Thus, when an imperfect front is mixed in the chamber between columns and applied to the next column, the more concentrated solution which follows the front will overtake the mixed and diluted solution in the second column and sharpen the front.

10.6. Apparatus. Just about all the techniques described for column utilization of ion-exchange materials can be effected with very simple equipment. The column can be any kind of inert tube with a porous plug in the bottom to support the exchanger bed. Usually the precaution is taken to keep the outlet of the column above the top of the exchanger bed. This is done to prevent air from entering the column and forming channels for the solution to pass through. Typical laboratory column designs are indicated in Fig. 10.10, but burets or short bits of glass tubing fitted with a rubber outlet tube and pinch clamp are quite effective. The length of the column is usually 10 to 20 times its diameter, although in ion-exchange chromatographic procedures it is not uncommon for the length to be as much as 100 times the column diameter. For convenience, the free volume in the column above the resin should be large enough to accommodate the entire sample. Columns can be jacketed for temperature control by passing hot liquids or vapors through the jacket.

It is preferable to add the resin to the column as a slurry and let the resin particles settle to form the bed. Columns must not be packed with dry resin because the exchanger can swell when wetted and burst the column. The resin is then converted to the desired form by washing

with the proper regenerant.   After regeneration is complete, the column
is washed with distilled water and is ready for the admission of a sample.

In an analysis the sample solution is introduced to the column and the
stopcock is adjusted to control the flow rate.   Frequently, the sample is
washed with a small volume of distilled water prior to the addition of the
eluting agent.   Elution of solutes is then achieved by either an elution or
displacement technique.

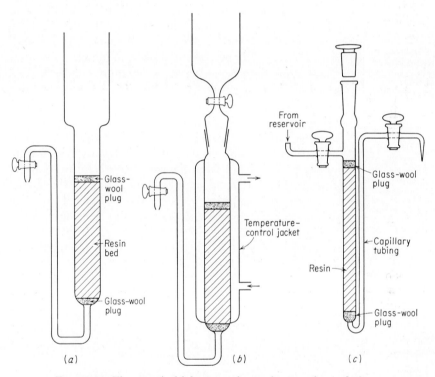

FIG. 10.10. Three typical laboratory ion-exchange column designs.

One of the more common techniques of achieving separations by ion-
exchange chromatography is to collect the effluent from the elution step
in a large number of fractions which are then analyzed by conventional
procedures.   Much time can be saved in the collection of these fractions
if an automatic fraction collector is used because the operator's constant
attention is not required.   Furthermore, the experiment can be continued
8 or 10 hr or more unattended.   Commercial models of collectors are
available which will collect fractions of effluent at regular time intervals
or in equal volumes.

Several simple collectors have been described in the literature[41,42] that can be built with a minimum of effort. These are quite effective in collecting fractions and are a tremendous aid to the analyst.

In some cases the collection of only the desired fractions can be effected by continuously recording some physical or chemical property of the effluent characteristic of the solutes. As the solute appears in the effluent, a mechanism to collect the fraction is triggered by the recording system. Once the fraction has been collected, the effluent is switched to a different fraction. Arrangements for the continuous recording of pH,[43] refractive index,[44] conductivity,[45] and radioactivity[46,47] have been described in detail.

10.7. Deionization of Aqueous Solutions. The deionization of water is generally effected in a two-step process in which the solution is passed successively through a cation exchanger in the hydrogen form and an anion exchanger in the hydroxyl form. In the cation exchanger the various solution cations are exchanged for hydrogen ions and the effluent from the exchanger bed is a solution of the acid of the anions. Subsequently, in the anion exchanger the solution anions are exchanged for the hydroxyl group which neutralizes the hydrogen ions, forming an equivalent amount of water. The two-step process is indicated in Fig. 10.11 for the demineralization of a sodium chloride–potassium sulfate solution.

One of the more serious problems encountered in the deionization of aqueous solutions by the above procedure is the leakage through the bed of cations that have not been exchanged for hydrogen ions. Obviously, leakage will reduce the quality of the deionized water and the capacity of the exchanger bed.

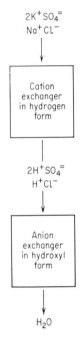

F I G. 1 0. 1 1. T w i n - b e d deionization of electrolyte solution.

The amount of leakage is determined by the flow rate through the bed, the type of cation exchanger used, the composition and concentration of the original solution, and the method of regeneration. Strongly acidic cation exchangers are preferred because they undergo exchange with the solution cations more readily than a weakly acidic exchanger. The monovalent ions are more likely to leak through the column than divalent or trivalent cations because their exchange affinity is lower. As the concentration of the influent increases, equilibrium exchange is less likely to occur and the flooding of the column with cations favors leakage. To counteract an increased concentration of solute, the flow rate through the column should be proportionately less. If a column is not fully regenerated before use, the bottom portion will contain cations other than hydrogen.   As the solution to be deionized percolates through the upper portion of the regenerated column, the exchanged hydrogen ions migrate downward and displace the cations from the unregenerated lower portion. Thus, leakage is more pronounced at the beginning of a cycle and near the exhaustion point of the bed.

Leakage can be controlled by using low flow rates, solution concentrations below 1000 ppm, and complete regeneration of the exchanger before use by backwashing the column with concentrated regenerant.   All strong acids are equally efficient for regenerating the exhausted resin to the hydrogen form, but some difficulties may be encountered unless there is a judicious selection of regenerant.   For example, if calcium ions are to be replaced, sulfuric acid should not be used as the regenerant.   The released calcium ions will precipitate as calcium sulfate, and the column may become clogged.

The capacity and effluent quality of the anion-exchanger column depend on the same factors enumerated for the cation exchanger. Strongly basic anion exchangers must be used for the quantitative uptake of the weak acids, such as H_2CO_3, H_2SiO_3, H_2S, and H_3BO_3.   Weakly basic anion exchangers do not take up the anionic forms of these acids. Strong alkalies are required for the regeneration of the strongly basic anion exchangers.

The effectiveness of a deionization process must be measured in terms of the quality of water produced.   Statements to the effect that the effluent water is comparable in purity to that obtained by distillation are false.   Ion exchange can remove only the dissolved electrolytes; non-electrolytes remain in the effluent water.   In fact, the slight dissolution of the exchanger tends to contaminate the water with soluble organic material.   It is possible, however, to reduce the electrolyte content of the effluent water to levels as low as that obtained by distillation.   Water having a conductivity of less than 10^{-6} mho per cm is easily attained if both anion and cation exchangers are carefully regenerated before use or the effluent is passed through a series of alternating cation- and anion-exchanger columns.

In certain cases it may be desirable to pass the solution to be deionized through the anion exchanger first to avoid the buildup of high acidity. The deionizations of sucrose and protein solutions are two examples. The acid formation in the normal procedure would produce an appreciable amount of sucrose inversion and the coagulation of the proteins.   The efficiency of this reversed order of deionization is controlled by the same factors as for the normal order, and the deionized water is of equal quality.

The most recent development in water deionization is the mixed-bed technique.   The aqueous solution is percolated through an intimate mixture of a strongly acidic cation exchanger and a strongly basic anion exchanger. If equivalent quantities of the cation and anion exchanger are used, a complete deionization is achieved in a single pass through the column and a neutral solution remains neutral throughout the deionization process. In the mixed-bed system the concentration of solution ions is decreased in stages and an analogy exists to the theoretical plates of a distillation column. Leakage is not a problem, and the effluent from the first mixed-bed column can exhibit a resistivity as low as 10^{-7} ohm-cm.

When a mixed bed is in operation, the resins are intimately mixed but they must be separated for regeneration. This is accomplished by several techniques: (1) Use resins with sufficiently different densities so that backwashing the column will carry the lighter resin to the top of the bed where it can be regenerated separately; (2) use resins of different particle size so that separation can be achieved by screening operations. After the individual exchangers are regenerated and rinsed, they are mixed and ready for a new cycle of deionization.

Mixed-bed deionization can be quite effective in a batch operation also. A common technique used to supply small quantities of deionized water is to place a mixture of anion and cation exchangers in the hydroxyl and hydrogen form, respectively, in a polyethylene wash bottle. Water to be deionized is added to the wash bottle. Provided the capacity of the exchangers is great enough to accommodate the solution ions, a quantitative deionization is effected. The quantitativeness of the reaction is determined by the neutralization reaction involving the displaced hydrogen and hydroxyl ions. Since the equilibrium point of this reaction is shifted far toward the formation of water, the exchange reaction is driven to completion.

10.8. Water Softening. The softening of water by means of ion exchange is one of the most important applications of exchange resins. The replacement of calcium and magnesium ions and lesser amounts of heavier metal ions with sodium ions constitutes the softening process. Softening is achieved by passing the hard water through a strongly acidic cation-exchanger bed in the sodium form. The reactions can be represented as

$$2NaR + Ca^{++} \rightleftharpoons CaR_2 + 2Na^+$$
$$2NaR + Mg^{++} \rightleftharpoons MgR_2 + 2Na^+$$

Once the exchanger has been exhausted, it is regenerated to the sodium form by washing with a brine solution. Carboxylic acid exchangers have such a great affinity for the alkaline-earth cations that the regeneration of the exchanger with brine is too inefficient for practical use. As a result, sulfonic acid exchangers are most frequently used because they can be efficiently regenerated with brine solutions and are efficient in taking up the alkaline-earth metal ions from solution.

10.9. Concentration of Electrolytes. One of the more interesting applications of ion exchange to analytical chemistry is the concentration of extremely dilute solutions of electrolytes. If a dilute solution of an electrolyte is passed through a column of an appropriate ion-exchange resin, the exchangeable ions will be adsorbed. The ions in question can then be washed free of nonexchanging impurities and eluted as a small volume of more concentrated electrolyte by regenerating the resin bed with a proper electrolyte solution. This enables one to identify and determine trace constituents in solutions where their primary concentration is well below the sensitivity limit of the available test method. The simplicity, speed, and quantitativeness of the method offer many advantages over the older concentration procedures depending on adsorption carriers or the evaporation of large volumes. The method has proved useful in many biological investigations and in the analysis of water and spent industrial fluids. Solutions containing as little as 10^{-4} ppm of such metals as copper, silver, manganese, iron, cobalt, nickel, and uranium can be concentrated 100- to 1000-fold quantitatively and brought to a concentration suitable for conventional analytical procedures.

Uranium[48] has been concentrated up to 1000 times its original concentration when a dilute solution of the uranyl ion in sulfuric acid solution (pH 1 to 2) is passed through a quaternary amine anion-exchange resin in the sulfate form, rinsed, and eluted with 1 M perchloric acid. In dilute sulfuric acid solutions hexavalent uranium is present as a complex anionic species, $UO_2(SO_4)_2^{-2}$ or $UO_2(SO_4)_3^{-4}$, which is readily adsorbed by a quaternary amine anion exchanger in the sulfate form.

Platinum can be recovered from the dissolved potassium chloroplatinate and the excess chloroplatinic acid reagent resulting from a potassium determination when the $PtCl_6^{-2}$ radical is collected on an anion exchanger in the chloride form. The platinum can be eluted with concentrated hydrochloric acid and concentrated by evaporation of the excess hydrochloric acid.

Burstall and Wells[49] developed a method for the concentration and recovery of gold from dilute alkaline cyanide solutions utilizing a strong-base anion-exchange resin. The complex cyanides of silver, copper, cobalt, nickel, zinc, and iron are also adsorbed, but they can be selectively eluted. Zinc and nickel can be eluted with 0.2 N hydrochloric acid, copper, and iron with strong sodium cyanide solution; gold and silver with a mixture of acetone and hydrochloric acid; and cobalt with a potassium thiocyanate solution. The gold and silver are then recovered by conventional means.

10.10. Preparation of Reagents. Standard solutions of acids and bases[50] are readily prepared by an ion-exchange technique from solutions of the pure salts of the acids and bases. If an accurately known amount of sodium chloride is dissolved in distilled water and passed through a strong-acid cation exchanger in the hydrogen form, a quantity of acid equivalent to the salt appears in the column effluent. If the displaced hydrogen ions are washed from the column, collected, and diluted to known volume, a standard acid solution is the result.

Similarly, silica- and carbon dioxide-free caustic solutions can be prepared by passing a solution of sodium or potassium sulfate through a quaternary ammonium anion-exchanger column in the hydroxyl form.

10.11. Dissolution of Insoluble Electrolytes. It is reasonable to suppose that almost any slightly soluble salt that ionizes in solution can be dissolved by an ion-exchange procedure, the criterion being that the final equilibrium favors the dissolution. Consider, for example, the dissolution of $CaSO_4$ when it is shaken with an aqueous suspension of a cation-exchange resin in the hydrogen form. The reaction can be represented by

$$2RSO_3H + CaSO_4(s) \rightleftharpoons (RSO_3)_2Ca + 2H^+ + SO_4^{--}$$

and the equilibrium constant as

$$\frac{[(RSO_3)_2Ca][H^+]^2[SO_4^{--}]}{[RSO_3H]^2} = K_{eq} = kK_{sp} \qquad (10.19)$$

where k is the equilibrium constant for the exchange reaction

$$2RSO_3H + Ca^{++} \rightleftharpoons (RSO_3)_2Ca + 2H^+$$

and K_{sp} is the solubility-product constant for the insoluble salt. As long as the product kK_{sp} is not too small, the reaction can be driven to completion if a moderate excess of the exchanger is added to the system. In practice, 0.3 g of calcium sulfate can be quantitatively dissolved in 15 min at 100° by shaking with about 10 g of a sulfonic acid exchanger in the hydrogen form.

Since the rate of the exchange reaction is proportional to the available concentration of the cation of the insoluble salt, dissolutions become impractical from a time standpoint if the solubility-product constant is very small. Increasing the temperature usually speeds up the dissolution and increases the value of the K_{sp}, thus favoring further dissolution.

Osborn[51] and Honda[52] were the first to report on this technique. Both showed that barium sulfate could be dissolved with cation-exchange resins. Osborn's technique consisted in shaking 0.25 g of barium sulfate with 10 g of cation exchanger in the hydrogen form in 100 ml of hot water. After 12 hr no barium sulfate remained and the quantity of acid liberated was equivalent to the amount of barium sulfate originally taken. The generalized technique is applicable to the dissolution of calcium carbonate, strontium sulfate, barium succinate, and a number of other common insoluble salts. Osborn also pointed out the feasibility of preparing hydrofluoric acid directly from calcium fluoride without the addition of sulfuric acid. A number of assay techniques for insoluble samples have been reported in which the liberated acid or anion is titrated directly after removal of the resin phase.[53]

One of the chief advantages of the technique is the dissolution of the insoluble material without the introduction of extraneous soluble electrolytes.

10.12. Removal of Interfering Ions. In many analytical procedures certain ions seriously interfere with the analysis and must be removed from the system prior to the determination. In some cases the interference is readily removed by an ion-exchange technique. For example, in the gravimetric determination of potassium as either the perchlorate or chloroplatinate, sulfate is a serious interference. The sulfate can be removed if the solution is passed through an anion exchanger in the chloride form. The alkali metal washes through and can be determined in the chloride solution. In the analysis of sulfate, sodium and iron are serious interferences. These contaminants can be removed if the sample solution is passed through a cation exchanger in the hydrogen form. The sulfate is present then in a solution containing hydrogen ions as the only cation, and the analysis can be completed with reliability. In the analysis of phosphate, calcium and other metal cations can be removed by collection of the cations on a cation exchanger in the hydrogen form. If some of the phosphorus is present as meta- or pyrophosphate, iron and aluminum can appear in the effluent as anionic species and still interfere in the subsequent determination.

In each of these examples, the ion that can interfere is of opposite charge to that to be determined and the interfering ion can be replaced easily with an ion that does not interfere. This is exactly what is done in water-softening procedures where calcium and magnesium ions are replaced with sodium.

In more complicated systems, such as the interference of lithium, sodium, rubidium, and cesium in the determination of potassium, the interference can be removed by ion-exchange chromatography. Such resolutions are discussed in the following section.

10.13. Ion-exchange Chromatography. In most instances the differences among similarly charged ionic species are not large enough to permit a separation by ion exchange unless an elution or displacement chromatographic technique is employed. The ions to be separated are adsorbed in a narrow zone at the top of the column and eluted with a developing solvent. Elution results in a series of adsorptions and desorptions of the ionic species which culminates with the ionic species of the lowest exchange potential moving through the column at the fastest rate. If the differences in exchange potentials are great enough, it is possible that a complete resolution will be achieved. The efficiency of the separation depends on a number of factors, such as the nature of the eluting agent, length of column, flow rate, resin particle size, temperature, size of sample, and differences in exchange potentials. Separation efficiency increases if one raises the temperature, lowers the flow rate, decreases the resin particle size, increases the length of the column, and uses a resin with a higher exchange capacity. These factors have been discussed in relation to the shape of elution or breakthrough curves and ion-exchange kinetics and will not be considered again. The complexing ability of the elutriant also plays an important role in elution of certain ionic species and will be considered further.

Samuelson,[54] Lederer and Lederer,[55] Kunin,[56,57] and Osborn[53] have cited numerous examples of chromatographic separations achieved with ion-exchange resins, but there are several separations that are especially noteworthy—the separations of the rare-earth metals and of the amino acids.

One of the most difficult separations to effect in inorganic chemistry has been the separation of the rare-earth metals from one another. The problem has been solved by an ion-exchange chromatographic procedure. Ketelle and Boyd[58] separated the rare earths on a 97-cm column of 270/325 mesh Dowex 50 at 100° using a 5 per cent citrate buffer (pH 3.28) at a flow rate of 0.64 cm per min. The cross-sectional area of the column was 0.26 sq cm. Figure 10.12 is the elution curve for a portion of this work. The very similar ionic radii (exchange affinities) of these metals preclude a separation by ion exchange of the simple ions alone. It is necessary that complexing agents, such as citric acid, be used to enhance the differences among the ions if a separation is to be achieved. The reactions which are postulated are as follows:

$$M^{3+} + 3NH_4R \rightleftharpoons MR_3 + 3NH_4^+$$
$$M(H_2Cit)_3 \rightleftharpoons M^{3+} + 3H_2Cit^-$$

Assuming the laws of mass action to hold, the equilibrium distribution of the metal between the resin phase and the complex is given by the coefficient K_d.

$$K_d = \frac{MR_3}{M(H_2Cit)_3} = \frac{K_{exchange}K_{complex}}{K_1^3} \frac{[NH_4R]^3}{[NH_4^+]^3} \frac{[H^+]^3}{[H_3Cit]^3} \quad (10.20)$$

where $K_{exchange}$ = exchange reaction equilibrium constant
$K_{complex}$ = complex instability constant
K_1 = first dissociation constant of citric acid

This equation shows the dependence of the distribution ratio on pH. The usual procedure for varying K_d is to add ammonia to the citrate buffer. A decrease in hydrogen-ion concentration is accompanied by an increase in ammonium-ion concentration, but the effect on K_d is partially offset by the decrease in the undissociated citric acid concentration, so that the change in K_d is not radical. The distribution ratio will remain constant in the course of an elution as long as the quantity of rare earth exchanged is small enough not to alter the activity of the ammonium ion in the

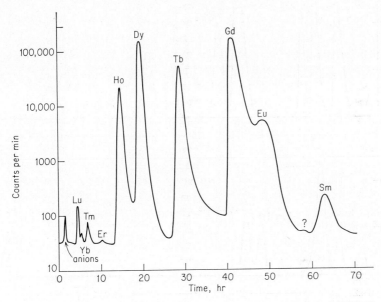

FIG. 10.12. Yttrium earth separations effected with a 97-cm column of 270/325 mesh Dowex 50 at 100° using 5 per cent citrate buffer at a flow rate of 0.64 cm per min. [*From B. H. Ketelle and G. E. Boyd, J. Am. Chem. Soc.,* **73,** 1862 (1951).]

exchanger phase. The activity of the ammonium ion in the exchanger phase will be relatively constant for low values of K_d, low rare-earth concentrations, and high-capacity resins.

The point of interest is the separation of the rare earths, and this can best be treated by considering the ratio of the distribution coefficients of two neighboring rare-earth ions M_1 and M_2 as a separation factor α. Thus,

$$\alpha = \frac{K_d^{M_1}}{K_d^{M_2}} = \frac{K^{M_1}_{\text{exchange}}}{K^{M_2}_{\text{exchange}}} \frac{K^{M_1}_{\text{complex}}}{K^{M_2}_{\text{complex}}} \tag{10.21}$$

It then follows that the separability of a pair of rare earths is independent of the ammonium- and citrate-ion concentrations in solution and of pH as long as the composition of the complex does not vary. The role of the citrate then is to enhance the difference in the adsorbabilities of the two metals by controlling the degree of complexation in the aqueous phase. Thus, if $K_d{}^{M_1} > K_d{}^{M_2}$, M_2 will appear in the effluent before M_1. The greater the value of α, the more efficient the resolution.

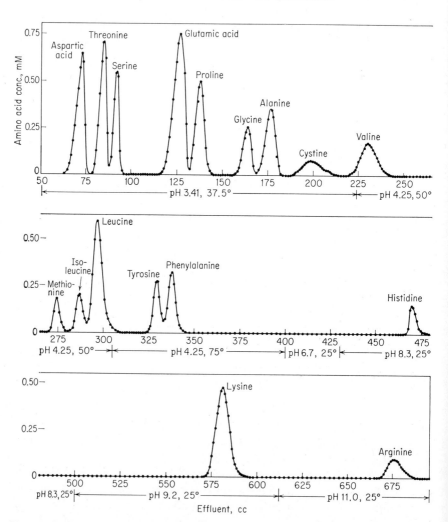

FIG. 10.13. Separation of amino acids from a synthetic mixture simulating the composition of a protein hydrolysate. The column of Dowex 50, 0.9 by 100 cm, was operated in the sodium form, with buffers of the pH and temperature indicated as eluants. A sample of about 6 mg of amino acids was chromatographed. The position of an amino acid peak is reproducible, on the average, to better than 5 per cent. [*From S. Moore and W. H. Stein, J. Biol. Chem.*, **192**, 663 (1951).]

Taken all together, the relative adsorbability of the rare earths is as follows:

La > Ce > Pr > Nd > Pm > Sm > Eu > Gd > Tb > Dy
> Y > Ho > Er > Tm > Yb > Lu

The progression is in the same order as that of crystal ionic radii and basicity.

Spedding et al.[59] have scaled the separation technique upward so as to effect a purification of macro amounts of the individual rare-earth elements.

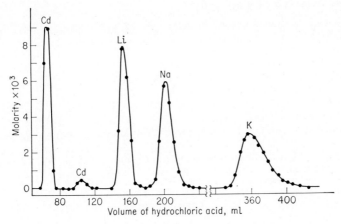

Fig. 10.14. Separation of approximately 0.2 millimole of cadmium, lithium, sodium, and potassium ions on a 37-cm by 2.4-sq cm column of colloidal Dowex 50. Ions eluted with 0.70 M HCl at a flow rate of 0.55 cm per min. [*From William Rieman, III, Record Chem. Progr.*, **15**, 85 (1954).]

Stein and Moore[60] developed an ion-exchange chromatographic technique for the separation of most of the common amino acids by means of a stepwise elution from a 9- by 1000-mm column of Dowex 50 in the sodium form. Elution was achieved with sodium citrate buffers of progressively increasing pH. The elution pattern for a synthetic mixture of amino acids is shown in Fig. 10.13.

Since the amino acids are amphoteric and exhibit isoelectric points which vary over a considerable pH range, it is possible under certain conditions to obtain separations into groups corresponding to the basic, neutral, and dicarboxylic amino acids.[61]

Other chromatographic separations of interest are the separations of the alkali metals depicted in Fig. 10.14 and the more common transition metals as chloro complexes on anion exchangers.[63,64]

In spite of the great usefulness of the ion-exchange technique, there are some weaknesses that should be mentioned. The theory fails if large samples or large flow rates are employed and does not indicate an allowable limit for these system variables. Ion-exchange chromatography is quite effective in separating sample components from one another, but it fails to isolate them in a pure form. Each component collected in the effluent of a column is mixed with a large amount of the eluant. In many cases this is not a serious handicap, but in other cases the eluant may seriously complicate the analyses of the small quantity of sample component.

10.14. Selected Bibliography

Ion Exchange, Analytical Reviews, *Anal. Chem.*, **32**, 67R (1960).
"Ion Exchange and Its Applications," Society of Chemical Industry, London, 1955.
Kitchener, J. A.: "Ion Exchange Resins," John Wiley & Sons, Inc., New York, 1957.
Kunin, R.: "Ion Exchange Resins," 2d ed., John Wiley & Sons, Inc., New York, 1958.
Lederer, E., and M. Lederer: "Chromatography," 2d ed., D. Van Nostrand Company, Inc., Princeton, N.J., 1957.
Nachod, F. C., and J. Schubert: "Ion Exchange Technology," Academic Press, Inc., New York, 1956.
Osborn, G. H.: "Synthetic Ion-exchangers," The Macmillan Company, New York, 1956.
Samuelson, O.: "Ion Exchangers in Analytical Chemistry," John Wiley & Sons, Inc., New York, 1953.

REFERENCES

1. Thompson, H. S.: *J. Roy. Agr. Soc. Engl.*, **11**, 68 (1850).
2. Way, J. T.: *J. Roy. Agr. Soc. Engl.*, **11**, 313 (1850); **13**, 123 (1852).
3. Boyd, G. E.: *Ann. Rev. Phys. Chem.*, **2**, 309 (1951).
4. Schubert, J.: *Anal. Chem.*, **22**, 1359 (1950).
5. Kunin, R.: "Ion Exchange Resins," 2d ed., John Wiley & Sons, Inc., New York, 1958.
6. Adams, B. A., and E. L. Holmes: *J. Soc. Chem. Ind.*, **54**, 1 (1935); British Pat. 450,309, 1936.
7. Kunin, R., and R. E. Barry: *Ind. Eng. Chem.*, **41**, 1269 (1949).
8. Boyd, G. E., J. Schubert, and A. W. Adamson: *J. Am. Chem. Soc.*, **69**, 2818 (1949).
9. Hogfeldt, E., E. Ekedahl, and L. G. Sillén: *Acta Chem. Scand.*, **4**, 1471 (1950).
10. Ketelle, B. H., and G. E. Boyd: *J. Am. Chem. Soc.*, **69**, 2800 (1947).
11. Bauman, W. C., and J. Eichhorn: *J. Am. Chem. Soc.*, **69**, 2830 (1947).
12. Gregor, H. P., J. Belle, and R. A. Marcus: *J. Am. Chem. Soc.*, **77**, 2713 (1955).
13. Kressman, T. R. E., and J. A. Kitchener: *J. Chem. Soc.*, 1949, pp. 1190, 1201, 1208, 1211.
14. Diamond, R. M.: *J. Am. Chem. Soc.*, **77**, 2978 (1955).
15. Reichenberg, D., K. W. Pepper, and D. J. McCauley: *J. Chem. Soc.*, 1951, p. 493.
16. Gregor, H. P.: *J. Am. Chem. Soc.*, **70**, 1293 (1948).
17. Glueckauf, E.: *Proc. Roy. Soc.*, **A214**, 207 (1952).
18. Boyd, G. E., and B. A. Soldano: *Z. Elektrochem.*, **57**, 162 (1953).

19. Davies, C. W., and C. D. Yeoman: *Trans. Faraday Soc.*, **49**, 968, 975 (1953).
20. Kornfeld, G.: *Z. Elektrochem.*, **23**, 173 (1917); V. Rothmund and G. Kornfeld, *Z. anorg. u. allgem. Chem.*, **103**, 129 (1918).
21. Pauley, J. L.: *J. Am. Chem. Soc.*, **76**, 1422 (1954).
22. Kunin, R., and R. J. Myers: *J. Am. Chem. Soc.*, **69**, 2874 (1947); *Discussions Faraday Soc.*, **7**, 114 (1949).
23. McBurney, C. H.: U.S. Pat. 2,613,200, 1952.
24. Gregor, H. P., M. Taifer, and E. I. Becker: *Ind. Eng. Chem.*, **44**, 2834 (1952).
25. Blasius, E., and G. Olbrich: *Z. anal. Chem.*, **151**, 81 (1956).
26. Boyd, G. E., A. W. Adamson, and L. S. Myers, Jr.: *J. Am. Chem. Soc.*, **69**, 2818 (1947).
27. Soldano, B. A.: *Ann. N.Y. Acad. Sci.*, **57**, 116 (1953); G. E. Boyd and B. A. Soldano, *J. Am. Chem. Soc.*, **75**, 6091 (1953).
28. Kunin, R., and R. E. Barry: *Ind. Eng. Chem.*, **41**, 1269 (1949).
29. Samuelson, O.: *Tek. Tidskr.*, **76**, 561 (1946).
30. Kunin, R., and R. E. Barry: *Ind. Eng. Chem.*, **41**, 1269 (1949).
31. Partridge, S. M.: *Discussions Faraday Soc.*, no. 7, p. 296, 1949.
32. Djurfeldt, R., and O. Samuelson: *Acta Chem. Scand.*, **4**, 165 (1950).
33. Mayer, S. W., and E. R. Tompkins: *J. Am. Chem. Soc.*, **69**, 2866 (1947).
34. Martin, A. J. P., and R. L. M. Synge: *Biochem. J.*, **35**, 1358 (1941).
35. Tompkins, E. R.: *J. Chem. Educ.*, **26**, 32, 92 (1949).
36. Beakenkamp, J., and W. Rieman, III: *Anal. Chem.*, **22**, 582 (1950).
37. Cornish, F. W.: *Analyst*, **83**, 634 (1958).
38. Claesson, S.: *Arkiv Kemi, Mineral. Geol.*, **A24**(16) (1947).
39. Hagdahl, L.: *Acta Chem. Scand.*, **2**, 574 (1948).
40. Tiselius, A., B. Drake, and L. Hagdahl: *Experientia*, **3**, 21 (1947).
41. Renshaw, A.: *Chem. & Ind.*, 1953, p. 294.
42. Eggenberger, D. N., and E. F. Cavanaugh: *Anal. Chem.*, **29**, 1116 (1957).
43. Partridge, S. M., and R. G. Westall: *Biochem. J.*, **44**, 418 (1949).
44. Tiselius, A.: *Arkiv Kemi, Mineral. Geol.*, **B14**(22) (1940); A. Tiselius and S. Claesson, *Arkiv Kemi, Mineral. Geol.*, **B15**(18) (1942).
45. Wickbold, R.: *Z. anal. Chem.*, **132**, 401 (1951).
46. Ketelle, B. H., and G. E. Boyd: *J. Am. Chem. Soc.*, **69**, 2800 (1947).
47. Spedding, F. H., A. F. Voigt, E. M. Gladrow, and N. R. Sleight: *J. Am. Chem. Soc.*, **69**, 2777 (1947).
48. Fisher, S., and R. Kunin: Peaceful Uses of Atomic Energy, **8**, 291 (1956), United Nations, Geneva.
49. Burstall, F. H., and R. A. Wells: "Ion Exchange and Its Applications," p. 83, Society of Chemical Industry, London, 1955.
50. Keattch, C. J.: *Lab. Practice*, **5**, 208 (1956).
51. Osborn, G. H.: *Analyst*, **78**, 220 (1953).
52. Honda, M., Y. Yoshino, and T. Wabiko, *J. Chem. Soc. Japan, Pure Chem. Sec.*, **73**, 348 (1952).
53. Osborn, G. H.: "Synthetic Ion-exchangers," The Macmillan Company, New York, 1956.
54. Samuelson, O.: "Ion Exchangers in Analytical Chemistry," John Wiley & Sons, Inc., New York, 1953.
55. Lederer, E., and M. Lederer: "Chromatography," 2d ed., D. Van Nostrand Company, Inc., Princeton, N.J., 1957.
56. Kunin, R.: "Ion Exchange Resins," 2d ed., John Wiley & Sons, Inc., New York, 1958.

57. Kunin, R.: Analytical Reviews—Ion Exchange, *Anal. Chem.*, **32,** 67R (1960).
58. Ketelle, B. H., and G. E. Boyd: *J. Am. Chem. Soc.*, **69,** 2800 (1947); **73,** 1862 (1951).
59. Spedding, F. H., E. I. Fulmer, T. A. Butler, E. M. Gladrow, M. Gobush, P. E. Porter, J. E. Powell, and J. M. Wright: *J. Am. Chem. Soc.*, **69,** 2812 (1947).
60. Moore, S., and W. H. Stein: *J. Biol. Chem.*, **192,** 663 (1951).
61. Tiselius, A., B. Drake, and L. Hagdahl: *Experientia*, **3,** 21 (1947).
62. Rieman, W., III: *Record Chem. Progr.*, **15,** 85 (1954).
63. Kraus, K. A., and F. Nelson: *Proc. Intern. Conf. on the Peaceful Uses of Atomic Energy*, Geneva, 1955, **7,** 113 (1956).
64. Kraus, K. A., and G. E. Moore: *J. Am. Chem. Soc.*, **72,** 4293 (1950).

CHAPTER 11

ION EXCLUSION

11.1. Introduction. Ion exclusion is a process for separating ionic materials from nonionic materials based on inherent differences in the distribution of the two types of solutes between an ion-exchange resin phase and a true aqueous solution. Numerous investigations have shown that, when an exchange resin is placed in a dilute aqueous solution of an electrolyte, the equilibrium electrolyte concentration is less in the resin phase than in the surrounding solution. On the other hand, when an exchange resin is placed in an aqueous solution of a nonelectrolyte, the nonelectrolyte tends to establish equivalent concentrations in the two phases.

Ion exchange is not involved in the absorption of electrolytes or non-electrolytes, and both types of solutes can be extracted from the resin phase simply by diluting the external solution with water. Thus, if a solution containing both ionic and nonionic materials is introduced to the top of a resin bed and washed through the column with water, the ionic material flows around the resin particles whereas the nonionic material diffuses into the resin particles as well as flowing into the void spaces. Therefore, the net forward migration rate of the nonionic material through the column is less than that for the ionic component. The ionic component will appear in the effluent first, and separations are possible. In a sense, this is the use of ion-exchange resins as the substrate or immobile phase in a partition chromatographic development. By alternately passing sample solution and water through the column, alternate fractions of electrolytes and nonelectrolytes can be collected in the effluent. Since there is no exchange taking place, the resin is never exhausted and does not require regeneration.

11.2. Distribution Phenomenon. An ion-exchange resin is quite unlike most common adsorbents. It imbibes large quantities of water when placed in aqueous solutions, becomes permeable to small ions and water-soluble small molecules, and behaves as a concentrated electrolyte solution. The ions attached to the polymeric structure are free to move only within the vibrational limits of that structure, whereas the counterions are mobile and free to move within the confines of the resin particle and even to leave the particle provided an equivalent charge takes its place to maintain electrical neutrality. Therefore, either the anion or the cation of an electrolyte free to diffuse into an exchange resin is confronted with a three-dimensional grid of fixed charges of like sign which repels the ion. Although only one ion of the electrolyte is excluded by the fixed charge network of the resin, the total amount of electrolyte diffusing into the resin is limited by the law of electrical neutrality.

Almost any type of ion-exchange resin can be used for the ion-exclusion process, but it is the more strongly ionized high-capacity resins that are most efficient. Consider, for example, the diffusion of sodium chloride into a cation-exchange resin NaR. (The sodium form of the resin must be employed; otherwise there is a conflicting exchange reaction between the cations.) If C_1 and C_2 are the initial concentrations of the salt solution and the resin phase, respectively, and X is the amount of sodium chloride diffusing into the resin in establishing equilibrium, the equilibrium condition

$$[Na^+]_{solution}[Cl^-]_{solution} = [Na^+]_{resin}[Cl^-]_{resin}$$

prescribed by the Donnan theory can be expressed as

$$(C_1 - X)(C_1 - X) = (C_2 + X)X$$

Rearranging terms gives

$$\frac{X}{C_1} = \frac{C_1}{C_2 + 2C_1} \tag{11.1}$$

The fraction X/C_1 gives the proportion of salt originally present which has diffused into the resin by the time equilibrium is established. Clearly, the proportion of salt that diffuses into the resin decreases as the exchange capacity (fixed charge density) of the resin increases. The net result is the exclusion of electrolytes by the resin phase when the concentration of the electrolytic solution is appreciably below that corresponding to the fixed ionic concentration of the resin. This is predicted by the Donnan membrane theory as applied to ion-exchange resins (see Sec. 10.3).

The distribution of solutes between the two phases can be conveniently expressed as a distribution coefficient K_d.

$$K_d = \frac{C_r}{C} \tag{11.2}$$

where C_r is the concentration of diffusible solute within the resin phase at equilibrium expressed as the weight of solute per unit volume of solution in the resin, exclusive of the resin itself, and C is the solute concentration in the solution external to the resin.

The exclusion of ionic solutes by a resin is exemplified with the system hydrochloric acid–water–Dowex 50–X8 (a sulfonated polystyrene cation-exchange resin with 8 per cent divinylbenzene). K_d for hydrochloric acid is about 0.1 for acid concentrations below 1.0 molal and climbs to about 0.4 for 5.0 molal solutions. This behavior is typical of the distribution of ionic solutes between water and high-capacity ion-exchange resins. None the less, no predetermined rule can be applied for predicting the behavior of ionic substances because K_d values vary with the functional group, capacity, type, and cross-linkage of a resin. Even less predictable is the distribution behavior of the nonionic materials.

Most low-molecular-weight water-soluble nonelectrolytes freely diffuse in and out of the resin phase regardless of the capacity of the resin and tend to exist at the same concentration in both phases at equilibrium in accord with the Donnan theory. Frequently, however, some additional absorption takes place because of the affinity of the nonelectrolyte for the hydrocarbon matrix of the resin, and the solute may highly favor the resin phase. In such cases, the absorption of nonelectrolytes generally follows isotherms which are qualitatively of the Langmuir or Freundlich type.

K_d values approach unity for a large number of the lower molecular-weight water-soluble nonionic materials[1,2] and usually increase with increased solution concentration and increased chain length of organic molecules in homologous series.[3] K_d values greater than 3 for nonionic materials are not common, however, unless there is an obvious adsorption of the solute, resulting in much higher values. For example, K_d values as high as 80 have been reported for phenol on certain types of resins.[4]

Higher molecular-weight nonionics are less readily differentiated from ionic materials than the lower molecular-weight nonionics by K_d values, which points up the fact that there are factors other than the degree of ionization which ensure exclusion. Molecules, for example, can be excluded from the resin structure because of their size. Sucrose and glucose cannot be separated from sodium chloride because all three substances are excluded from the resin. Presumably the sugar molecules are too large to enter the resin network.

For that matter, a simple distinction between ionic and nonionic materials is not always possible. At best, the dividing line is arbitrary; what may be considered ionic for one separation may be nonionic in another separation. As an example of this, hydrochloric and trichloroacetic acid can be separated to a fair degree and mixtures of trichloroacetic ($K_i = 2 \times 10^{-1}$) and dichloroacetic ($K_i = 5 \times 10^{-2}$) acid can be resolved. In each case the stronger electrolyte suppresses the ionization of the weaker electrolyte and effectively produces a nonionic. Therefore, it should be possible to separate mixtures of weak acids or weak bases by adjusting the pH of the system to a value at which the stronger component is converted to the salt form. Generally speaking, though, substances with ionization constants smaller than 10^{-3} behave as nonionics in ion-exclusion procedures.

The important point is that, as long as there is a difference in the K_d values for different solutes, separations are possible. It matters not whether the sample components are grouped as ionic and nonionic or are all nonionic. The rather wide variation in the adsorption affinities (K_d values) of various nonionics definitely establishes the possibility of separating mixtures of nonionics by a partition chromatographic technique in which the resin phase behaves as the immobile phase. The nonionics are removed from the resin with water by liquid extraction when the external phase is diluted. Such a technique ties in very closely with ion exclusion because no regenerants or elutriants, other than water, are necessary.

In any distribution study of this nature, the rate factor must not be overlooked. Although two substances may have equal distribution constants, their behavior on a column will not necessarily be the same. The rate at which equilibrium is obtained may be much greater for one solute than the other, particularly if one of the solutes is a large bulky molecule with a slow diffusion rate. Fortunately, most low-molecular-weight ionic and nonionic materials establish equilibria rapidly.

11.3. Theory. As long as there is a difference in the K_d values for different solutes, separations are possible and one can predict the order of elution from the column. The actual position of the solute in the effluent is determined, however, by the resin-bed characteristics.

The resin bed must be considered to exist in several parts: the interstitial volume V_1, which makes up approximately 30 per cent of the total column for a uniform spherical resin product; the occluded volume V_2, which is the solution volume within the resin particles and which may be as great as 40 per cent of the total column volume; and the solid resin volume V_r.

If a small quantity of an aqueous solution containing an electrolyte and a nonelectrolyte is added to the top of a resin column (in the same form as the added electrolyte) and washed through with water, the ionic material will appear in the effluent as soon as the influent volume equals the interstitial volume and quickly build up to its maximum concentration. The nonelectrolyte will not appear until the influent volume at least equals $V_1 + V_2$. If the sample volume V_3 is held less than V_2, there should be a complete separation of A and B in the effluent. This is, of course, assuming that ideal conditions, namely, complete exclusion of the ionic material and no exclusion of the nonionic material, prevail through the course of the operation. In practice, it is found that V_3 must be much less than V_2 if the boundaries between fractions remain well defined.

With known K_d the location of the leading edge of a zone can be more accurately predicted with the equation

$$V_{max} = V_1 + K_d V_2 \tag{11.3}$$

obtainable from a material-balance treatment.[5] V_{max} is the volume of effluent measured from the introduction of an infinitely small sample to the appearance of the maximum concentration of solute in the effluent.

Using a plate-by-plate material balance[5] and the plate theory of Mayer and Tompkins[6] the number of theoretical plates p is given by the expression

$$p = \frac{2C'(C' + 1)}{(W')^2} \tag{11.4}$$

where $C' = \dfrac{\text{amount of solute in resin phase at equilibrium}}{\text{amount of solute in liquid phase at equilibrium}}$

$$= \frac{C_r V_2}{C V_1} = K_d \frac{V_2}{V_1} = \frac{V_{max} - V_1}{V_2} \frac{V_2}{V_1} = \frac{V_{max} - V_1}{V_1}$$

$W' =$ half-width of elution curve at an ordinate value of $1/e$ of the peak concentration. e is the log base

Substitute the value of C' into Eq. (11.4) and

$$p = \frac{2V_{max}(V_{max} - V_1)}{(W)^2} \tag{11.5}$$

if $W = W' V_1$

The HETP of the column equals the length of the column divided by p. Thus, the resolution efficiency of a resin bed can be determined by the elution of a single component, since all the terms of Eq. (11.5) are measurable quantities.   In practice, the HETP is found to be directly proportional to the resin-particle diameter and to the square root of the flow rate and is independent of column height.   It varies only slightly with the degree of resin cross-linking and feed volume.   However, as the degree of cross-linking approaches zero, K_d for ionic materials approaches unity.

Since ion exclusion depends on a Donnan equilibrium, it can be assumed that separations will be more efficient at low ionic concentrations. Although there appears to be no sharp distinction between high and low electrolyte concentrations, experiments[7] clearly indicate that separations are improved as the electrolyte concentration is lowered.

The concentration of the nonelectrolyte is much less important to separation efficiency.   This is predicted from the theory and suggests a broad area of application for ion exclusion, namely, the deionization of concentrated nonelectrolytes without the need of introducing extraneous materials.

11.4. Applications. One of the first conceived separations for the exclusion process was the separation of sugar and salt.   Such separations are not possible, however, because of the size and relative inability of the sucrose and glucose molecules to diffuse rapidly into the resin phase. Nevertheless, it is in the separation of strong electrolytes from neutral molecules that ion exclusion will prove most useful.   An example of the separation potential of ion-exclusion processes is the purification of commercial glycerin.

Essentially all commercial processes for producing glycerin have a common problem of removing ionic impurities from the product.   Conventional distillation and ion-exchange techniques are used satisfactorily in the purification, but ion exclusion offers some advantages over these

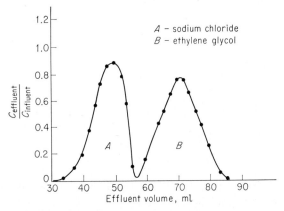

Fig. 11.1. Separation of sodium chloride and ethylene glycol by ion exclusion.   [(*From D. W. Simpson and R. M. Wheaton, Chem. Eng. Progr., ***50,*** 45 (1954).*]

methods, particularly when high ionic concentrations are encountered that make ion exchange prohibitive in cost.   Several studies[8,9] have indicated the feasibility of using ion exclusion for glycerol purification, and procedures[10] have been worked out which make it possible to separate up to 90 per cent of the total dissolved ionic salts from soap lye crude glycerin while holding glycerin losses to approximately 0.6 per cent by weight. Although it was not possible to remove all the ionic material by exclusion, the remaining ionic material was removed by ion exchange to produce CP glycerin.

Of lesser importance perhaps than the deionization of glycerol, but nevertheless significant, are the separations of sodium chloride and ethylene glycol[5] (see Fig. 11.1), hydrochloric acid and acetic acid, trichloroacetic acid and dichloroacetic acid, and sodium chloride from ethyl alcohol, formaldehyde, alkanolamines, ethylenediamine, and boric acid.[7]

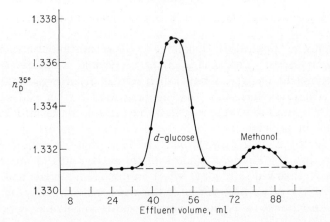

FIG. 11.2. Separation of *d*-glucose and methanol. Resin: Dowex 50-X8, 50 to 100 mesh, H⁺. Column: 62 by 1.5 cm. [*From R. M. Wheaton and W. C. Bauman, Ann. N. Y. Acad. Sci.*, **57**(3), 159 (1953).]

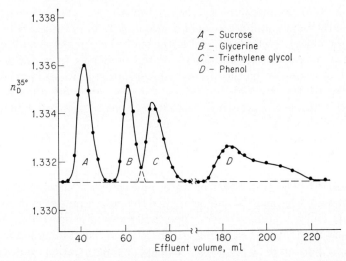

FIG. 11.3. Separation of a multicomponent system. Resin: Dowex 50-X8, 50 to 100 mesh, Na⁺. [*From R. M. Wheaton and W. C. Bauman, Ann. N. Y. Acad. Sci.*, **57**(3), 159 (1953).]

Included in the applications here are the separations of mixtures of nonionic materials by partition chromatography using ion-exchange resins, since the technique is identical with that for ion exclusion. The effectiveness of such separations is clearly indicated in Figs. 11.2 and 11.3. Clark[11] separated glycerol from a polyhydric alcohol mixture and concentrated the other components into two fractions containing sorbitol, xylitol, and erythritol and 1,2-propanediol and ethylene glycol, respectively.

Reichenberg[12] applied the technique to the separation of members of a homologous series. The separation of acetic and n-butyric acid was nearly complete on a sulfonated polystyrene resin cross-linked with 5.5 per cent divinylbenzene. Reichenberg went further and suggested the possibility that any organic resin with a suitable matrix which imbibes water can in principle be used. Ionic functional groups need not be present in the resin matrix at all. In fact, there is evidence which indicates that the strongly acidic sulfonic acid groups of an exchange resin exert a marked salting-out effect on organic materials and tend to counteract the adsorptive effect of the resin matrix. This, of course, leads to an increase in R_f values of such solutes in column operations.

Sargent and Rieman[13] report a much improved separation of nonionics if a salt solution instead of water is used as the eluent. Diethylene glycol and dipropylene glycol can be quantitatively separated on a 10-cm column of a strong-base anion exchanger in the sulfate form utilizing 3 M ammonium sulfate as the eluent. The separation of methanol, ethanol, and n-propanol is also greatly improved by the use of this same eluent. The beneficial effect of the salt in the eluent is probably due to a selective salting-out of the nonionics from the solution phase. It is known that, as the salt concentration in water increases, the solubility of the nonionic decreases. It was observed that a linear increase in the salt concentration produced a near-exponential increase in the breakthrough points of the nonionics.

11.5. Advantages and Disadvantages. An outstanding advantage of ion exclusion is that it is cheaper than conventional ion exchange because no chemicals are required for regeneration and operating costs are limited to the circulation of water and sample components through the system. The method can be applied to a wide range of materials and is simple and adaptable to continuous and automatic operation. Excellent separations have been achieved in solutions containing nonionics in concentrations up to 40 per cent. The upper concentration limit for ionic materials is about 8 per cent.

There are several rather serious disadvantages associated with ion exclusion that almost preclude its widespread acceptance by industry. Perhaps of greatest importance is the requirement that the resin must be in the same ionic form as the electrolyte in solution. The sample composition is thus limited to a single cationic or anionic species, and there appear to be few industrial systems that satisfy these requirements. Furthermore, exclusion works the wrong way by removing the major component in separations of ionics from nonelectrolyte solutions.

The volume of the sample solution is theoretically limited by the volume of solution absorbed by the resin and in practice is found to be considerably less than the occluded volume. One volume of sample solution is followed by several volumes of rinse solution, which results in a dilution of the nonionic component and a subsequent reconcentration step. This latter disadvantage is overcome, however, by recycling steps which produce a greater solute concentration in the effluent than in the influent. Clearly, the resin column can be used to its fullest capacity only if as little water as possible appears between the ionic and nonionic fractions. If sample and rinse water are alternately introduced in set proportions, several zones of solutes can be present in the column at one time. A typical elution curve is given in Fig. 11.4. The ratio of rinse volume to sample volume for each resolution was $3:1$; therefore, the concentration of each fraction is about one-half the original sample concentration.

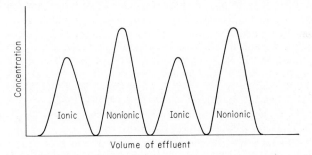

Fig. 11.4. Typical liquid chromatogram of continuous ion-exclusion operation.

Simpson and Bauman[14] have overcome this dilution of sample components and actually separated and concentrated in one step the nonionic component by a recycling procedure.

11.6. Ion Retardation. Ion retardation is a column operation very similar to ion exclusion but employs an exchange resin containing both anionic *and* cationic functional groups within the resin matrix. Therefore, the resin will absorb both anions and cations from sample solutions. The high concentrations of positive and negative charge sites within the resin partially neutralize each other's charge, however, and the adsorbed ions are held weakly by the resin. The absorption affinity is so weak, in fact, that water can be used as a regenerant for the ions. Ion retardation differs from ion exclusion in that ions are also retarded as they flow through a column.

Ion retardation, thus, can effect separations of electrolytes from large nonelectrolytes (which is impossible by ion exclusion) and electrolytes from electrolytes if distribution constants are sufficiently different. Of particular interest is the separation of two electrolytes such as sodium hydroxide from sodium chloride, ammonium chloride from zinc chloride, and ferrous sulfate from zinc sulfate.

11.7. Selected Bibliography

Bauman, W. C., R. M. Wheaton, and D. W. Simpson: Ion Exclusion, chap. 7 in "Ion Exchange Technology," F. C. Nachod and J. Schubert (eds.), Academic Press, Inc., New York, 1956.

Kunin, R.: "Ion Exchange Resins," 2d ed., John Wiley & Sons, Inc., New York, 1958.

Osborn, G. H.: "Synthetic Ion Exchangers," The Macmillan Company, New York, 1956.

Wheaton, R. M., and W. C. Bauman: Ion Exclusion, *Ind. Eng. Chem.*, **45**, 228 (1953).

REFERENCES

1. Wheaton, R. M., and W. C. Bauman: *Ann. N.Y. Acad. Sci.*, **57**, 159 (1953).
2. Gregor, H. P., F. C. Collins, and M. Pope: *J. Colloid Sci.*, **6**, 304 (1951).
3. Davies, C. W., and G. G. Thomas: *J. Chem. Soc.*, 1951, p. 2624.
4. Anderson, R. E., and R. D. Hansen: *Ind. Eng. Chem.*, **47**, 71 (1955).
5. Simpson, D. W., and R. M. Wheaton: *Chem. Eng. Progr.*, **50**, 45 (1954).
6. Mayer, S. W., and E. R. Tompkins: *J. Am. Chem. Soc.*, **69**, 2866 (1947).
7. Wheaton, R. M., and W. C. Bauman: *Ind. Eng. Chem.*, **45**, 228 (1953).
8. Asher, D. R., and D. W. Simpson: *J. Phys. Chem.*, **60**, 518 (1956).
9. Shurts, E. L., and R. R. White: *A.I.Ch.E. J.*, **3**, 183 (1957).
10. Prielipp, G. E., and H. W. Keller: *J. Am. Oil Chem. Soc.*, **33**, 103 (1956).
11. Clark, I. T.: *Anal. Chem.*, **30**, 1676 (1958).
12. Reichenberg, D.: *Chem. & Ind.*, 1956, p. 958.
13. Sargent, R., and W. Rieman, III: *J. Org. Chem.*, **21**, 594 (1956).
14. Simpson, D. W., and W. C. Bauman: *Ind. Eng. Chem.*, **46**, 1958 (1954).

CHAPTER 12

DIALYSIS

12.1. Introduction. Dialysis is the fractionation of solutes by their differential rates of diffusion through porous membranes and was first described by Graham in his work on liquid-diffusion phenomena. Graham[1] observed that, when a solution of salt was separated from water by a thin membrane such as parchment, animal tissue, pig's bladder, or sized paper, the salt diffused through the membrane and ultimately equalized the solute concentration on both sides of the membrane. The same studies revealed that certain other substances in solution, such as starch and gum arabic, were incapable of diffusing through the membranes. Thus, it was possible to effect separations of mixtures of sodium chloride and starch and sugar and gum arabic by dialysis. More importantly, the studies were the first real introduction to colloid chemistry and were used to classify substances as *colloids* or *crystalloids*. Substances of the first type were distinguished by their very slow rate of diffusion through membranes when in solution and by their tendency to form a gelatinous mass of noncrystalline character. Contrariwise, crystalloids diffused rather rapidly through the membranes and readily crystallized from solution. At the present time *colloid* refers to a *state* of matter and not to a *kind* of matter as Graham supposed. No sharp distinction exists between the colloidal and crystalloidal states; there is only a gradual transition in size of the dispersed particles in going from true solutions to colloid suspensions. The generally recognized limits for colloidal particle diameters are 10^{-7} to 10^{-5} cm (1 to 100 mμ).

Primarily, then, the dialyzing membrane is used to filter dispersions by permitting certain solution components to pass through while offering a high resistance to the passage of other solution components. Colloids do diffuse through the membranes, but only slowly. It must not be imagined, though, that the dialyzing membrane acts merely as a sieve whose selectivity depends only on pore size. There are other factors which must be taken into consideration.

As to the nature of the force which determines diffusion in solution, it is essentially the same force we associate with osmotic pressure. When one substance is dissolved in another, the solvent in the solution has a chemical potential different from that of the pure solvent. The tendency toward equalization of this difference when the two liquids are separated by a membrane permeable to the solvent is manifested as osmosis. The number of collisions made by solvent molecules per unit of time on a given area of the membrane will be less on the solution side than on the solvent side; there will be a flow of solvent into the solution until the number of these collisions on both sides of the membrane is equalized or until the flow of solvent through the membrane is the same in both directions. In an analogous fashion, if the solute can permeate the membrane, there will be a spontaneous migration of solute particles from the solution into the pure solvent. The phenomenon is dialysis.

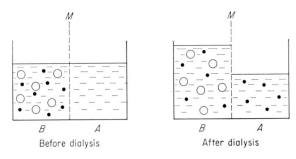

FIG. 12.1. A simple dialysis cell.

A simple case of dialysis is illustrated in Fig. 12.1. M is a dialyzing or semipermeable membrane which prevents gross intermixing of the solvent in A and the solution in B but permits the passage of the solvent and at least one of the solutes from one solution to the other. In time, in order for solute and solvent concentrations to be equal in both compartments, a portion of the solvent will diffuse from compartment A to compartment B by osmosis and a portion of the smaller solute will diffuse from compartment B to A by dialysis. The diffusing solute is referred to as the *diffusate*, and the solution from which solutes migrated is referred to as the *dialyzed liquid* or the *dialyzate*. If the receiving solution in compartment A is periodically replaced with pure solvent, a condition will be approached wherein the diffusate will be completely extracted from the dialyzate. Theoretically at least, dialysis should be capable of separating not only colloids from simple ions but also colloids from colloids, ions from ions, molecules from ions, and molecules from molecules. The criterion for separation is simply that the various solution components diffuse through the membrane at different rates.

Two factors determine the effectiveness of dialysis as a separation process: the diffusion rate of solutes through the membrane and the membrane properties. Concentration gradients provide the driving force, whereas the nature of the membrane determines which solutes can pass through. Graham's studies of diffusion in aqueous solutions established the dependence of the rate of diffusion on the nature of the diffusate and temperature, while other studies clearly indicated that the rate of diffusion was determined, at least in part, by the concentration gradient of the diffusing species. The only impediment, then, to the fractionation of complex mixtures of solutes by dialysis is the development of porous membranes sufficiently selective to distinguish among solutes of similar sizes and properties.

Ultrafiltration has been considered dialysis by many workers, but there are basic differences. Ultrafiltration is basically a mechanical (screening) process, whereas dialysis is a rate process determined by multiple factors. A further distinction is that ultrafiltration actually separates the dispersed phase from the dispersing medium. Ultrafiltration is more rapid than dialysis and is preferred to dialysis when the method is applicable.

12.2. Theory. The rate at which a substance diffuses through a solution is related to the concentration gradient across the diffusing path by Fick's general law of diffusion, which can be expressed as

$$dS = -Dq \frac{dc}{dx} dt \qquad (12.1)$$

S represents the amount of substance diffusing through a diffusion plane of thickness x and area q in time t under a concentration gradient dc/dx. D is the specific diffusion coefficient defined by the amount of substance diffusing across unit area per unit time under a concentration gradient of unity. The minus sign denotes that the substance diffuses in the direction of decreasing concentration. Thus, Fick's law provides an explanation for both dialysis and osmosis. For example, when a solution is separated by a permeable membrane from a pure solvent or a less concentrated solution of the same solute, the law foretells that the solute will have a tendency to diffuse from the more concentrated solution to the less concentrated solution. From the point of view of the solvent, the law predicts that the solvent will move from the region of its highest concentration to the lowest. Obviously, if the membrane is permeable to both solute and solvent, dialysis and osmosis will occur simultaneously. On the other hand, if the membrane is permeable to the solvent but not the solute, only osmosis occurs and the equilibrium condition is different.

If an aqueous solution is separated by a thin porous membrane from pure water (or a more dilute solution of the same solute), and if the liquids on both sides of the membrane are stirred, the only diffusion process of any importance occurs entirely within the membrane. The rate at which the concentrations of the two solutions are equalized will then be proportional to the diffusion coefficient provided no disturbing influences are set up in the membrane itself. Under these suppositions the driving force for the equalization of concentrations will be the concentration gradient across the membrane. For a thin membrane of uniform thickness the equation can be rewritten as

$$dS = k_1 A (C_1 - C_2) \, dt \qquad (12.2)$$

where A = area of membrane
C_1 and C_2 = solute concentrations on either side of membrane
   k_1 = constant
Integrated with respect to t, Eq. (12.2) becomes

$$S = kA (C_1 - C_2) t \qquad (12.3)$$

which on rearrangement gives

$$k = \frac{S}{At(C_1 - C_2)} \qquad (12.4)$$

k is the permeability coefficient and is considered a constant for a given membrane-solute combination, although it often varies with solute concentration. The permeability coefficient is reasonably constant for many nonelectrolyte solutes, whereas it is generally variable with electrolytes and, as expected for a diffusion process, increases with an increase in temperature.[2]   The equation for temperature dependence is

$$k_{T,2} = k_{T,1}[1 + B(T_2 - T_1)]^2 \qquad (12.5)$$

where T_1 and T_2 are the two temperatures and B is a constant. The temperature coefficient B is apparently some function of the diffusion coefficient, since it decreases with an increase in solute mobility.

One might suppose from the preceding discussion that a substance capable of diffusing through a membrane would distribute itself evenly on both sides of the membrane independently of other substances present. Such is not the case. Fick's diffusion law holds reasonably well for small neutral molecules but not for electrolytes. With salts dissociated in solution the problem is more complex. Independent diffusion of the anions and cations through the membrane does not occur, although it might be expected because of their different mobilities. A separation of ions on this basis would create electrostatic potentials on the faces of the membrane which would retard the faster moving ions and speed up the slower ones. The opposing forces of diffusion and electrostatic attraction ensure that the diffusion of anion and cation will occur at equal rates.

Complications arise in a system containing an electrolyte which can dissociate into a diffusible and a nondiffusible ion. In such a system, another electrolyte whose ions will permeate the membrane will be distributed unevenly on the two sides of the membrane at equilibrium. For clarification, consider the case of an electrolyte NaR dissolved in water and separated from an aqueous solution of sodium chloride by a membrane impermeable to R^- but permeable to the other ions present. Sodium ions cannot diffuse from the solution of R^- because of the electrostatic affinity for R^-. There is nothing, however, to prevent the migration of both sodium and chloride ions into the solution of NaR. Donnan's membrane theory will give a quantitative interpretation to the equilibrium distribution of the ions in such a system. Let C_1 and C_2 be the initial concentration of the sodium chloride and NaR solution, respectively, and x be the amount of sodium chloride diffusing into the NaR solution to establish an equilibrium. Following the treatment of Donnan's theory in Sec. 10.3, the equilibrium condition of

$$[\text{Na}^+]_{\text{solution 1}}[\text{Cl}^-]_{\text{solution 1}} = [\text{Na}^+]_{\text{solution 2}}[\text{Cl}^-]_{\text{solution 2}}$$

can be written as

$$(C_1 - x)(C_1 - x) = (C_2 + x)x \qquad (12.6)$$

Rearranging terms gives

$$\frac{x}{C_1} = \frac{C_1}{C_2 + 2C_1} \qquad (12.7)$$

x/C_1 is the fractional amount of the diffusible solute that has diffused into the solution of NaR by the time equilibrium is established. Clearly, the amount of solute diffusing through the membrane will vary from 50 per cent of the original amount present when the nondiffusible electrolyte concentration is negligible to only 1 per cent when the concentration of the diffusible electrolyte is $\frac{1}{100}$ that of the nondiffusible electrolyte. It is apparent that the presence of an electrolyte with one nonpermeable ion can drastically reduce the permeability of the diffusing electrolyte and can, if present in sufficient quantities, prevent the normal diffusion of the second substance. The same equilibrium conditions result, of course, regardless of the initial relative concentrations of the diffusible species on opposite sides of the membrane.

The above-described effect is not limited to cases where there is a common ion between the electrolyte and nondialyzing substance. The presence of NaR, for example, causes the membrane to show an extraordinarily high permeability to the cation of the diffusible electrolyte, while the anions are effectively repelled.

Conclusions of a practical nature can be drawn from the preceding theoretical treatment. Clearly, the rate at which solute is transported through a membrane is directly proportional to the area of the membrane, the concentration gradient of diffusate across the membrane, and the temperature. Each of these factors should be adjusted to the optimum, consistent with mechanical and other requirements of the operation. In practice, it is customary to use large membrane surfaces and to maintain the highest possible concentration gradient of diffusate by continually or periodically replacing the receiving solution with pure solvent or by collecting the diffusate in a volume of solution that is quite large relative to the volume of dialyzate. Dialysis at temperatures of 80 to 100°C is frequently many times more rapid than dialysis at room temperature. For instance, the diffusion rate of electrolytes has been observed to increase as much as 2.5 per cent per degree rise in temperature.

A factor not yet discussed which influences the rate of dialysis is the membrane porosity or permeability. The rate of dialysis is, of course, increased by increasing the porosity of the membrane. The extremes in membrane porosity are exhibited by membranes which show no selectivity toward solutes, passing all, and those membranes which completely exclude the passage of solute because of the relative solute and pore dimensions. Since the extremes in membrane porosity are seldom encountered, the subject will not be discussed further.

12.3. Membranes. Semipermeable membranes are thin barriers which permit the passage of one or more solution constituents but offer high resistance to the passage of other solution components. Practical considerations require that the membranes be as thin as possible, have a large surface area, and be somewhat selective in the passing of solutes. Such membranes are typified by the natural plasma membranes of living cells, skins and tissues, and a multitude of artificial or synthetic materials, such as cellophane and collodion.

Numerous explanations have been offered regarding the mechanism of selective permeability, but they are adequate for particular systems only and are not generally applicable. The principal theories proposed to account for the selective permeability of membranes are as follows: The membrane acts as a molecular sieve, screening out particles strictly on the basis of size; the membrane behaves as a series of fine capillary tubes which selectively retard the migration of the various solutes; permeation of the membrane is possible only if there is a combination of solvent and membrane or the solvent is soluble in the membrane substance. Since none of the theories advanced is entirely satisfactory, it is probable that a variety of mechanisms brings about the observed changes. A cursory investigation of some common membranes and their properties substantiates this viewpoint and strongly suggests that the nature of selective permeability is quite complex.

Cellophane consists of many relatively large pores and approximates being a molecular sieve, but it differs from a conventional sieve by its heteroporosity. The pores are not uniform straight holes or passages through the membrane but are irregular channels with cross connections, dead ends, and widely varying diameters and cross sections. Because of this heteroporosity it is possible to separate solutes quantitatively only if the components differ greatly in size. The leakage of the larger solutes through the membrane can be prevented only if all effective pore sizes are reduced below the diameter of the solute molecules. There can be no doubt, however, that permeability is a product of factors other than pore size, for it has been demonstrated that membranes with pore diameters many times larger than the smallest dimension of the solute can prevent the passage of the solute.

Membranes with pronounced physicochemical characteristics behave quite differently from the molecular sieve type. Any one or a combination of several factors can limit permeability: the very chemical nature and physical structure of the membrane, the affinity of the membrane for solvent and solute, the degree of membrane swelling and hydration, the creation of charged surfaces by adsorption, and the solubility of the solute in the membrane material.

In partial explanation of the exclusion of solutes by membranes with pore diameters larger than the smallest dimension of the solute, it can be said that, if the molecules of solvent are adsorbed on the walls of the capillaries of the membranes, a continuity of solvent is established which permits the ready movement of solvent through the membrane. But the preferential adsorption of solvent effectively reduces the diameter of the capillary and prevents the passage of solute molecules.

The most important factor in the dialysis of electrolytes, though, is the electrochemical behavior of the membrane. Cellulose nitrate membranes, as an example, have been studied extensively, and it has been established that acidic groups situated in the membrane skeleton impart a negative charge to the membrane which then repels anions. Since the maintenance of electrical neutrality demands an equal number of positive and negative ions on either side of the membrane, the restriction on anion permeability directly impedes the diffusion of cations into pure solvent. The same loss of electrolyte permeability results if the membrane becomes positively charged owing to the adsorption of strongly positive groups such as certain proteins, dyes, etc. Collodion, parchment, and cellulose membranes are always negative, but membranes of gelatin and proteins are positive or negative depending on conditions.

Electrochemical effects are also mainly responsible for the difference between the free rate of diffusion of ions and their diffusion rate through membranes. The two diffusion rates are generally quite similar for univalent ions but differ markedly for polyvalent ions.

The complication of chemical forces arising in the membrane is demonstrated quite well with precipitate membranes. Precipitate membranes are prepared by the direct precipitation of a substance within the pores of a coarse film or by the careful deposition of the precipitate to form a film. These membranes are impermeable to ions in solution which are common to the precipitate or which form an insoluble compound with an ion of the precipitate. For example, a copper ferrocyanide membrane is impermeable to both copper and ferrocyanide ions but will pass a number of small ions and various small solvent molecules.

The very simplicity of dialytic separations has prompted investigations directed toward the preparation of membranes with a greater selectivity than the naturally occurring membranes. The need for improvements is great. Dialysis with parchment is slow. Animal sacs such as pig, ox, or fish bladders, peritoneal membranes of cattle, and other animal membranes are usually very efficient for certain separations, but they lack versatility and controlled permeability. Natural membranes cannot be readily formed to any desired shape and frequently lack the mechanical strength needed to withstand a hydrostatic head. Most of these difficulties have been overcome to a remarkable extent with the preparation of synthetic membranes of graded porosity or permeability, but there is still a great need for the development of even more selective barriers.

Collodion membranes made from nitrocellulose dissolved in a mixture of alcohol and ether are among the more easily prepared membranes of graded porosity.[3,4] Collodion can be molded in almost any desired shape, thickness, and size, and the porosity can be regulated over a fairly wide range by controlling the degree and rate of drying of the collodion film and the ratio of alcohol to ether in the solvent. The conditions for preparing a membrane of desired porosity are arrived at empirically. A closed tube is dipped into the solution of collodion and slowly turned or drained in an atmosphere of collodion to give uniform thickness to the adhering film. The film is then air dried. At the proper state of dryness the coated tube is plunged into water to leach out the solvent and leave an open pore structure. A high ether content yields highly impermeable membranes, whereas a high alcohol content yields highly permeable membranes. The film is then removed from the tube and air dried overnight to remove the alcohol. Once the membrane has been dried, it can be swelled by placing it in an alcoholic solution. Grading is possible because the permeability of the membrane is proportional to the degree of swelling, which is proportional to the alcoholic content of the solution. The degree of swelling increases gradually up to 90 per cent alcohol mixtures and then increases very rapidly with increased percentage of alcohol. Some dissolution of the membrane occurs at the higher alcohol concentrations, which partially accounts for the greatly increased porosity.   When the desired swelling is complete, the membrane can be "fixed" by washing in water.

By this technique it is possible to prepare a series of graded membranes which allow slower and slower diffusion rates for a given solute until eventually a membrane in the series excludes the solute entirely.   Thus, the membranes can be characterized by a number which represents the percentage of alcohol in the swelling solution used in membrane preparation.   Such a number is termed the *alcohol index* of the membrane. Similarly, solutes can be characterized by the alcohol index of the most porous membrane which is impermeable to the solute.   Some of these

TABLE 12.1. ALCOHOL INDICES FOR SOME COMMON SOLUTES*

Solute	Alcohol index of most porous membrane that is impermeable to solute
Water†	
NaCl, NH₄Cl†	
KMnO₄	30–40
Picric acid	35–40
K oxalate	60–70
Bismarck brown	65
Methylene blue	70
Neutral red	72.5–75
Safranine	75–77.5
Dextrin	85–87.5
Starch	90
Aniline blue	92
Litmus (neutral)	93
Congo red	96
Night blue	96

* From W. Brown, *Biochem. J.*, **9**, 611 (1915).

† Water, sodium chloride, and ammonium chloride diffuse through membranes with indices below 30, but only very slowly.

indices are given in Table 12.1.   Copper sulfate, sodium sulfate, potassium ferrocyanide, and a number of other salts have alcohol indices similar to that of potassium oxalate.   Further examples of the controlled porosity achieved are illustrated in Tables 12.2 and 12.3.   Other solvents also affect the permeability of the membrane.   Acetone increases permeability, and amyl alcohol decreases it.

Vaughan[5] has discussed the characterization of semipermeable membranes for osmotic measurements and described a method for improving the solute selectivity of such membranes.   It is quite likely that the techniques are applicable to dialytic processes as well and that certain practical separations can be achieved as a result of improved solute selectivity.

By the oxidation of cellulose nitrate, Sollner and coworkers[6] have obtained membranes which exhibit high membrane potentials and

TABLE 12.2. COMPARISON OF TIMES REQUIRED FOR MEMBRANE PENETRATION BY VARIOUS SOLUTES USING MEMBRANES WITH DIFFERENT ALCOHOL INDICES*

0.5% KMnO$_4$		0.1% methylene blue	
Alcohol index	Time of penetration	Alcohol index	Time of penetration
70	1 min	95	12 min
60	5 min	90	70 min
50	25 min	85	4 hr
40	120 min	80	10 hr
30	None in 24 hr	75	24 hr
		70	6 days

* From W. Brown, *Biochem. J.*, **9**, 605 (1915).

TABLE 12.3. RESULTS OF TESTS FOR SOLUTE IN RECEIVING SOLUTION AFTER A 24-HR DIALYSIS PERIOD USING MEMBRANES WITH DIFFERENT ALCOHOL INDICES*

Concentration	Mixed solutes	Test for solute in diffusate through membranes of index		
		50	85	92
1 M	NaCl	+	+	+
0.2 M	Glucose	0	+	+
0.5%	Dextrin	0	0	+
0.5%	Starch	0	0	0

* From W. Brown, *Biochem. J.*, **9**, 613 (1915).

undergo ion-exchange reactions with electrolytes. The permeability of these membranes can be controlled to a marked extent by mechanical treatment during drying.

Efforts have been directed toward the production of semipermeable membranes suitable for the desalting of brackish waters.[7] Cellulose acetate membranes show a practical degree of semipermeability, which can be varied with pressure. When compressed sufficiently the membrane is effective in screening out or retarding sodium chloride. The desirability of producing such selective membranes is great. The development of an economical desalinization process is one of the most pressing problems facing the chemist today. With suitable membranes, dialysis can be the answer.

Recently, highly selective membranes of ion-exchange resins have been developed which are almost perfectly selective toward anions or cations. These membranes will be discussed in the chapter on electrodialysis.

12.4. Apparatus. Many arrangements have been tried in the design of equipment for dialytic processes, but none is simpler or more generally useful than the arrangement illustrated in Fig. 12.2. A cellulose nitrate, cellophane, collodion, parchment, or animal-tissue bag or thimble is filled with the solution to be dialyzed and suspended in pure solvent.

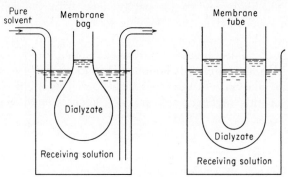

Fig. 12.2. Two simple dialysis cells for laboratory separations.

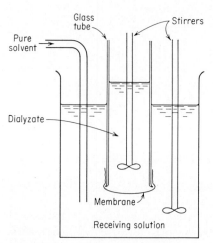

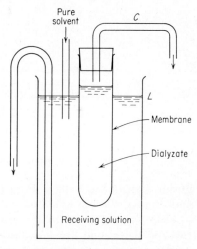

Fig. 12.3. A simple modification of the dialysis cell which provides for continuous stirring of both the receiving solution and dialyzate.

Fig. 12.4. Dialysis cell for semicontinuous operation.

The receiving solution is continually or periodically replaced with the pure solvent to maintain the highest possible concentration gradient across the membrane. When dialysis is complete, the dialyzate and diffusate are recoverable.

A simple modification of this basic design (Fig. 12.3) is to close off the open end of a glass or metal tube with membrane material, fill the tube with dialyzate, and suspend it in the receiving solution. This arrangement makes it convenient to stir both diffusate and dialyzate so as to destroy concentration gradients which develop near the surface of the membrane and impede the dialysis.

Semicontinuous dialysis can be achieved with the apparatus shown in Fig. 12.4. The dialyzing bag is partly filled with the solution to be dialyzed and suspended in the receiving solvent. As dialysis proceeds, the volume of dialyzate increases owing to osmosis and ultimately overflows through C. Pure solvent is continually added to B to maintain the liquid level L while the diffusate is siphoned from the bottom of the vessel. The recovered dialyzate is the most highly purified fraction. The disadvantages of this arrangement are its slowness and the inefficient

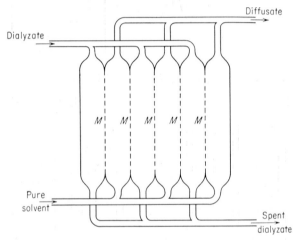

FIG. 12.5. Dialysis cell for continuous operation.

purification of the bulk of the dialyzate in the bag. Only the overflow and some of the top liquid are adequately dialyzed.

A simple continuous dialyzer is illustrated in Fig. 12.5. It consists of two end plates and five membranes arranged to form six compartments. Alternate compartments are for the dialyzate and diffusate, respectively.

A fairly thorough coverage of laboratory dialyzers can be found in Weissberger's "Technique of Organic Chemistry," vol. III.

12.5. Applications. Dialysis is one of the most universally used separation techniques in the laboratory and industry. It is often a preparatory step in processing samples and is indispensable in the recovery and purification of materials in the chemical, food, biological, pharmaceutical, and atomic-energy fields. In recent years the technique has become useful in the separation of azeotropes and close-boiling mixtures of water and oxygenated hydrocarbons, mixtures of different types of organic compounds such as aromatics and aliphatics, and low-molecular-weight organic compounds. A few typical separations are given below to illustrate the effectiveness of dialysis as a separation tool.

In general it can be said that dialytic processes are indicated when salts must be removed from colloidal suspensions or when low-molecular-weight water-soluble organic compounds are to be separated from higher molecular weight species. Graham's work in the middle nineteenth century clearly proved the worthiness of the technique for such separations.

The most important commercial use of dialysis is in the recovery of caustic soda from industrial wastes, such as viscose "press liquor" from the rayon industry and mercerizing solutions. Caustic recovery is only 90 to 93 per cent complete, but this amounts to a great saving in caustic and reduces greatly the caustic that must be dumped.

The recent development of acid-resistant vinyl membranes opens up many new separation possibilities. Sulfuric, nitric, hydrochloric, hydrofluoric, and chromic acid, for example, may be recoverable from waste liquors in a variety of metallurgical processes. For some time now sulfuric acid has been separated from copper and other metal salts in electrolytic bath liquors with cellulose or parchment membranes, although all components will permeate the membrane. Separations are effected by virtue of the differences in respective diffusion rates. Copper transfers at only one-tenth the rate of acid; nickel is slightly slower. Chamberlin and Vromen[8] list the diffusion coefficients of a number of the common acids, alkalies, salts, carbohydrates, and alcohols and illustrate the calculations necessary for predicting separation factors in dialytic procedures. Certain conclusions can be drawn from these values regarding the possible resolution of certain commercial wastes.

Stauffer[9] gives an excellent bibliography on the applications of dialysis and electrodialysis for the separation of organic substances. Specific references are given to the purification of proteins, hormones, enzymes, antitoxins, starches, sugars, and gums, and general references are given for apparatus, theory, and applications.

Pseudocountercurrent distributions or multiple-dialysis procedures analogous to the multiple-extraction pattern of Bush and Densen (see Sec. 3.7) have been described by Craig and King[10] as a preliminary step in the purification of polypeptide mixtures. Multiple dialyses considerably simplified the more precise fractionation procedures by definitely limiting the complexity of the sample on the basis of molecular size or weight. Efforts are now being made to produce operable countercurrent dialysis equipment, since it has been shown that many pure substances dialyze at such a rate that a plot of the log C versus time is a straight line. Therefore, the simple calculations of the binomial theorem can be applied to predict the distribution of the diffusate after multiple equilibrations.[11]

Hoch and Williams[12] have investigated the usefulness of dialytic rate measurements for the detection of differences in molecular size and sample heterogeneity. Neutral species, such as benzoic acid and phenylacetic acid, in 0.01 N hydrochloric acid solutions passed through cellophane membranes at rates predictable by the equation

$$\log C = -kt$$

where C = concentration of solute
$\quad t$ = time
$\quad k$ = constant

The precision with which pure substances obeyed this equation suggested to the authors that deviations from the equation might be interpreted as sample heterogeneity or as a change in membrane permeability. Dialysis rates of electrolytes deviate greatly from the equation because the negatively charged membrane tends to exclude salts, particularly at low salt concentrations. The method, apart from being a test for sample heterogeneity, might be useful for characterizing mixtures of unknowns as well as for characterizing membranes by the dialysis of known mixtures.

One of the latest advances in membrane permeation separations is not truly a dialytic process, but it does merit mention. Azeotropes and close-boiling mixtures of water and oxygenated hydrocarbons have been separated by the use of semipermeable polymeric membranes.[13] The key to such separations is that one component of the mixture be preferentially soluble in the polymer of the membrane and, as a consequence, diffuse through the membrane. The diffusate is then removed from the outside of the membrane by evaporation. The process has unique selectivity, since the membrane can be tailored to fit the system. As an example of the technique, the water content of an isopropyl alcohol–ethyl alcohol–water mixture can be lowered to less than 0.5 per cent.

Many products are awaiting the development of suitable membranes. Attempts to purify molasses, fruit juices, raw-sugar juice, lactose solutions, etc., by dialysis have been abandoned, yet the nature of such systems suggest purification by dialysis. The development of stronger and more selective membranes should open the door to economical purification of these and many other commercial products.

The synthesis of more selective membranes should also make possible the separation of low-molecular-weight species which differ in molecular weight by only 20 to 25 units. It is not expecting too much to anticipate the development of membranes which can remove fairly small anions and cations from solution by osmotic or dialytic procedures.

12.6. Selected Bibliography

Dialysis, in "Encyclopedia of Chemical Technology," R. E. Kirk and D. F. Othmer (eds.), vol. 5, The Interscience Encyclopedia, Inc., New York, 1950.

Hartman, R. J.: "Colloid Chemistry," 2d ed., p. 294, Houghton Mifflin Company, Boston, 1947.
Stauffer, R. E.: Dialysis and Electrodialysis, in "Technique of Organic Chemistry," vol. III, part I, p. 65, A. Weissberger (ed.), Interscience Publishers, Inc., New York, 1956.
Thomas, A. W.: "Colloid Chemistry," p. 68, McGraw-Hill Book Company, Inc., New York, 1934.

REFERENCES

1. Graham, T.: *Trans. Roy. Soc. London,* **151,** 183 (1861).
2. Bethe, A., H. Bethe, and Y. Terada: *Z. physik. Chem.,* **112,** 250 (1924).
3. Brown, W.: *Biochem. J.,* **9,** 591 (1915); **11,** 40 (1917).
4. Elford, W.: *Trans. Faraday Soc.,* **33,** 1094 (1937).
5. Vaughan, M. F.: *Nature,* **182,** 1730 (1958); **183,** 43 (1959); *J. Appl. Polymer Sci.,* **1,** 255 (1959).
6. Gregor, H. P., and K. Sollner: *J. Phys. Chem.,* **50,** 53 (1946).
7. Reid, C. E., and E. J. Breton: *J. Appl. Polymer Sci.,* **1,** 133 (1959).
8. Chamberlin, N. S., and B. H. Vromen: *Chem. Eng.,* **66**(9), 117 (1959).
9. Stauffer, R. E.: Dialysis and Electrodialysis, in "Technique of Organic Chemistry," A. Weissberger (ed.), vol. III, p. 106, Interscience Publishers, Inc., New York, 1956.
10. Craig, L. C., and T. P. King: *J. Am. Chem. Soc.,* **77,** 6620 (1955).
11. Craig, L. C., T. P. King, and A. Stracher: *J. Am. Chem. Soc.,* **79,** 3729 (1957).
12. Hoch, H., and R. C. Williams: *Anal. Chem.,* **30,** 1258 (1958).
13. Sanders, B. H., and C. Y. Choo: *Petrol. Refiner,* **39**(6), 138 (1960).

CHAPTER 13

ELECTRODIALYSIS AND ION-EXCHANGE MEMBRANES

13.1. Introduction. Dialytic diffusion of charged species can be accelerated by the application of an electromotive force across the membrane as indicated in Fig. 13.1. Assuming that the membrane is permeable to

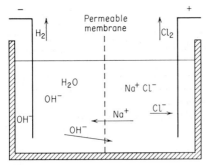

FIG. 13.1. Schematic of a simple electrodialysis cell.

both the anion and cation of the electrolyte, the ions will migrate toward the appropriate electrode and effectively desalt the dialyzate. The process is referred to as *electrodialysis*. Concomitantly, certain solution species are discharged at the anode and cathode, which leads to the formation of acids and alkalies in the respective compartment. No current can pass through the system without this effect. Electrodialysis has been used extensively for the removal of electrolytes from lyophobic colloidal systems and biocolloids and for the desalting of brackish waters.

The major impediment to a more widespread use of electrodialysis in separations work has been the preparation and selection of suitable membranes. The membranes must be mechanically strong to resist the pressures of solutions, permeable, selective to either anions or cations for high efficiency, and have a high electrical conductivity. In the absence of membranes, ions migrate at a rate depending on their individual mobilities. The membrane, however, can slow down or restrict entirely the diffusion of ions to the appropriate electrode. If, for example, the cathode is adjacent to an anion-permeable membrane (cation-impermeable) and the anode adjacent to a cation-permeable membrane, the electrolyte is confined between the membranes. If, on the other hand, the positions of the membranes are switched, the electrolyte is concentrated in the electrode compartments and the solution between the membranes is freed of ions.

A qualitative interpretation of why certain membranes are selectively permeable to either anions or cations follows in the next section.

13.2. Principles of Membrane Selectivity to Anions or Cations.   In electrodialysis there are two side effects of great practical importance: the electroosmotic transport of water through the membrane, which tends to dilute the dialyzate, and the tendency of all membranes placed in solution between electrodes to take on surface charges.   The surface nearest the cathode becomes positive, and the surface nearest the anode negative. This results in an accumulation of hydroxyl ions at the anode face and hydrogen ions at the cathode face.   The charges can be attributed to the difference in relative transport numbers of the ions in the solution and membrane phases.[1]   The magnitude and direction of the effect are dependent on the acidity of the solution, the nature of the membrane, and the composition of the electrolyte.   The second mentioned effect is used practically as a means of improving the selective permeability of membranes.

The selective permeability of membranes to ions can be explained by the existence of ionic functional groups within the membrane.   If the fixed groups are cationic and the mobile groups or counterions are anionic, the membrane will be preferentially permeable to anions.   Fixed anionic groups and mobile cations give a cation-permeable membrane.   Consider, for example, a cation-permeable membrane which is equilibrated with a solution of potassium chloride.   A Donnan equilibrium (see Sec. 10.3) is established, and unequal numbers of the oppositely charged ions enter the membrane.   At equilibrium

$$[K^+]_{membrane} = [Cl^-]_{membrane} + [anion]_{fixed\ in\ membrane}$$

The larger the fixed anionic concentration in the membrane, the greater the difference in the potassium- and chloride-ion concentrations in the membrane.   Since the transport number of ions in solution depends on their relative concentration and mobilities, it is apparent that the transport number of the potassium ion within the membrane is greater than that in the free solution whereas the transport number of the chloride ion is less in the membrane than in solution.   As a consequence, the membrane is more permeable to cations than anions.   If the fixed anionic concentration of the membrane is quite large relative to the electrolytic solution concentration, the transport number of the chloride ion in the membrane will approach zero and the membrane will exclude anions. Obviously, as the electrolytic solution concentration increases, the selectivity of the membrane decreases.

The mobility of the ions within the membrane will be sharply reduced from that in free solution because of somewhat complex electrostatic and interionic attractions.   Thus, the conductivity of the membrane is expected to be less than that of a free electrolyte solution of equivalent concentration, but it does increase with an increase in solution concentration.

Teorell[2] and Meyer and Sievers[3] have derived from the above considerations an expression for the potential across a membrane separating two solutions of different concentrations. From this has evolved the basic theory for the electrochemical behavior of the membranes. It is beyond the scope of this chapter, however, to treat in detail the theory of ion transport across membranes and the electrochemical properties of porous membranes. For a source of such information the reader is referred to the selected bibliography. It is quite apparent, though, that, if electrodialytic membrane materials are going to be highly selective and have high conductivities, they must have a high fixed ionic concentration and be porous.

13.3. Ion-exchange Membranes. Both organic and inorganic membranes which exhibit some degree of selectivity toward anions and cations have been tried in separations experiments. Cellulose, impregnated cellulose, oxidized cellulose and cellulose nitrate, cellophane, cloth, skin, protein, gelatin, precipitated silica, copper ferrocyanide films, canvas, and felt have all been used with varying degrees of success, but in general, membranes of these types have one serious deficiency. The concentration of ionic functional groups within the membrane material is very low, and/or the concentration of adsorbed charged species is low. In either case, the ionic selectivity of the membrane is poor. The only ion-selective membranes that are highly selective and generally applicable for electrodialytic separations are membranes made from ion-exchange resins. Refer to Chap. 10 for a discussion of the makeup of ion-exchange resins.

Homogeneous ion-exchange membranes can be prepared by casting the resin as a thin film. Heterogeneous membranes are prepared by incorporating finely ground ion-exchange resins into a plastic but inert matrix. The significant features of each type of membrane are that they imbibe water and swell, are good electrolytic conductors, are permeable by most small ions, and possess a high concentration of fixed ionic groups of similar sign. Membranes prepared from cation-exchange resins are permeable to cations but not anions; the high concentration of fixed negative charges in the resin matrix offers a high resistance to the passage of anions, so high, in fact, that membranes of cation-exchange resins are almost perfectly impermeable to anions in low solution concentrations. In a like fashion, membranes of anion-exchange materials readily pass anions and almost completely exclude cations.

The degree of permselectivity of the membrane can be conveniently expressed in terms of the change in the transport number of the mobile ion in a solution when a membrane is placed in the solution in electrical series with the solution.   The permselectivity P is then defined as

$$P = \frac{t_{\text{mobile ion}} - t^0_{\text{mobile ion}}}{1 - t^0_{\text{mobile ion}}}$$

where $t_{\text{mobile ion}}$ and $t^0_{\text{mobile ion}}$ refer to the transport number of the permeable ion in the membrane and in the free electrolyte solution, respectively. The actual difference in transport number of the mobile ion in the two phases is given by $t_{\text{mobile ion}} - t^0_{\text{mobile ion}}$, whereas the maximum possible difference in the transport number for the membrane and solution phase is given by $1 - t^0_{\text{mobile ion}}$.   Thus, P is the fraction of the maximum possible increase in the transport number of the mobile ion observed when the membrane is placed in the solution.   In general, the permselectivity of a given membrane approaches ideality, namely, unity, for the permeable ion as its solution concentration decreases.   Permselectivities of the order of 0.90 to greater than 0.99 are not at all unusual for solutions with concentrations below 1 N.   The selectivity offered by these resin membranes is so far superior to the many other natural and synthetic membranes mentioned that they are virtually the only ones worth considering for practical applications.

13.4. Apparatus.   Electrodialytic separations can be achieved with simple equipment and be quite versatile when highly selective membranes are used.   The basic equipment design is one consisting of a two- (see Fig. 13.2) or a three- (see Fig. 13.3) compartment cell.   Thus, electrolytes can be collected in or discarded from particular compartments as desired.   Multicompartment cells will be considered in Sec. 13.6.

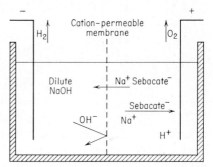

FIG. 13.2. Schematic of a two-compartment electrodialysis cell using a cation-permeable membrane.

Inert electrodes are essential in most systems because highly reactive electrode products are encountered.   Platinum, gold, and dense graphite are generally satisfactory in laboratory equipment.

Low-voltage d-c power sources are satisfactory in most cases because of the high conductivity of the membranes and the electrolyte solutions. As solution resistance increases, as is the case with low electrolyte concentrations and multiple-compartment cells, higher voltages are necessary to maintain a significant current through the cell.

13.5. General Applications.   From a survey of the chemical literature it is apparent that only a few specific applications of ion-exchange membranes are being employed in electrodialytic separations.   Nevertheless, the potential for effecting separations and purifying solutions is great. The following examples will serve to illustrate the potentialities of the method.   The paramount use of cation- and anion-exchange membranes is as partitions which hamper the passage of anions and cations, respectively.

Salts of pH-sensitive organic acids and bases can be converted into the free acid or base by membrane hydrolysis or by dialytic ion exchange against an acid or base without ever coming in contact with the latter, as occurs in precipitation reactions.   Specific examples are the preparation of sebacic acid from sodium sebacate and ethylenediamine from ethylenediamine hydrochloride.   Sebacic acid is readily prepared by placing a

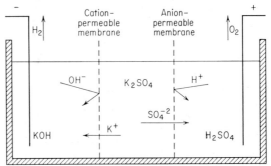

Fig. 13.3. Schematic of a three-compartment electrodialysis cell using a cation- and anion-permeable membrane.

solution of sodium sebacate in the anode compartment of a two-compartment cell (Fig. 13.2) and separating it from a dilute solution of sodium hydroxide in the cathode compartment with a cation-permeable membrane.   Under an impressed potential, sodium ions migrate from the anode compartment through the membrane into the cathode compartment while hydrogen ions are produced at the anode.   As the acidity of the anode compartment increases, sebacic acid precipitates.   The migration of hydroxyl ions into the anode compartment is effectively stopped by the cation-exchange membrane.   Contrast this simple electrochemical procedure with the usual precipitation of sebacic acid from its salt solution by the addition of sulfuric acid.

Ethylenediamine is usually prepared by neutralizing the amine hydrochloride with caustic.   The salt formed presents a problem in product purification.   The difficulty is overcome, however, if the hydrochloride is placed in the cathode compartment of a two-compartment cell and separated from a dilute hydrochloric acid solution in the anode compartment by an anion-exchange membrane.   During electrolysis, chloride ions migrate from the cathode compartment through the membrane into the anode compartment.   Hydroxyl ions are formed at the cathode and neutralize the amine hydrochloride. The migration of hydrogen ions from the anode compartment is prevented by the anion-exchange membrane.

Each of the above methods points up advantages of the electrodialytic process. No additional chemical reagents are added to the reaction vessel, the desired product is not contaminated by added salts, and electrode products such as caustic, hydrogen, oxygen, and chlorine are recoverable as by-products.

A three-compartment cell which employs a cation- and anion-permeable membrane can be used to deplete the electrolyte content of the central compartment. The electrodialysis of a potassium sulfate solution in such a cell is illustrated in Fig. 13.3. As the electrolysis proceeds, the electrolyte content of the central compartment is depleted by the migration of potassium ions into the cathode compartment and sulfate ions into the anode compartment. The diffusion of anions and cations from the cathode and anode compartments, respectively, into the central compartment is prevented by the cation- and anion-permeable membranes. This basic technique is also suitable for isolating an electrode from a given electrolyte when undesirable reactions might occur otherwise.

Zarinskii et al.[4] have used the technique for the quantitative removal of iron, copper, lead, and cadmium salts from suspensions of SiO_2 and WO_3. This separation differs from the above in that the membrane must be impermeable to the suspended particles, which can become charged and migrate to the appropriate electrode unless movement is hampered by the presence of an impermeable membrane.

The most notable use of ion-exchange membranes in electrodialytic separations is for the desalinization of brackish waters.

13.6. Desalinization of Brackish Water. First experiments in the desalting of water by electrodialysis were effected in apparatus with three compartments separated by porous but not selective membranes such as asbestos. Electrodes were in the outer compartments. When a current was passed through the system, the ions in the middle compartment migrated toward the appropriate electrode, thus depleting the electrolyte content in the central compartment. Electrical efficiency of such a system is never more than about 18 per cent because of the overvoltage at the electrodes and the back diffusion of ions which consume energy but do not contribute to the purification of the water. This back diffusion of ions can be understood by considering the electrolysis of a solution of potassium sulfate in the three-compartment cell illustrated in Fig. 13.4.

Under the influence of the applied potential, potassium ions move toward the cathode and sulfate ions toward the anode. Potassium hydroxide and hydrogen are formed in the cathode compartment, while oxygen and sulfuric acid are formed in the anode compartment. The hydrogen and oxygen are evolved as gases, but the hydrogen ions and hydroxyl ions are attracted toward the cathode and anode, respectively. Since the hydrogen and hydroxyl ions migrate more rapidly than the potassium and sulfate ions, they are the preferential charge carriers. Consequently, the electrical efficiency is reduced.

A partial solution to the above problem in efficiency is obtained if the porous membranes are replaced with ion-exchange membranes as illus-

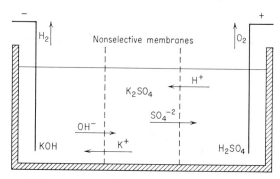

FIG. 13.4. Schematic of a three-compartment electrodialysis cell using nonselective membranes.

trated in Fig. 13.3. If the membrane next to the anode were an anion-exchange membrane, it would not allow the back diffusion of hydrogen ions but it would allow the free diffusion of sulfate ions into the anode compartment. A cation-exchange membrane next to the cathode would inhibit the back diffusion of hydroxyl ions without interfering with the diffusion of potassium ions into the cathode compartment.

Having thus substantially reduced the transport of current through the cell by hydrogen and hydroxyl ions, the chief remaining obstacle to high-efficiency separations is the overvoltage at the electrodes. The effects of overvoltage can be minimized by working with a many-compartment cell formed by alternating cation- and anion-exchange membranes, as illustrated in Fig. 13.5. In such a cell the absolute value of the over-voltage is the same as for the three-compartment cell, but the effects are now averaged over many compartments. Desalting occurs in every other cell as indicated by the movement of ions in Fig. 13.5. Each ion ulti-mately finds in its path a nonpermeable membrane; thus, only the potassium and sulfate ions which enter the electrode compartments consume energy. Electrical efficiencies as high as 80 per cent have been achieved in 100-compartment cells. The limiting factors appear to be the finite electrical resistance of the membranes and the purified water. Although it is theoretically possible to demineralize water completely by such a technique, the power losses become excessive when electrolyte

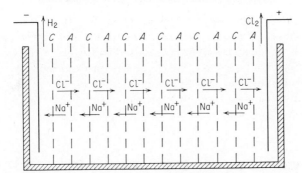

FIG. 13.5. Schematic of a multicompartment electrodialysis cell formed by alternating the positions of the anion- and cation-exchange membranes. A is the anion-permeable membrane; C is the cation-permeable membrane.

concentrations drop below 500 ppm. Kressman,[5] Kunin,[6] Osborn,[7] and Spiegler[8] give a critical evaluation of the desalinization program.

13.7. Selected Bibliography

"Amberplex Ion Permeable Membranes," Rohm and Haas Co., The Resinous Products Division, Washington Square, Philadelphia 5, Pa., 1952.

Clarke, H. T. (ed.): "Ion Transport across Membranes," Academic Press, Inc., New York, 1954.

Collection of papers presented at the University of Nottingham in a symposium on Membrane Phenomena, *Discussions Faraday Soc.*, no. 21, 1956.

Electrodialysis, in "Encyclopedia of Chemical Technology," vol. 5, R. E. Kirk and D. F. Othmer (eds.), The Interscience Encyclopedia, Inc., New York, 1950.

Kunin, R.: "Ion Exchange Resins," 2d ed., John Wiley & Sons, Inc., New York, 1958.

Nachod, F. C., and J. Schubert: "Ion Exchange Technology," Academic Press, Inc., New York, 1956.

Osborn, G. H.: "Synthetic Ion Exchangers," The Macmillan Company, New York, 1956.

Stauffer, R. E.: Dialysis and Electrodialysis, in "Technique of Organic Chemistry," vol. III, part I, p. 65, A. Weissberger (ed.), Interscience Publishers, Inc., New York, 1956.

REFERENCES

1. Bethe, A., and T. Toropoff: *Z. physik. Chem.*, **88**, 686 (1914); **89**, 59 (1915).
2. Teorell, T.: *Z. Electrochem.*, **55**, 460 (1951).
3. Meyer, K. H., and J. F. Sievers: *Helv. Chim. Acta*, **19**, 649 (1936).
4. Zarinskii, V. A., M. M. Farafonov, and V. V. Zateeva: *Zhur. Anal. Khim.*, **12**, 677 (1957).
5. Kressman, T. R. E.: *Ind. Chemist*, **30**, 99 (1954).
6. Kunin, R.: "Ion Exchange Resins," 2d ed., John Wiley & Sons, Inc., New York, 1958.
7. Osborn, G. H.: "Synthetic Ion Exchangers," The Macmillan Company, New York, 1956.
8. Spiegler, K. S.: "Ion Exchange Technology," F. C. Nachod and J. Schubert (eds.), p. 118, Academic Press, Inc., New York, 1956.

CHAPTER 14

PRECIPITATION

14.1. Introduction. Some of the most delicate nondestructive methods available for the separation of similar chemical species depend on a difference in the solubility of the components in the chosen solvent system. All the common schemes of qualitative analysis and many of the conventional gravimetric procedures used for the quantitative determination of constituents are based on the selective solubility (or insolubility) of specific chemical substances or small groups of chemically similar substances. Most of our earlier atomic-weight determinations were based directly or indirectly on the isolation of the element in question in some insoluble form with a definite, known composition. Actually, the majority of the analytically significant reactions occurs in solution and is influenced by the solubilities of the various constituents. In fact, one of the factors for driving a chemical reaction to completion is the formation of an insoluble product that effectively removes certain reactants from the reaction mixture. It is not surprising then that much effort has been devoted to the study of solubility phenomena.

There are several excellent monographs[1,2] that delve into the theoretical aspects of solubility phenomena. Suffice it to say, though, that if a solubility must be known accurately (within 10 per cent or so of the correct value), it must be determined experimentally. One still cannot accurately calculate the solubility from the physical and chemical properties of the pure components. This should not be interpreted to mean that there are no criteria for the prediction of solubilities. We do not have to rely completely on the adage "like dissolves like." Empirical and semiempirical approaches to predicting solubilities are rapidly being replaced with creditable equations derived from sound thermodynamic principles. As molecular-structural data become more convincing, greater reliance will be placed on theoretical calculations, but we may never be able completely to supplant experience with theory in the determination of solubilities. Certainly, theoretical advancements are not going to supersede our present semiempirical techniques in the immediate future.

The criterion which must be satisfied for precipitation to occur is that the solution must become supersaturated with respect to the solute. The metastable state produced eventually reverts to a stable state by the release of the excess solute as a solid. The new phase is the result of either direct chemical action which forms a new chemical species that is insoluble in the solution or changes in the system which decrease the solubility of the solute in the parent solution. Since there are numerous ways of producing and relieving a state of supersaturation, the following discussions will consider independently the factors that influence the solubility of a precipitate, for it is largely through a knowledge of the principles and limitations of precipitation processes that new and better analytical separations will be devised. The factors which determine the solubility of solid solutes to the greatest extent are temperature, pressure, particle size, degree of supersaturation, solvent-solute interactions, complexation, and variations in pH and salt concentration.

14.2. The Effect of Temperature on Solute Solubility. A reasonably accurate and useful equation that relates the solubility of a solid to the absolute temperature can be derived from thermodynamics. The basic equation that relates the vapor pressure of a solid to the absolute temperature for a system involving an equilibrium between a solid and its vapor at constant external pressure is the Clausius-Clapeyron equation.

$$\frac{d \ln p^s}{dT} = \frac{\Delta H^s}{RT^2} \qquad (14.1)$$

where p^s = vapor pressure of solid
$\quad \Delta H^s$ = molar heat of sublimation of solid
$\quad T$ = absolute temperature
$\quad R$ = molar gas constant

For a system involving an equilibrium between liquid and vapor the equation becomes

$$\frac{d \ln p^L}{dT} = \frac{\Delta H^v}{RT^2}$$

where p^L = vapor pressure of liquid
$\quad \Delta H^v$ = molar heat of vaporization

Assuming that the latter equation holds true for a supercooled solution or melt, then the two forms of the equation should be applicable at the same temperature and

$$\frac{d \ln (p^s/p^L)}{dT} = \frac{\Delta H^s - \Delta H^v}{RT^2} = \frac{\Delta H^F}{RT^2} \qquad (14.2)$$

where ΔH^F is the molar heat of fusion of the solid.

An important aspect of this equation is its application to the calculation of solubilities. Strictly speaking, the equation involves no assumption concerning the nature of the solid in equilibrium with the solution. Therefore, the equation can be applied to a saturated solution. At the freezing (saturation) point of the solution, that is, at the point where solid solute separates from the solution and establishes an equilibrium, the partial pressure p of the solute must equal the vapor pressure of the pure solid. Then, if Raoult's law is applicable, p^s/p^L equals p/p^L, which is the mole fraction x of the solute in the system. Thus

$$\frac{d \ln x}{dT} = \frac{\Delta H^F}{RT^2}$$

When x is unity, T is the freezing temperature of the pure solute. Integration of the above equation between T and T_f (the freezing point) of the solute results in

$$\int_i^1 d \ln x = \int_T^{T_f} \frac{\Delta H^F}{RT^2} \, dT$$

$$\ln 1 - \ln x_i = \frac{\Delta H^F}{R} \left(\frac{1}{T} - \frac{1}{T_f} \right) = \ln \frac{1}{x_i}$$

$$\ln \frac{1}{x_i} = \frac{\Delta H^F}{R} \frac{T_f - T}{TT_f}$$

$$\log \frac{1}{x_i} = \frac{\Delta H^F}{4.575} \frac{T_f - T}{TT_f} \qquad (14.3)$$

which gives the mole fraction x_i of solute present in solution at any temperature T if the heat of fusion and melting point of the solute are known. This equation is valid, though, only if the system conforms to ideality and ΔH^F is constant with temperature. If the temperature difference is small, ΔH^F can be taken as an average value without affecting the results grossly. Greater accuracy can be achieved in predicting solubilities if the change in heat capacity of reactants and products with temperature is taken into consideration. An extension of Eq. (14.3) to incorporate the variation in heat capacity of the system with temperature yields

$$\log \frac{1}{x_i} = \frac{\Delta H_m^F}{4.575} \frac{T_f - T}{TT_f} - \frac{\Delta C_p}{4.575} \frac{T_f - T}{T} + \frac{\Delta C_p}{1.987} \log \frac{T_f}{T} \qquad (14.4)$$

where ΔH_m^F is the molar heat of fusion at the melting point and ΔC_p is the change in molar heat capacity. Although this leads to a more accurate expression, the intricacy of most chemical systems is such that the assumption of ideality introduces a greater error than the omission of the terms in ΔC_p. Besides, the terms in ΔC_p are usually not known. Consequently, the simpler equation is usually adequate.

An example will illustrate the effectiveness of Eq. (14.3). The heat of fusion of naphthalene has been reported as 4,550 cal per mole, and the melting point as 353°K. Substitution of these data into Eq. (14.3) indicates a theoretical solubility of naphthalene at 20°C in an ideal solution of 0.264 mole fraction. A saturated solution of naphthalene in any solvent thus should contain sufficient solute at 20°C to give a mole fraction of 0.264. The measured solubility of naphthalene in benzene,[3] chlorobenzene, and toluene[4] at 20° is 0.260, 0.276, and 0.259 mole fraction, respectively. This is reasonably good agreement considering the assumption of ideality, which is not obtained. On the other hand, if a polar solvent such as acetone or aniline is selected, the departure from ideality is anticipated and the equation does not predict the solubility as accurately. Actually, the solubility is much less than that predicted by the equation and corresponds to a positive deviation from Raoult's law; that is,

$$x < \frac{p}{p^L}$$

Positive deviations generally are the result of great differences in the types of molecular attractive forces existent in solute and solvent. Negative deviations (abnormally great solubilities) occur most frequently when both components are highly polar and there is an unusually great attraction, either physical or chemical, between solute and solvent. The result is that

$$x > \frac{p}{p^L}$$

A satisfactory graphic representation of ideal solubility can be obtained by plotting $\log x$ versus $1/T$. The result is a straight line with a slope of $-\Delta H^F/4.575$. The upper limit is where $\log x = 0$ at the melting point of the solute. Therefore, if the melting point of the solute and its solubility at one other temperature are known, the straight-line relationship will give the approximate solubility at other temperatures. Similarly, if ΔH^F is known, the slope of the line is established and only one other point (such as the melting point) is needed to fix the position of the plot.

The quantitative nature of Eq. (14.3) must not be emphasized too greatly, however. The gross departure of most systems from ideality precludes the application of this equation for calculating solubilities except as an approximation.

Qualitative deductions based on the thermodynamic calculations are quite helpful, however. For substances with similar molar heats of fusion, the one with the higher melting point is less soluble at a given temperature than the one with the lower melting point. Theoretical significance also is shown for the adage that the solubility of a substance increases with temperature, since T is always less than T_f.

A variation of Eq. (14.3) is the Van't Hoff equation

$$\log \frac{K_1}{K_2} = \frac{-\Delta H}{4.573}\left(\frac{1}{T_1} - \frac{1}{T_2}\right)$$ (14.5)

where ΔH is the heat of reaction or dissolution and K is the equilibrium constant (K_{sp}). This equation is perhaps of greater importance to the analytical chemist than Eq. (14.3) because it can be used effectively in calculating the solubility of insoluble strong electrolytes (common precipitates) at different temperatures. The Van't Hoff equation also is only an approximation that does not take into consideration the change in heat capacities of reactants and products at different temperatures. ΔH is an average value for the temperature range considered. For a narrow temperature range, though, the equation gives satisfactory values. Probably the greatest use of this equation is in determining heats of reaction and not in predicting solubilities.

It is apparent then that the influence of temperature on the solubility of solids in liquids is a function of the differential heat of solution. The heat of solution consists of two neutralizing quantities: the heat evolved upon solvation of the dissolved solute and the heat required to separate the particles from one another in the solid state. If the heat of solvation is greater than the lattice energy, the dissolution process is exothermic. If the lattice energy is the greater of the two, the dissolution is endothermic. When the two energy terms are roughly equal, the heat of dissolution approaches zero and temperature has little effect on the solubility. The dissolution of most salts is endothermic, which accounts for their greater solubility at higher temperatures. There are, however, some salts that go into solution by an exothermic process and are less soluble at higher temperatures.

14.3. The Effect of Pressure on Solute Solubility. Just as an increase in temperature effects an increase in the solubility of a solid that dissolves by an endothermic process, so an increase in pressure increases the solubility of a solid that dissolves with a decrease in volume. The ideal equation relating pressure and solubility is

$$\frac{d \ln x}{dP} = \frac{V^s - V^L}{RT}$$ (14.6)

where V^s and V^L are the molal volume of the solid and the solid in the pure liquid state, respectively. The other terms have been identified in the preceding section. It is well known that most solids expand upon melting. Therefore, V^L is usually larger than V^s and $V^s - V^L$ is negative. Thus, the solubility or mole fraction of a solute in equilibrium with the solution decreases with an increase in pressure. It is possible, though, that under conditions where the system gives a negative deviation from Raoult's law the solubility will increase with an increase in pressure. This is the result of a decrease in the molal volume of the solid as it goes into solution. Both effects are qualitatively predicted by the principle of Le Châtelier.

Gibson[5] has derived some empirical equations from data collected on the compressibility of solutions at low pressures that will permit the calculation of the solubility of certain salts in water at high pressure. The equations are based on accurate data collected at the lower pressures where the compressibility of the solution is greatest. Extrapolation of these equations into the region of higher pressures and lower compressibility gives surprisingly good results. So far there has been little or no analytical application of these equations for predicting solubilities under pressure.

It should be emphasized, though, that the effect of pressure on the solubility of solids is small and can be neglected for most purposes unless pressures are quite large. This can be demonstrated by integration of Eq. (14.6) between limits of p_1 and p_2.

$$\int_{x_1}^{x_2} d \ln x = \frac{V^s - V^L}{RT} \int_{p_1}^{p_2} dp$$

$$\ln \frac{x_2}{x_1} = \frac{\Delta V}{RT} (p_2 - p_1)$$

$$\log \frac{x_2}{x_1} = \frac{\Delta V}{2.303 RT} (p_2 - p_1) \tag{14.7}$$

From this equation one can evaluate the exact effect of pressure on solubility provided the system is ideal. For example, theoretically a change of 0.010 liter in the molal volume of solute at 25°C would require a pressure change of 231 atm to effect a 10 per cent change in solute solubility.

$$\log \frac{0.55}{0.50} = \frac{0.010(p_2 - p_1)}{2.303 \times 0.08205 \times 298}$$
$$\Delta p = \log 1.1 \times 2.303 \times 0.08205 \times 298 \times 10^2$$
$$= 0.041 \times 2.303 \times 0.08205 \times 298 \times 10^2$$
$$= 231 \text{ atm}$$

It is indeed unusual to consider the effect of pressure on the solubility of solids. The solubility of $NaCl$ in water increases only from 26.42 to 27.20 g per 100 g of solution (a 3 per cent increment) as the pressure increases from 1 to 1500 atm.[6] The solubility of cadmium sulfate in water increases by only 1.5 per cent (from 43.44 to 44.08 g per 100 g of solution) for a pressure change from 1 to 1000 atm.

14.4. The Effect of Particle Size on Solute Solubility. It is a well-documented fact that many colloidal and other very finely divided precipitates undergo a spontaneous change upon digestion in contact with the mother liquor. The fine particles become coarser and fewer in number with the smallest actually disappearing. The phenomenon is known as *Ostwald ripening*. The process is obviously not an equilibrium one because the change of solute in one state of aggregation to another is spontaneous. The escaping tendency of solute from the smaller particles is greater than that from the larger particles. Such a system can be treated thermodynamically to obtain an equation that will relate particle size to solubility.

Consider the change in free energy that accompanies the spontaneous dissolution of the smaller particles with the deposition of this material on the surface of the larger particles. Assume that the shape of the small particle is spherical with a radius of r. The volume V then is $\frac{4}{3}\pi r^3$. If there is n moles of solute in the small particle,

$$nv = \tfrac{4}{3}\pi r^3 = V$$

when v is the molal volume of the solid. If dn moles of the particle dissolves, the change in the radius of the sphere is given by

$$dn = \frac{4\pi r^2}{v}\, dr \qquad (14.8)$$

and the surface area, $\sigma = 4\pi r^2$, of the particle changes as

$$d\sigma = 8\pi r\, dr \qquad (14.9)$$

Now, if F and F^0 are the molal free energy of the small solute particle and solute macroparticle, respectively, the change in free energy accompanying a transfer of dn moles of solute is given by

$$dF = (F - F^0)\, dn$$

Assuming that the surface area of the macroparticle is not changed appreciably by the deposition of dn moles of solute, the change in free energy is equal to the change in surface energy of the microparticle. That is,

$$dF = \gamma\, d\sigma = (F - F^0)\, dn \qquad (14.10)$$

when γ is the surface tension of the solid. By substitution of terms from Eqs. (14.8) and (14.9) into Eq. (14.10),

$$\gamma 8\pi r\, dr = \frac{\gamma 8\pi r v}{4\pi r^2}\, dn = (F - F^0)\, dn$$

or

$$\frac{2\gamma v}{r} = (F - F^0) = RT \ln\frac{f}{f^0}$$

where f and f^0 are the fugacity of the small particles and large particles, respectively. Substitution of the ratio of solubility of microparticles S to macroparticles S^0 for the ratio of fugacities yields

$$RT \ln \frac{S}{S^0} = \frac{2\gamma v}{r} = \frac{2\gamma M}{rd} \tag{14.11}$$

M is the molecular weight of the solute and d the density. This is known as the Ostwald-Freundlich equation and relates the solubility of a solute to its state of subdivision.

To illustrate the effect of particle size on solubility it is possible to calculate the particle diameter required to increase the solubility by 10 per cent at 25°C. Assume an intermediate value of 200 dynes for the surface tension of the solid and 50 ml as the molal volume. Then

$$2.303RT \log \frac{S}{S^0} = \frac{2 \times 200 \times 50}{r}$$

$$2.303 \times 8.316 \times 10^7 \times 298 \times \log 1.10 = \frac{20,000}{r}$$

$$r = \frac{20,000}{235 \times 10^7} = 8.50 \times 10^{-7}$$

$$= 8.5 \times 10^{-6} \text{ cm}$$

It immediately becomes apparent that one need consider the effect of particle size on solubility only if the particles are extremely small.

A number of workers have experimentally substantiated the fundamental premise of Eq. (14.11). Hulett[7] has shown that the equilibrium solubility of small particles is greater than that of large crystals. He was able to increase the solubility of gypsum ($CaSO_4 \cdot 2H_2O$) by 20 per cent and barium sulfate by 80 per cent by using very finely divided materials. Dundon and Mack[8] determined the increase in solubility due to a reduction in particle size for a number of common substances and used the Ostwald-Freundlich equation to evaluate the surface energy of solids from solubility data. Consult Table 14.1 for the increase in solubility noted for a particular particle size. Hardness and calculated surface energies are given for comparison purposes. Solubility increases are determined by the measured increase in the conductivity of solutions in equilibrium with macrocrystals of the salts as the finely divided material is added to the system. These are not truly equilibrium solubilities because, if the solutions are digested long enough, the solubility of the solute will be reproducible with that of large crystals because of the spontaneous reduction of surface area. Such was the case in these studies where conductivities returned to the original saturated solution value or nearly so. The attainment of maximum solubility (conductivity) was

rapid in most cases with a gradual reduction to the original value. In
some instances the increase in solubility was accompanied by a disappear-
ance of the fine particles. It would thus appear that Dundon has shown
that the Ostwald-Freundlich equation is basically correct and that a
proportionality exists between surface energy and hardness.

Balarew[9] and Cohen and Blakkingh[10] have criticized the conductimetric
measurements of Dundon and actually reported no increase in solubility
for BaSO$_4$ particles of 0.1 μ diameter. In view of these criticisms, May
and Kolthoff[11] undertook an investigation of the solubility of lead
chromate as a function of particle size under experimental conditions

TABLE 14.1. INCREASE IN SOLUTE SOLUBILITY WITH SMALL PARTICLE SIZE*

Salt	Minimum particle diameter, μ	Average increase in solubility, %	γ	Hardness
PbF$_2$	0.3	9	900	$\sim$2
PbI$_2$	0.4	2	130	Very soft
SrSO$_4$	0.3	25	1400	3.0–3.5
Ag$_2$CrO$_4$	0.3	10	575	$\sim$2
CaF$_2$	0.2–0.3	18	2500	4
BaSO$_4$	0.1	80	1250	2.5–3.5
CaSO$_4$·2H$_2$O	0.2–0.5	4.4–12	370	1.6–2

* From M. L. Dundon, *J. Am. Chem. Soc.*, **45**, 2658 (1923).

that would eliminate factors that might invalidate the work of previous
investigators. Solubility measurements were made on freshly prepared
and aged lead chromate in 0.1 M perchloric acid. Chromate concentrations were determined amperometrically, and lead and chromate concentrations by polarography. The freshly prepared lead chromate had
an average diameter of 0.17 μ and was 70 per cent more soluble than the
aged product. Aging of the fresh precipitate occurred rapidly at 25°C
with a normal solubility being found after a 20-min digestion period, at
which time the average particle diameter had increased to 0.56 μ. May
and Kolthoff concluded that the greater solubility of the fresh precipitate
must be attributed to its very small particle size.

The reported failure of small barium sulfate particles to dissolve in
saturated solutions can be explained on the basis that, after a portion of
the small particles have entered solution, the acquisition of a surface
charge by adsorption decreases their solubility. The Ostwald-Freundlich
equation does not take into consideration the possible ionic dissociation
of a solid in solution or the surface energy of the solid derived from any
electric charge on the surface, but Knapp[12] has extended the equation to

include these terms.   Knapp's equation is

$$\frac{RT}{M} \ln \frac{K_r}{K} = \frac{2\sigma}{rd} - \frac{q^2 \delta}{4\pi D d r^5} \qquad (14.12)$$

where K_r and K = activity products of small and large particles, respectively

q = electrical charge on each layer of electrical double layer produced by adsorption

δ = distance between layers

D = dielectric constant of the medium

and the other symbols possess the significance assigned them above. According to the Ostwald-Freundlich equation the solubility of a particle should increase exponentially with decreasing particle size.   The Knapp equation, however, predicts that the solubility increase with decreasing particle size would be tempered by the electrical charge and actually approach zero for very small particles.   The explanation of why small barium sulfate particles failed to dissolve in a saturated solution is at least in harmony with Knapp's equation.   Frankly, it is fruitless to pursue the modifications of the basic equation further here because there are certainly many factors other than surface energy to be taken into consideration.   A qualitative interpretation of this equation is adequate for most purposes because empirical correction factors must be introduced into the equation to correlate closely experimental and theoretical solubilities.

In view of the above discussion it seems that the Ostwald-Freundlich equation can be used for qualitatively predicting solubilities on the basis of particle size only if the particles are very small, less than 1 μ in diameter.

14.5. The Effect of Supersaturation on Solute Solubility.   Prior to the development of present-day nucleation and crystal growth theory, von Weimarn[13] proposed that the speed of precipitation depends on the absolute concentration of the solute and its equilibrium solubility. Expressed in mathematical form von Weimarn's equation is

$$D = K \frac{Q - S}{S} \qquad (14.13)$$

where D = dispersion coefficient = speed of precipitation

Q = total concentration of substance in solution

S = equilibrium solubility of coarse crystals

$Q - S$ = supersaturation at the moment of nucleation

$(Q - S)/S$ = degree of supersaturation

K = constant

Von Weimarn's simple equation indicates that a precipitation can be slowed down by increasing the solubility of the precipitate or by decreasing the concentration of reactants.

The results of an extensive study by von Weimarn on the variation of precipitate form and time required for precipitation of $BaSO_4$ with various concentrations of the barium and sulfate ions are summarized by Kolthoff and Sandell.[14] The data tend to confirm von Weimarn's theory, but in view of modern nucleation concepts, it is too simplified an expression to be completely valid. At best it is only an empirical effort that can be depended on to predict qualitatively the relationship between solute concentration and the rate at which the precipitate forms.

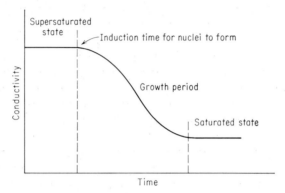

Fig. 14.1. Variation of conductivity of a solution prepared by mixing electrolytes that form an insoluble product.

Two stages are involved in the initial formation of a precipitate: an induction period required for the first nuclei to form and act as centers for the deposition of additional solute and the period of crystal growth until the attainment of a final stable condition. Figure 14.1 diagrams these stages for the deposition of an ionic precipitate. The conductivity of the solution decreases as the crystal nuclei grow and ultimately becomes the same as the conductivity of a saturated solution of the insoluble salt. The rate at which the precipitate is produced is thus dependent upon two factors: the rate of nucleation and the rate of crystal growth. These two factors are largely independent of each other, but both are dependent on the solute solubility.

The rate of nucleation increases very rapidly with increasing supersaturation. Nucleation does not occur readily in saturated solutions as evidenced by the ease with which supersaturated solutions are prepared by gradually lowering the temperature of a saturated solution. Nuclei of a new phase can be produced only after a certain degree of supersaturation exists. The nuclei then grow by assimilating more material until the supersaturation is alleviated.   If the degree of supersaturation is only slight, precipitation may not begin for weeks or even months.   A solution only slightly supersaturated in respect to macrocrystals will allow only the larger nuclei to increase in size to the detriment of the smaller nuclei, since the solubility of the newly formed nucleus is greater than the solubility of larger particles.   Further hindrance to nucleation in slightly supersaturated solutions is the great improbability of large nuclei ever forming.   On the other hand, in more concentrated solutions, there is a greater probability for a nucleus to form that is sufficiently stable to grow further.   Nuclei once formed grow rather rapidly initially, thereby diminishing the supersaturation and their own solubility.   Subsequent growth is slower.   Nuclei appear so quickly and in such profusion in more concentrated solutions that the supersaturation is relieved immediately by the formation of a gel, colloid, or amorphous precipitate.

Stated rather plainly, this implies that in order for spontaneous nucleation to occur there must be a relatively high degree of supersaturation. Davies and Jones[15] have shown that the spontaneous precipitation of AgCl does not occur unless the product of the silver- and chloride-ion concentrations is at least twice the value of the solubility-product constant.   LaMer and Dinegar[16] observed that for the precipitation of $BaSO_4$ the ionic concentrations must be twenty-one times as great as the equilibrium concentration.   A recalculation of some of von Weimarn's data agrees very closely with the observations of LaMer and Dinegar. The supersaturation ratio required for the precipitation of $SrSO_4$ is about 3.

A corollary to von Weimarn's theory is that the degree of supersaturation is the chief factor in determining the physical characteristics of the precipitate.   That is, the general physical appearance of different precipitates should be the same if obtained under similar conditions. Immediately many exceptions come to mind.   Barium sulfate and silver chloride have roughly equal molar solubilities, but if precipitated with equal degrees of supersaturation with respect to macroparticles, the barium sulfate will appear as microcrystals and the silver chloride as a curdy flocculated colloid.   The difference is explained in part by the fact that the solubility of the primary particles of the two is not necessarily the same, since their surface tensions are unequal (refer to Sec. 14.4). The silver chloride precipitate is soft with a low surface tension, whereas the barium sulfate is hard with a higher surface tension.   Therefore, the silver chloride solubility is less dependent on particle dimension than is that of barium sulfate.   The relative supersaturation of the solution is actually greater with respect to the primary particles of silver chloride than barium sulfate.   Consequently, many more nuclei of silver chloride than barium sulfate are formed.   A low surface tension inhibits rapid

Ostwald ripening, and the silver chloride precipitate is colloidal. Conversely, the lower relative supersaturation and the higher surface tension of the barium sulfate account for fewer nuclei, rapid recrystallization, and a microcrystalline precipitate.

During nucleation the number of particles in the precipitate and their final size are fixed. The nucleation process determines the surface area on which further precipitation can occur and consequently establishes the rate of the precipitation.

Klein and Gordon[17] give an excellent discussion of the conflicting theories on nucleation and stress the need for better understanding of the process if we are to increase the sensitivity and delicacy of separations by precipitation.

The relation between the rate of crystal growth and the degree of supersaturation appears to be rather complicated. Crystal growth can be determined either by the rate at which solute particles migrate to the surface of the nucleus or by the rate of actual deposition of dissolved solute on the crystal lattice. If the crystal growth is governed by a diffusion mechanism, the rate of growth should be directly proportional to the degree of supersaturation. If the crystal growth is controlled by the rate of deposition, concentration should have little effect. Doremus[18] has shown for a limited number of systems that the crystal growth rate is controlled by an interface process rather than by bulk diffusion of the solute to the surface of the crystal. As a result, it is proposed that the adsorption of a surface layer is the first stage in crystal growth from solution.

Although there is considerable controversy regarding the mechanism and rate-determining factors of crystal growth, it is apparent that in very dilute solutions diffusion is slow because the concentration gradient is so small. The few nuclei that do form grow slowly and form distinct crystals. In more concentrated solutions nuclei appear so quickly and in such great numbers that the supersaturation is relieved before an appreciable amount of diffusion can occur. Resulting crystals are imperfect and give the appearance of being amorphous. The important point is that the most perfect crystals are consistently obtained where the rate of nucleation and rate of crystal growth are inhibited by low concentrations of reagents.

There is substantial evidence thus to support the empirical approach of precipitating substances from dilute solutions under conditions of maximum solubility for optimum purity and perfection. A case in point is the conventional precipitation of barium sulfate from hot, dilute acid solutions. Precipitate solubility is increased by the higher temperature and by the equilibrium

$$H^+ + SO_4^{--} \rightleftharpoons HSO_4^-$$

but not sufficiently to prevent a quantitative precipitation. At low enough concentrations the rate of crystal growth is diffusion controlled and the resulting crystals are reasonably perfect. Some of Fischer's[19] electromicrographs of barium sulfate precipitates obtained under various conditions substantiate these concepts well.

There are numerous disadvantages associated with the use of large excesses of reacting species. Precipitates formed under such conditions are grossly imperfect, amorphous, voluminous, and difficult to filter and readily occlude impurities. Thanks mainly to the work of von Weimarn, it is known that these characteristics are influenced more by the conditions under which the precipitate is formed than by its chemical composition. Certain precipitation techniques introduced in recent years overcome many of these difficulties by carefully controlling the precipitant concentration so that there is never even a localized excess of reagent. See Sec. 14.10 on precipitation from homogeneous media.

14.6. The Effect of Solvent on Solute Solubility. The influence of solvent on solute solubility can best be realized by considering the dissolution process as consisting of two steps: the complete separation of crystal components and the solvation of the independent particles. The dissolution of a solid electrolyte M^+B^- in water can be represented as follows:

$$\text{Crystalline } M^+B^- \xrightarrow[\text{energy}]{-\text{lattice}} M^+ + B^- \xrightarrow[\text{energy}]{+\text{hydration}} M(H_2O)_x^+ + B(H_2O)_y^-$$

The energy required for the parting of the crystal components is an intrinsic property of the solid and is not affected by the presence of solvent. This energy, usually designated as lattice energy, is defined as the decrease in energy associated with the process of bringing the components, when separated by infinity, to the positions they occupy in the stable lattice. The prime source of energy required for the dispersal of the crystal components is the solvation process, which is exothermic. The spontaneous association of solute and solvent is the direct result of dipole-dipole interactions, induced dipole interactions, coulombic or electrostatic forces, hydrogen-bond formation, dispersion forces, and/or conventional chemical bonding by the sharing of electrons.

Since the solvation energy is a function of both the solvent and the solute, the effect of the solvent on the solubility of a solute is determined by the magnitude of the solvation energy relative to the lattice energy. It is generally conceded that polar substances are more soluble in polar solvents than in nonpolar solvents. The converse is also true. Polar compounds are usually characterized by high lattice energies, high melting points, high solvation energies, and appreciable solubility in water or other highly polar solvents. Relative to the polar substances, the nonpolar substances are characterized by generally lower lattice energies, lower melting points, lower solvation energies, and much lower solubilities in water and other polar solvents. As would be expected, polar compounds are quite insoluble in nonpolar solvents because the lattice energies are high and the solvation energies low. The molecular interaction decreases as the solvent polarity decreases. Polar solutes separating from solution associated with water of hydration are commonly encountered, less frequently with alcohol of crystallization, and seldom with benzene of crystallization. It is almost impossible to verify the existence of solvates involving nonpolar paraffins of crystallization.

TABLE 14.2. THE SOLUBILITIES OF SODIUM AND POTASSIUM PERCHLORATES IN
VARIOUS SOLVENTS*
(Solubilities expressed in grams of solute per 100 ml of solution at 25°C.)

Solvent system	$NaClO_4$	$KClO_4$
Water	113.88	2.0394
Methyl alcohol	35.833	0.0830
Ethyl alcohol	11.134	0.0094
n-Butyl alcohol	1.495	0.0036
Ethyl acetate	8.425	0.0013
Acetone	36.596	0.1179
Ethyl ether	Insol.	Insol.

* From H. H. Willard and G. F. Smith, *J. Am. Chem. Soc.*, **45**, 286 (1923).

The analytical significance of the preceding discussion is the implication that the solubility of a salt can be altered by changing the properties of the solvent or by actually changing the solute to a different environment. This is a very common practice. In instances where excessive solute solubility in water is observed, the solubility is frequently reduced by the addition of a miscible organic solvent in which the solute is but slightly soluble. For example, strontium chromate is appreciably soluble in water but can be quantitatively precipitated from an alcohol-water mixture. The solubility of lead sulfate in water is reduced greatly by introducing 10 to 20 volume per cent of alcohol. In the perchlorate method for the determination of potassium, the $KClO_4$ is precipitated from alcoholic or nonaqueous media rather than water because of the lower solubility in the organic solvent. The effect of changing solvent environment on the solubility of sodium and potassium perchlorate is illustrated in Table 14.2. Note the general decrease in solubility with decreased solvent polarity.[20]

In spite of the widespread applicability of the influence of nonaqueous media on the solubility of inorganic compounds, there are several serious disadvantages associated with its use, namely, the dilution effect accompanied by the decreased activity of the precipitant and the determination of the type and amount of organic solvent to be added. The dilution effect is encountered because the organic solvent-water mixture is not used as the solvent per se. Rather, the organic solvent is added to a fixed volume of aqueous solution, and although the solubility of the solute per unit volume of the mixture is then less than that for an equal volume of water, the total volume is increased. For instance, if the composition of the solvent were changed from 100 per cent water to 90 per cent organic solvent, there would be a tenfold increase in volume. The solubility of the solute in the mixed solvent would have to be less than one-tenth its solubility in water to effect a further precipitation of solute. Almost as important as the dilution is the maintenance of a high precipitant concentration. If the precipitant (common ion) is a strong electrolyte, its solubility can also be lessened by the addition of an organic solvent and cause a shift in the solute solubility toward higher values.

Generally the type and the amount of organic solvent to be used have been determined empirically by trial and error, but Jentoft and Robinson[21] have proposed a graphical method for selecting the optimum organic solvent-water mixture for analytical precipitations. Let S_w and S_x represent the solubility of the solute per unit volume of water and mixed solvent, respectively, and x the volume fraction of organic solvent in the mixture. The dilution function D_x is then defined as

$$D_x = \frac{1}{1 - x} \tag{14.14}$$

D_x is a measure of the dilution of a fixed volume of water as a miscible organic solvent is added and varies from one to infinity as the volume fraction of organic solvent varies from zero to 1. The solubility of the solute per unit volume of water in the mixture is given by $D_x S_x$, and the ratio $D_x S_x / S_w$ is a direct measure of the reduction of the solubility relative to water effected by the addition of the organic solvent. S_x is a function of x and must be determined experimentally for a given organic solvent. Therefore

$$D_x S_x = D_x f(x) = \frac{f(x)}{1 - x} \tag{14.15}$$

Since only the minimum value of $D_x S_x / S_w$ is of interest, it can be obtained by differentiating Eq. (14.15) and setting the first derivative equal to zero:

$$\frac{dD_x S_x}{dx} = \frac{d}{dx} \frac{f(x)}{1 - x} = \frac{f(x)}{(1 - x)^2} + \frac{f'(x)}{1 - x} = 0$$

A rearrangement of terms gives

$$f'(x) = \frac{-f(x)}{1 - x} = -(D_x S_x)_{\min}$$

which is the slope of the tangent to the solubility curve, $S_x = f(x)$, at the mixed solvent composition $x_{\min}$ corresponding to the minimum value of $D_x S_x$. The equation for the tangent is

$$S_x = mx + C$$

where m is the slope and C a constant. C can be evaluated at the point $(x_{\min}, S_x)$ and be shown equivalent to $(D_x S_x)_{\min}$. Thus, for x equal to 1, S_x equals zero and for x equal to zero, S_x equals $(D_x S_x)_{\min}$.

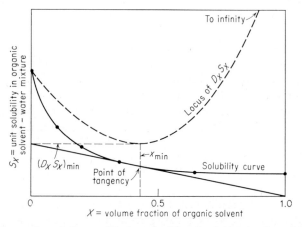

Fig. 14.2. Illustration of the graphical method for the determination of the optimum composition of mixed solvent to be used to reduce solute solubility. The solid line is a hypothetical solubility curve. The dashed line is the locus of values for $D_x S_x$. The point of tangency gives the value for $x_{\min}$. [*After R. E. Jentoft and R. J. Robinson, Anal. Chem.*, **26**, 1156 (1954).]

This approach provides a graphical method for the determination of the optimum composition of mixed solvent to be used to reduce solute solubility. Simply plot the solubility of solute versus volume fraction of organic solvent, and draw a tangent to the curve that passes through point ($x = 1$, $S_x = 0$). The point of tangency gives the value for $x_{\min}$, which is the composition sought. Figure 14.2 illustrates the technique with a hypothetical solubility curve. The dashed curve is the locus of values for $D_x S_x$. If several different organic solvents are tried, the one giving the smallest value of the tangent intercept is the most efficient.

The method has not been used extensively, but it deserves further consideration. It is convenient and can be applied to existing solubility data provided sufficient data exist to construct a solubility curve. Jentoft and Robinson[21] used it effectively to establish the optimum composition of ethanol-water mixtures desired for the precipitation of potassium metaperiodate.

14.7. The Effect of Salt Concentration on Solute Solubility. It has been well established that saturated solutions of strong electrolytes in contact with the solid solute are dynamic equilibrium systems subject to the provisions of the law of chemical equilibrium. For the generalized equation

$$mA + nB + oC + \cdots \rightleftharpoons rD + sE + tF + \cdots$$

representing an equilibrium chemical system, the mass-action law imposes the condition that

$$\frac{a_D{}^r a_E{}^s a_F{}^t \ \cdots}{a_A{}^m a_B{}^n a_C{}^o \ \cdots} = K_{eq}$$

where a represents the activity of a given chemical species and K is a true thermodynamic constant characteristic of the particular chemical system.

The activity of a substance is defined in terms of the work that must be done to transfer a mole of the substance from one environment to another; that is,

$$\Delta F \equiv RT \ln \frac{a_2}{a_1}$$

It is apparent then that the activity of a substance can be expressed only in terms of a ratio and not as an absolute quantity. Therefore, it is practical to choose for each substance a reference or standard state in which the activity is arbitrarily taken as unity. The activity of any component is then simply the ratio of its immediate value to that in the standard state. It might be well to point out here that the standard state for liquids is the pure solvent and for solids the pure substance. The standard state for solid solutes is chosen so that the activity is equal to the concentration at infinite dilution. Then

$$\lim_{C \to 0} \frac{a_1}{C_1} = \lim_{C \to 0} f_1 = 1$$

where C_1 is the molar concentration of the solute and f_1 is the activity coefficient for the solute. This is in line with the fact that solutions approach ideality as they approach infinite dilution. The activity and concentration of the solute are therefore related by the equation

$$a_1 = C_1 f_1$$

When the solution is ideal, the activity of a solute equals the concentration.

In the study of dilute saturated solutions of insoluble binary electrolytes, the general equilibrium reaction reduces to

$$A_x B_n \rightleftharpoons xA + nB$$
$$\text{(solid)} \qquad \text{(solution)}$$

and concentrations are substituted for activities in the equilibrium condition. The term involving the activity of the solid is eliminated because of the assumption that the pure solid is the standard state. The ion product

$$[A]^x [B]^n = K_{sp}$$

is designated as the solubility-product constant K_{sp} and gives the approximate relationship between solute concentration and the solubility of the salt. For example, saturated solutions of AgCl, $BaSO_4$, CaF_2, $Ca_3(PO_4)_2$, and $PbSO_4$ have the following conditions imposed on them by the law of chemical equilibrium:

$$[Ag^+][Cl^-] = 1.63 \times 10^{-10}$$
$$[Ba^{++}][SO_4^{--}] = 1.1 \times 10^{-10}$$
$$[Ca^{++}][F^-]^2 = 4.0 \times 10^{-11}$$
$$[Ca^{++}]^3[PO_4^{3-}]^2 = 1 \times 10^{-25}$$
$$[Pb^{++}][SO_4^{--}] = 1.93 \times 10^{-8}$$

The equations tell us that, if in a saturated aqueous solution of one of the salts the concentration of one of the ions is increased, the concentration of the other must decrease by forming more solid to maintain equilibrium. Conversely, if the concentration of one ion is decreased, there must be a compensating increase in the other ionic concentration by the dissolution of solid. Such effects have long been qualitatively predicted from LeChâtelier's principle, but through mass-action-law concepts the effect of altering concentrations on the solubility of a salt can be predicted quantitatively. To begin with, the criterion for precipitation to occur is that the product of the ionic concentrations of the solute must exceed the solubility-product constant and form initially a supersaturated solution. This means, of course, that no precipitate of AgCl will be produced when NaCl is added to a solution of silver ions until the concentration product of the silver and chloride ions exceeds 1.63×10^{-10}. Thereafter, further additions of NaCl will reduce the silver-ion concentration by precipitation of AgCl so as to maintain a constant ionic product. Stated in terms of solubility, this means that a maximum of $(1.63 \times 10^{-10})^{1/2}$ mole of AgCl will dissolve in 1 liter of distilled water at 25° but only 1.63×10^{-7} mole will dissolve in 0.001 M sodium chloride solution since

$$[Ag^+][Cl^-] = 1.63 \times 10^{-10}$$
$$[Ag^+] = \frac{1.63 \times 10^{-10}}{0.001} = 1.63 \times 10^{-7}$$
$$= \text{molar solubility of AgCl in 0.001 } M \text{ NaCl solution}$$

This is in rather good agreement with the observed solubility of 4.7×10^{-7} mole per liter in 0.001 M sodium chloride. Similarly, the actual solubility of lead sulfate in 5.1×10^{-4} M sulfuric acid is 4.3×10^{-4} mole per liter compared with 3.8×10^{-4} mole per liter calculated from the solubility-product constant. It is really surprising how well the solubility-product principle predicts the solubility of salts as a function of solute concentrations because the K_{sp} is not a true thermodynamic constant.

TABLE 14.3. SOLUBILITY OF AgCl IN AQUEOUS SOLUTIONS OF NaCl AT 25°*

Concentration of NaCl, moles per liter	Solubility of AgCl, moles per liter	Calculated solubility of AgCl from K_{sp}, moles per liter
0.00	1.278×10^{-5}	1.278×10^{-5}
1.0×10^{-4}	0.277×10^{-5}	0.163×10^{-5}
1.0×10^{-3}	0.047×10^{-5}	0.0163×10^{-5}
1.0×10^{-2}	0.047×10^{-5}	0.00163×10^{-5}
1.0×10^{-1}	0.292×10^{-5}	
5.0×10^{-1}	2.41×10^{-5}	3.26×10^{-10}
10.0×10^{-1}	8.45×10^{-5}	

* From A. Pinkus and A. M. Timmermans, *Bull. soc. chim. Belges,* **46,** 46 (1937).

The solubility-product principle predicts a decreasing solubility for a salt as the concentration of a common ion increases. An anomaly is observed, however, for as the concentration of the common ion increases, a concentration is soon reached where the solubility of the salt increases also. See the effect of increasing common ion concentrations on the solubility of silver chloride[22] and lead sulfate in Tables 14.3 and 14.4. This reversal of the "common ion" effect is anticipated from the theory if the true activity-product constant is used rather than the solubility-product constant. The activity-product constant for the equilibrium of the solid binary electrolyte A_xB_n and its ions is

$$a_A{}^x a_B{}^n = K_{ap}$$

Expressed in terms of solute concentrations and activity coefficients, the equation becomes

$$[A]^x f_A{}^x [B]^n f_B{}^n = K_{ap}$$

Ordinarily the activity of a dissolved solute is less than unity because of interionic attractions and various types of dipole interactions. Therefore, as the concentration of the solute ion increases, there is a greater deviation from ideality and the activity coefficients decrease in value. In order for the system to maintain the activity-product constant, there must be an accompanying increase in the concentration (solubility) of the

TABLE 14.4. SOLUBILITY OF PbSO₄ IN AQUEOUS SOLUTIONS OF
SULFURIC ACID AT 20°

Concentration of H_2SO_4, moles per liter	Solubility of $PbSO_4$, moles per liter	Calculated solubility of $PbSO_4$, from K_{sp}, moles per liter
0.00	1.39×10^{-4}	1.39×10^{-4}
5.1×10^{-4}	0.429×10^{-4}	0.378×10^{-4}
10.2×10^{-4}	0.330×10^{-4}	0.189×10^{-4}
25.8×10^{-4}	0.231×10^{-4}	0.075×10^{-4}
51×10^{-4}	0.181×10^{-4}	
102×10^{-4}	0.132×10^{-4}	
258×10^{-4}	0.132×10^{-4}	
510×10^{-4}	0.148×10^{-4}	
10.2×10^{-1}	0.330×10^{-4}	1.89×10^{-8}

solute. But before one can quantitatively predict the effect of increased solubility with increased common ion concentration, the variation of the activity coefficient with concentration must be established. To facilitate this, Lewis and Randall introduced the concept of the ionic strength μ, which is a measure of the intensity of the electric field produced by ions in solution. Ionic strength is defined by the equation

$$\mu = \tfrac{1}{2}\Sigma c_i z_i{}^2 \tag{14.16}$$

where c_i is the actual concentration of each ionic species and z is its valence. In solutions of uni-univalent strong electrolytes the ionic strength is equal to the molar concentration of the electrolyte. In solutions of unibivalent strong electrolytes the ionic strength is equal to three times the molar concentration of the electrolyte.

Numerous observations verify that in dilute solutions the activity coefficient of a given electrolyte is approximately the same in all solutions of the same ionic strength. Therefore, the solubility of slightly soluble electrolytes should be enhanced by the presence of any added electrolyte and not by just the common ion.   Table 14.5 is typical of such data.[23]

TABLE 14.5. SOLUBILITY OF BARIUM SULFATE IN DILUTE AQUEOUS SOLUTIONS
OF SALTS AT 25°C*

Salt	Molarity of salt	$\mu^{1/2}$ Ionic strength of aqueous salt solution	Molar solubility BaSO$_4$
None	....	0.0000	0.957×10^{-5}
KCl	0.000020	0.00814	1.002×10^{-5}
	0.002526	0.05082	1.274×10^{-5}
	0.03501	0.1874	2.320×10^{-5}
MgCl$_2$	0.00001002	0.00874	1.002×10^{-5}
	0.002113	0.08003	1.547×10^{-5}
	0.01064	0.1790	2.340×10^{-5}
LaCl$_3$	0.0000067	0.00930	1.007×10^{-5}
	0.0001550	0.03137	1.194×10^{-5}
	0.002400	0.1204	2.014×10^{-5}
	0.004296	0.1609	2.394×10^{-5}

* From E. W. Neuman, *J. Am. Chem. Soc.*, **55**, 879 (1933).

The anomalous behavior or change in activity coefficients of ions in solution is related to the ionic strength of the solution by the limiting equation of the Debye-Hückel theory, which is

$$- \log f = K z^2 \mu^{1/2} \tag{14.17}$$

where
$$K = \left[\frac{2\pi N \epsilon^6}{1000(DkT)^3} \right]^{1/2}$$

and
N = Avogadro's number

ϵ = charge on the electron

D = dielectric constant of medium

k = Boltzmann constant

T = absolute temperature

For aqueous solutions at 25°C, K is approximately equal to 0.5.

The significance of Eqs. (14.16) and (14.17) can readily be shown by the simple calculation of the solubility of AgCl in 0.01 M Ba(NO$_3$)$_2$ solution.   First we must determine the activity-product constant for AgCl. From Table 14.3 we see that the experimentally determined molar solubility of silver chloride in water is 1.278×10^{-5}.   Therefore,

$$K_{sp} = [Ag^+][Cl^-] = (1.278 \times 10^{-5})^2 = 1.633 \times 10^{-10}$$

and the true thermodynamic constant

$$K_{ap} = [Ag^+][Cl^-]f_{Ag^+}f_{Cl^-}$$

The ionic strength μ is equal to the salt concentration.

$$
\begin{aligned}
- \log f_{Ag^+} = - \log f_{Cl^-} &= 0.5z^2\mu^{1/2} \\
&= 0.5 \times 1^2 \times (1.278 \times 10^{-5})^{1/2}
\end{aligned}
$$

and
$$f_{Ag^+} = f_{Cl^-} = 0.996$$

Therefore
$$
\begin{aligned}
K_{ap} &= 1.633 \times 10^{-10} \times (0.996)^2 \\
&= 1.62 \times 10^{-10}
\end{aligned}
$$

Now to calculate the solubility of silver chloride in 0.01 M $Ba(NO_3)_2$. The ionic strength of the solution is

$$
\begin{aligned}
\mu &= \tfrac{1}{2}\{[Ag^+] \times 1^2 + [Cl^-] \times 1^2 + [Ba^{++}] \times 2^2 + [NO_3^-] \times 1^2\} \\
&= \tfrac{1}{2}[(1.278 \times 10^{-5} \times 1^2) + (1.278 \times 10^{-5} \times 1^2) \\
&\qquad\qquad\qquad\qquad + (0.01 \times 2^2) + (0.02 \times 1^2)] \\
&\cong 0.03
\end{aligned}
$$

if the small contribution made by the silver and chloride ion is considered negligible. Thus

$$- \log f_{Ag^+} = - \log f_{Cl^-} = 0.5 \times 1^2 \times (0.03)^{1/2}$$

and
$$f_{Ag^+} = f_{Cl^-} = 10^{-0.086} = 0.82$$

Since
$$[Ag^+] = [Cl^-]$$

$$
\begin{aligned}
K_{ap} &= [Ag^+][Cl^-]f_{Ag^+}f_{Cl^-} \\
&= [Ag^+]^2(0.82)^2 = 1.62 \times 10^{-10}
\end{aligned}
$$

and
$$
\begin{aligned}
[Ag^+] &= 1.54 \times 10^{-5} \\
&= \text{molar solubility of AgCl in 0.01 } M \text{ } Ba(NO_3)_2
\end{aligned}
$$

The calculated value compares most favorably with the experimentally determined solubility of 1.54×10^{-5} mole per liter. On the other hand, the solubility-product principle predicts a solubility of 1.28×10^{-5} mole per liter, which differs from the experimental value by 20 per cent.

Although the effects of added salts and interionic attractions are great enough to alter solubilities appreciably, the foregoing treatment is not intended to belittle the effectiveness of applied solubility-product principles for calculating solute solubilities. A large percentage error in calculations often can be tolerated because the actual solubility error in an analysis is usually small compared with other errors. Furthermore, true equilibrium solubilities are rarely attained in analyses because the equilibration of sparingly soluble salts with their solutions takes place

slowly.   A source of solubility error of much greater magnitude than that
due to the diverse ion effect is the interaction of solute particles with other
ions or molecules in solution to form complexes and/or undissociated
molecular species.

14.8. The Effect of Complex Ion Formation on Solute Solubility.   The
influence of complexation on solute solubility is variable but there is in
general an enhancement of the solubility of sparingly soluble salts.   As
a consequence, the phenomenon is responsible for large solubility losses
when it occurs unexpectedly and is put to excellent use in separation
techniques when predicted.   Some knowledge of complexation is obviously necessary if one is to anticipate its occurrence and utilize or cope
with it intelligently.

Attention is directed to the complexes of metal ions because these
species form systems that are familiar and analytically most profitable.
The more common complexing agents (ligands) are fluoride, chloride,
bromide, iodide, thiocyanate, cyanide, phosphate, oxalate, tartrate,
citrate, thiosulfate, ammonia, amines, and water.   All these reagents are
similar in so far as they are electron donors (Lewis bases) capable of
establishing a coordinate covalent link with an acceptor (Lewis acid) such
as a metal ion.   All the common metals, with the exception of rubidium
and cesium, form complexes.   Typical examples of such complexes are:

$$Ag(CN)_2^-$$
$$Cd(CN)_4^{--}$$
$$AgS_2O_3^-$$
$$FeF_6^{3-}$$
$$Co(CNS)_6^{3-}$$
$$Mg(C_2O_4)_2^{--}$$
$$Cu(H_2O)_4^{++}$$
$$Cu(NH_3)_4^{++}$$
$$Ag(NH_3)_2^+$$

$$AuCl_4^-$$
$$PtCl_6^{--}$$
$$Fe(PO_4)_2^{3-}$$
$$HgI_4^{--}$$
$$AgCl_2^-$$
$$CdI_4^{--}$$
$$Al(C_4H_4O_6)_3^{3-}$$
$$SiF_6^{--}$$
$$Ca(C_{10}H_{12}N_2O_8)^{--}$$ calcium
ethylenediamine tetra-
acetate complex

The number of coordinating groups about the central metal atom is
determined by the coordination number of the metal and by steric factors.
Complexes of this type are weak electrolytes that dissociate and establish
equilibria with their dissociation products.

The cations most likely to form a covalent bond are those with a high
charge and small radius and should not have an inert gas structure.
Thus, Co^{++} and Fe^{3+} and other transition metals are more likely to form
complexes than Ca^{++} and Mg^{++}, and Mg^{++} forms stronger complexes

than Ca^{++}. The alkali-metal ions form only a few relatively weak complexes.

Theoretically, all anions are complexing agents because they are potential electron-pair donors. But unlike the cations, greater complexing ability resides with those anions which are unsymmetrical with a high charge, large radius, and highly electronegative center. The readily polarizable iodide, cyanide, thiocyanate, and carboxyl ions are excellent complexing agents, whereas the symmetrical perchlorate and sulfate radicals, as well as the nitrate and acetate radicals, form few stable complexes. Beyond these generalizations it is difficult to compare relative complexing strength of donors except when the central metal atom is held the same, for when the metal ion is changed, an entirely new order of complexing strength may evolve for the donors.

A fine example of what can happen when complexation is overlooked as a solubilizing factor is encountered in the pedagogically overworked silver chloride system. It is almost universally inferred that the common ion effect will reduce the solubility of silver chloride to a ridiculously low and predictable value if the chloride-ion concentration is increased to as much as $0.1\ M$, whereas, in fact, the predicted solubility of silver chloride in aqueous sodium chloride solutions is grossly in error. Compare the usual calculated values with experimental values in Table 14.3. Corrections of calculations for nonideality do not compensate for the difference. The discrepancy between theoretical and experimental values at the higher concentrations can be readily accounted for, however, by the formation of the complex $AgCl_2^-$. Stop to consider then what might be the effect of complexation in less well-known systems involving stronger complexing agents than chloride ion. When solubility anomalies are encountered, investigate the probability of complex formation; complexation is more common than generally believed. The existence of at least 25 different metal-ion–chloride-anionic complexes has been demonstrated.

Although the effect of complexation of solute solubility has been frequently ignored, it is not always unpredictable. With only a meager quantity of data, the alteration of solute solubility by complexation can be treated quantitatively. The complexes are weak electrolytes that partially dissociate and form equilibrium mixtures. If the dissociation (instability) constants and some solute concentrations are known, the alteration in solute solubility by complexation can be predicted. Consider, for example, the dissolution of silver cyanide with excess cyanide. The reaction can be represented either as

$$AgCN\ (s) + CN^- \rightleftharpoons Ag(CN)_2^-$$

or as

$$Ag[Ag(CN)_2]\ (s) + 2CN^- \rightleftharpoons 2Ag(CN)_2^-$$

The complex in turn is instable and dissociates.

$$Ag(CN)_2^- \rightleftharpoons Ag^+ + 2CN^-$$

The K_{sp} for AgCN is 1.2×10^{-16} and for $Ag[Ag(CN)_2]$ is 5×10^{-12}. The dissociation constant for the $Ag(CN)_2^-$ is 2×10^{-21}. After sufficient cyanide has been added to make the solution 0.01 M in cyanide, the sum is

$$[CN^-] + [Ag(CN)_2^-] = 10^{-2} \text{ mole per liter}$$

because 1 mole of complex is produced for each mole of cyanide reacted. At equilibrium, however, the mole ratio is

$$\frac{[CN^-]}{[Ag(CN)_2^-]} = 1.7 \times 10^{-5}$$

Therefore, the concentration of the $Ag(CN)_2^-$ is for all practical purposes 0.01 M and the cyanide concentration is $1.7 \times 10^{-7} M$.

The conclusion is simply this: The complex is so stable that the reaction is essentially quantitative, and 1 mole of silver cyanide dissolves for each mole of cyanide ion added. The Liebig method for the determination of cyanide is entirely dependent on the complete conversion of added silver ion (titrant) to the soluble cyano complex up to the point at which the silver-to-cyanide ratio exceeds 1:2. A precipitate of AgCN or $Ag[(Ag(CN)_2]$ appears when the reactant ratios are very near this stoichiometric ratio and serves as an indicator for the titration.

Notable examples of the use of complexation in selective separations are the following: Silver chloride is selectively dissolved from photographic emulsions with sodium thiosulfate to form the stable $AgS_2O_3^-$. In gravimetry calcium is precipitated quantitatively as CaC_2O_4 in the presence of magnesium, which forms the soluble $Mg(C_2O_4)_2^{--}$ under the same conditions. Thus, by forming a complex ion, one ion can be kept in solution while another is precipitated. Zinc and cadmium can be successfully precipitated as the sulfides in the presence of copper if the sample is first treated with cyanide solution. The copper is stabilized in solution as the cyano complex. The gravimetric determination of iron and aluminum is low if conducted in the presence of fluoride because of the formation of AlF_6^{3-}. Silver can be isolated from mixtures of AgCl, $PbCl_2$, and $HgCl_2$ with ammonia water because of the formation of the soluble $Ag(NH_3)_2^+$. Tartrate ion is added to alkaline Fehling's solution to prevent the precipitation of the hydrous oxide of cupric ion. Ethylenediaminetetraacetic acid will keep all the divalent and trivalent metal ions in solutions at pH values above which their hydrous oxides normally precipitate because of the formation of complexes such as CaY^{--} and $AlY(OH)^{--}$, where Y represents the ethylenediaminetetraacetate ligand. A more refined example of complexation in precipitation phenomena is the use of nitrilotriacetic acid, $N(CH_2COOH)_3$, for the selective precipitation of the rare-earth oxalates.[24] The stability of the rare-earth complexes with nitrilotriacetic acid increases with the atomic weight of the metal. Consequently, in the presence of oxalate ion, as the pH is lowered, successive complexes are destroyed and the metals precipitate in the order from lanthanum to lutetium. In such instances it is impossible to isolate the solubilizing factor and call it explicitly complexation. Hydrogen-ion concentration plays such a dominant role in the stability of chemical species in aqueous solution that it should be considered as a separate factor.

14.9. The Effect of pH on Solute Solubility.   Probably the single greatest factor to consider in studying the solubility of solutes in aqueous solutions is the pH.   The anions of all weak acids associate with protons in aqueous solutions to form the weak acid and an equilibrium mixture. Sparingly soluble salts of weak acids such as calcium oxalate, barium carbonate, and silver chromate are soluble in dilute solutions of strong acids.   In each case, the anion is removed from the salt to form the weak electrolyte in the following manner:

$$CaC_2O_4 \downarrow \rightleftharpoons Ca^{++} + \boxed{\begin{array}{l} C_2O_4^{=} \\ + \\ H^+ \rightleftharpoons HC_2O_4^- \end{array}}$$

$$Ag_2CrO_4 \downarrow \rightleftharpoons 2Ag^+ + \boxed{\begin{array}{l} CrO_4^{=} \\ + \\ H^+ \rightleftharpoons HCrO_4^- \end{array}}$$

The criterion for the dissolution of the sparingly soluble salt is that the equilibrium concentration of the anion of the weak acid is less than the equilibrium concentration of the anion of the salt.   Under such conditions the formation of the weak acid is favored and the salt must dissolve to supply the necessary anionic component.   Even the very refractory $BaSO_4$ becomes more soluble in acid medium than in pure water because of the association of hydrogen and sulfate ions to form bisulfate.   The increased solubility is the result of HSO_4^- being a weak acid with an ionization constant of 1.0×10^{-2}.   Obviously, the solubility of certain salts can be varied over a wide range simply by regulating the anion concentration with controlled pH.   This can be well illustrated by following the variation in the solubility of $MgNH_4PO_4$ with pH.   The appropriate equilibrium expressions are:

$$[Mg^{++}][NH_4^+][PO_4{}^{3-}] = 2.5 \times 10^{-13}$$

$$\frac{[H^+][H_2PO_4^-]}{[H_3PO_4]} = K_1 = 7.5 \times 10^{-3}$$

$$\frac{[H^+][HPO_4{}^{--}]}{[H_2PO_4^-]} = K_2 = 6.2 \times 10^{-8}$$

$$\frac{[H^+][PO_4{}^{3-}]}{[HPO_4{}^{--}]} = K_3 = 1 \times 10^{-12}$$

For a solution with a total phosphate concentration of 0.1 M,

$$[H_3PO_4] + [H_2PO_4^-] + [HPO_4{}^{--}] + [PO_4{}^{3-}] = 0.1$$

and the concentration ratios of the various phosphate species can be evaluated in terms of the hydrogen-ion concentration. For a pH of 2,

$$\frac{[H_3PO_4]}{[H_2PO_4^-]} = \frac{[H^+]}{K_1} = \frac{10^{-2}}{7.5 \times 10^{-3}} = 1.3$$

$$\frac{[HPO_4{}^{--}]}{[H_2PO_4^-]} = \frac{K_2}{[H^+]} = \frac{6.2 \times 10^{-8}}{10^{-2}} = 6.2 \times 10^{-6}$$

$$\frac{[PO_4{}^{3-}]}{[H_2PO_4^-]} = \frac{K_2K_3}{[H^+]^2} = \frac{6.2 \times 10^{-8} \times 10^{-12}}{10^{-4}} = 6.2 \times 10^{-16}$$

$$[PO_4{}^{3-}]:[HPO_4{}^{--}]:[H_2PO_4^-]:[H_3PO_4] = 6.2 \times 10^{-16}:6.2 \times 10^{-6}:1:1.3$$

The concentration ratios of the various phosphate species at different pH values are given in Fig. 14.3a. Note that certain species are dominant over limited pH ranges. Figure 14.3b depicts the variation of the solubility of $MgNH_4PO_4$ (namely, the Mg^{++} concentration) with pH. The solubility of magnesium ammonium phosphate is much greater in acid medium than in alkaline medium. In practice, the salt is precipitated from a buffered solution with a final pH in the range 9 to 10. Although the monohydrogen phosphate ion is the dominant phosphate species at this pH, the concentration of the phosphate ion is sufficiently high to cause a quantitative removal of the magnesium ammonium phosphate. Higher pH values are avoided because of the reduction in ammonium-ion concentration, the possible formation of magnesium hydroxide, and the normal complications of analysis in strongly alkaline media.

A classic example of selective precipitation by controlled pH is the separation of the metal sulfides into acid-insoluble and acid-soluble groups. The precipitant, sulfide ion, concentration is supplied by hydrogen sulfide and is readily controlled by controlling the pH. The various equilibria which govern the sulfide-ion concentration are

$$H_2S \rightleftharpoons H^+ + HS^-$$
$$HS^- \rightleftharpoons H^+ + S^{--}$$

and the respective dissociation constants are

$$\frac{[H^+][HS^-]}{[H_2S]} = K_1 = 5.7 \times 10^{-8}$$

$$\frac{[H^+][S^{--}]}{[HS^-]} = K_2 = 1.2 \times 10^{-13}$$

If the hydrogen-ion concentration is determined by the presence of a strong acid in the system, a simpler expression relating reagent (H_2S), precipitant (S^{--}), and hydrogen-ion concentrations is valid; namely,

$$\frac{[H^+]^2[S^{--}]}{[H_2S]} = K_1K_2 = 6.8 \times 10^{-21}$$

Now visualize a 1 N strong acid solution saturated (0.1 M) with hydrogen sulfide gas at atmospheric pressure. Any divalent metal ion present that can form an insoluble sulfide is a potential precipitate provided its

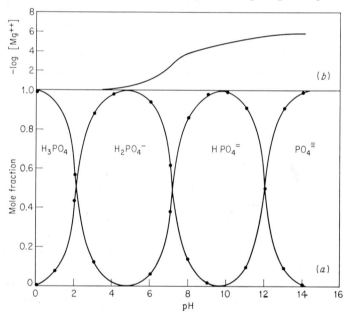

FIG. 14.3. (a) Variation of mole fraction of phosphate species with pH. (b) Variation of solubility of magnesium ammonium phosphate with pH.

solubility product is exceeded. If, for simplicity, one assumes an arbitrary value of 10^{-3} M for each metal-ion concentration, it is possible to calculate which salts will precipitate and which will not.

$$[M^{++}][S^{--}] \text{ must be} > K_{sp}$$

if MS is to precipitate.

The solubility-product-constant value which must be exceeded to produce a precipitate can be calculated in the following manner:

$$[H_2S] = 0.1\ M$$
$$[H^+] = 1\ M$$
$$[M^{++}] = 10^{-3}\ M$$
$$[S^{--}] = \frac{K_1K_2[H_2S]}{[H^+]^2} = \frac{6.8 \times 10^{-21} \times 0.1}{1^2} = 6.8 \times 10^{-22}$$

Now, by substituting the sulfide- and metal-ion concentrations into the solubility-product expression, we see that the arbitrary limit for determining solute solubility under these conditions is a

$$K_{sp} = 1 \times 10^{-3} \times 6.8 \times 10^{-22} = 6.8 \times 10^{-25}$$

MS compounds with a $K_{sp} > 6.8 \times 10^{-25}$ will be soluble; those divalent metal sulfides with a $K_{sp} < 6.8 \times 10^{-25}$ will be insoluble under the prescribed conditions. Just how well this describes the actual precipitation can be seen by comparing the solubility-product-constant values for the conventionally recognized acid-soluble and acid-insoluble sulfides in Table 14.6. Naturally, there is considerable dependence of solute

TABLE 14.6. COMPARISON OF K_{sp} VALUES FOR ACID-SOLUBLE AND -INSOLUBLE SULFIDES

Acid-soluble sulfides		Acid-insoluble sulfides	
FeS	3.7×10^{-19}	CuS	8.5×10^{-45}
CoS	1×10^{-27}	PbS	1×10^{-29}
NiS	1.4×10^{-24}	CdS	4×10^{-29}
MnS	1.4×10^{-15}	HgS	4×10^{-53}
ZnS	1.2×10^{-23}		

solubility on acid- and metal-ion concentrations. Therefore, the above calculations are intended merely to show how pH can be used in selective precipitations. In alkaline sulfide solutions the sulfide-ion concentration approaches a maximum, and many more metal sulfides form in alkaline solutions than in acid solutions. More refined separations can now be considered in subsequent sections.

14.10. Precipitation from a Homogeneous Medium. A precipitation is generally effected by the addition of a suitable reagent to a solution of the substance to be precipitated. Even though the precipitant is dilute and is added very slowly with mixing, there is always a localized excess of the reagent where the two solutions mix. This localized concentration of reagent is conducive to the rapid formation of a large number of small crystals and a large precipitate surface area. Because of their rapid formation, the crystals are imperfect and tend to adsorb and occlude impurities from solution. The precipitates are voluminous and sometimes difficult to filter. The localized excess of precipitant also can cause the precipitation of substances more soluble than the expected precipitate.

Once formed, even under conditions where they should dissolve once the solution is thoroughly mixed, these spurious precipitates may be entrained by the desired precipitate and rendered insoluble. These sources of error can be avoided to a great extent, however, if the solution is homogeneous at all stages of the precipitation process. Such a condition can be achieved by the slow internal generation of the precipitant from a solute dissolved in the sample solution.

A prime example of what precipitation from a homogeneous medium can do to improve precipitate characteristics is the precipitation of the metal hydrous oxides by homogeneously raising the pH of the solution. The precipitates are still gelatinous but much denser and easier to filter than those obtained by conventional means. Coprecipitation is reduced to a minimum and under some circumstances is almost eliminated. Fractional precipitations can be achieved where formerly they were difficult or impossible.

The most useful reaction for homogeneously raising the pH of a solution is the hydrolysis of urea:

$$H_2N-\overset{\overset{\textstyle O}{\|}}{C}-NH_2 + H_2O \rightleftharpoons CO_2 + 2NH_3$$

The rate of hydrolysis is almost independent of solution pH but varies appreciably with temperature.[25] The reaction is slow at room temperature, but at 100° ammonia is liberated rapidly enough to be of practical use in neutralization processes. The rate of change of pH can be controlled by varying the quantity of urea and/or the temperature. Urea is water soluble, nonreactive to most common metal ions, and negligibly basic itself. Ordinarily the sample solution is made sufficiently acidic just to prevent the precipitation of the desired component, then 10 to 15 g of urea is added for each 250 to 500 ml of sample solution, and the solution is boiled until the precipitation is complete, usually in 1 to 2 hr. The hydrolysis can be terminated at any desired pH by cooling the reaction mixture.

Another reagent recommended for the homogeneous generation of hydroxyl ions is hexamethylenetetramine. It is an exceedingly weak base whose aqueous solutions are neutral to litmus. In acid medium it hydrolyzes to formaldehyde and ammonia.

$$(CH_2)_6N_4 + 6H_2O \rightleftharpoons 4NH_3 + 6CH_2O$$

Usually enough hydrogen ions are produced by the hydrolysis of salts already in solution for hydrolysis of the hexamine to proceed. The formaldehyde generated does not interfere with the precipitation of metal hydrous oxides.

Thiosulfate serves the same purpose as urea or hexamine because it consumes hydrogen ions in the following manner:

$$S_2O_3^{--} + 2H^+ \rightleftharpoons H_2S_2O_3 \rightleftharpoons S^0 + H_2O + SO_2$$

The sulfur dioxide escapes from the hot solution, but colloidal sulfur contaminates the precipitate.

Moser and Singer[26] utilized the hydrolysis of ammonium nitrite for controlling pH, and Stock[27] proposed the use of mixtures of iodide and iodate because of the consumption of hydrogen ions:

$$5I^- + IO_3^- + 6H^+ \rightleftharpoons 3I_2 + 3H_2O$$

Some difficulty is encountered because of the generation of the strong oxidizing agent iodine.

Acetamide hydrolyzes readily to form ammonium acetate:

$$CH_3\overset{\overset{\displaystyle O}{\|}}{C}-NH_2 + H_2O \rightleftharpoons NH_4^+ + CH_3COO^-$$

and thereby raises the pH within limits.

Trichloroacetate salts release carbonates in hydrolysis and are used to raise the pH of a solution slowly and homogeneously.

$$Cl_3CCOO^- + H_2O \rightleftharpoons CHCl_3 + HCO_3^-$$

Willard and Tang[28] were the first to show that more than just a homogeneous change in pH is required if the hydrous oxides are to be dense, easily filtered, and relatively free of coprecipitation. They proved that a particular anion was required for the formation of a dense precipitate, presumably because of the formation of a basic salt. If the required ion is furnished by an organic acid such as formic, benzoic, or succinic, there are the added advantages of the buffering action and the ease of removal of the organic anion by ignition. The basic salts also precipitate at lower pH values than the normal hydroxides and thereby improve the separation from interfering ions.

It is most important, though, that the proper anion be included in the precipitation of the basic salts or hydrous oxides homogeneously if optimum results are expected. Aluminum precipitated in the presence of formate ion gives a dense precipitate, whereas in the presence of acetate ion the product is flocculent. Formate is preferred for the precipitation of iron and thorium, succinate for aluminum, and sulfate for titanium and stannic tin. Tin(IV) precipitates as an extremely compact basic sulfate. It might be worth mentioning that, although an organic anion is present during precipitation, it does not necessarily enter the reaction to form a basic salt.   An isolated instance of this is shown in Fig. 14.4, curve *D*, where the horizontal portion of the pyrolysis curve of alumina between 94 and 221° affirms the absence of succinate.   Duval states that the loss in weight above 221° is attributable to the loss of 12 moles of water per mole of alumina.

The precipitation of basic salts with urea is characterized by the adherence of thin films of the precipitate to glass surfaces.   The few milligrams of precipitate involved can usually be dissolved with hydrochloric acid, but the basic stannic sulfate can be removed only with hydrofluoric acid or some other rigorous treatment.   This phenomenon led Willard to hope that some day it will be possible to make all the precipitate adhere to the beaker. Then it will be necessary only to dry and weigh the beaker after discarding the solution.[25]

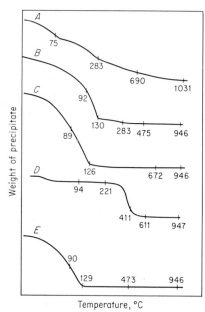

FIG. 14.4. Pyrolysis curves of aluminum hydroxide precipitated by: (*a*) aqueous ammonia; (*b*) gaseous ammonia; (*c*) urea; (*d*) urea-succinic acid; (*e*) hexamine. (*After C. Duval, "Inorganic Thermogravimetric Analysis," p. 106, Elsevier Publishing Company, Amsterdam, 1953.*)

In addition to the basic salts, many other common precipitates are formed by neutralizing an acidic medium.   The technique has been effective for the precipitation of calcium oxalate, nickel dimethylglyoxime, and magnesium ammonium phosphate.

The advantages of precipitation from homogeneous media are not limited to neutralization processes, however.   Numerous precipitants, other than the hydroxyl ion, can be generated internally at controlled rates.   The most common procedure liberates the precipitant by the hydrolysis of esters.

Sulfate ion is generated by the hydrolysis of methyl or ethyl sulfate or sulfamic acid:

$$(CH_3O)_2SO_2 + 2H_2O \rightleftharpoons 2CH_3OH + H_2SO_4$$
$$NH_2SO_3H + H_2O \rightleftharpoons NH_4^+ + SO_4^{--} + H^+$$

Elving and Van Atta[29] quantitatively precipitated barium, strontium, and calcium as readily filterable sulfates by supplying sulfate ions by the hydrolysis of dimethyl sulfate.

Willard and Freund[30] separated zirconium and hafnium by the fractional precipitation of their phosphates. Phosphate was generated by the hydrolysis of triethyl phosphate:

$$(C_2H_5O)_3PO + 3H_2O \rightleftharpoons 3C_2H_5OH + H_3PO_4$$

Phosphate can also be generated by hydrolysis of metaphosphoric acid in hot acidic solutions or by homogeneously raising the pH of an acid phosphate solution by the hydrolysis of urea.

Oxalate can be generated by the hydrolysis of dimethyl or diethyl oxalate or by raising the pH of an acid oxalate solution by the hydrolysis of urea.

Chloride can be liberated from chlorohydrin by hydrolysis:

$$\begin{array}{ccc} \text{Cl} & \text{OH} & \text{OH} \\ | & | & | \\ \text{CH}_2\!-\!\text{CH}\!-\!\text{CH}_2 \end{array} + H_2O \rightleftharpoons HCl + \begin{array}{ccc} \text{OH} & \text{OH} & \text{OH} \\ | & | & | \\ \text{CH}_2\!-\!\text{CH}\!-\!\text{CH}_2 \end{array}$$

Hoffman and Brandt[31] obtained large, pure crystals of lead chromate by slowly oxidizing chromium(III) to chromate with bromate in buffered acetate solution.   The reactions can be represented by

$$2Cr^{3+} + BrO_3^- + 5H_2O \rightleftharpoons CrO_4^{--} + Br^- + 10H^+$$
$$5Br^- + BrO_3^- + 6H^+ \rightleftharpoons Br_2 + 3H_2O$$

Quill and Salutsky[32] dissolved a mixture of lanthanum, neodymium, and samarium oxides in trichloroacetic acid and precipitated the normal carbonates by the slow hydrolysis of the trichloroacetate.   The great advantage of this method is the preparation of rare-earth carbonates free of alkali-metal contamination.

Gordon and coworkers[33] obtained crystals of AgCl up to 0.2 mm in diameter by slowly releasing the silver ion from the silver-ammonia complex in the presence of chloride and hydroxyethyl acetate.

Note that each ester hydrolysis can be used as a homogeneous source of hydrogen ions. Because of this, most precipitants generated by ester hydrolysis must be released in buffered solution to control the acidity.

The production of sulfide ions has probably received the greatest attention of all the homogeneously produced precipitants, but of all the compounds studied, only thioacetamide has been generally accepted as a source of sulfide ions.   Hydrogen sulfide is one of the hydrolysis products of thioacetamide.

$$CH_3CSNH_2 + 2H_2O \rightleftharpoons CH_3COO^- + H_2S + NH_4^+$$

There are many advantages obtained by using thioacetamide.   The rate of precipitation can be controlled by controlling the rate of hydrolysis of thioacetamide through temperature, pH, or reagent concentration.

There are the usual advantages associated with precipitation from a homogeneous medium, and there is no necessity for handling hydrogen sulfide. Neutral aqueous solutions of thioacetamide are stable for

several months, and if a slight turbidity develops, they need only be filtered before use. The reagent has been widely substituted for gaseous H_2S in qualitative analysis, but one must be careful in selecting the procedure. Thioacetamide cannot be substituted for hydrogen sulfide, however, without some modification of procedure. Butler, Peters, and Swift[34] showed a predominant hydrolysis of the thio group in acid solutions and of the amide group in alkaline solutions. Consequently, thioacetamide can be substituted for hydrogen sulfide as a source of sulfide ions in acid solutions, but not in alkaline solutions when different reaction conditions are established.

FIG. 14.5. Comparative volumes of identical quantities of thorium precipitated as the iodate: (1) from homogeneous solution; (2) by the direct addition of iodate ion. [*After C. R. Stine and L. Gordon, Anal. Chem.*, **25**, 1519 (1953).]

Only limited quantitative procedures using thioacetamide are available because precipitates are contaminated by sulfur just as they frequently are when hydrogen sulfide is used. Flaschka[35] summarizes the recommended procedures for the precipitation of the sulfides of antimony, bismuth, copper, lead, tin, mercury, arsenic, and cadmium with thioacetamide. The precipitates in general are coarsely crystalline, dense, easily filterable, and less contaminated than those obtained by regular H_2S precipitations.

Numerous workers have employed this internal method of generating the precipitant, but the main credit for developing the technique must go to Willard and Gordon and their coworkers. The early reviews of Willard[36] and Gordon[25] are still useful, but their monograph with Salutsky[37] on precipitation from homogeneous media supersedes the other work.

A visual comparison (Fig. 14.5) of the precipitates formed by conventional processes and by precipitation from a homogeneous medium indicates the superiority of the homogeneous method for producing a denser precipitate. The work by Duval (Fig. 14.4) indicates in another way the desirability of precipitating solutes from homogeneous solutions. The hydrous oxide of aluminum obtained from a homogeneous medium can be ignited to constant weight at temperatures at least 500° lower than that required by conventional procedures. The effect that precipitation from a homogeneous medium has on the degree of coprecipitation taking place is discussed in Chap. 15.

14.11. Fractional Precipitation. Two or more substances can be separated by fractional precipitation provided they react with the same precipitant to form insoluble salts with markedly different values for the respective solubility products. The number of practical applications of this technique is limited but certainly worthy of mention. Iodide and chloride can be resolved by precipitation of the silver halides. Silver iodide ($K_{sp} = 1.7 \times 10^{-16}$) is much less soluble than silver chloride ($K_{sp} = 1.2 \times 10^{-10}$) and will precipitate first if the silver ion is added to a mixture of the soluble halides. At the instant chloride begins to precipitate, silver ions will be in equilibrium with both insoluble salts and

$$\frac{[I^-]}{[Cl^-]} = \frac{K_{sp} \text{ for AgI}}{K_{sp} \text{ for AgCl}} = \frac{1.7 \times 10^{-16}}{1.2 \times 10^{-10}} = 1.4 \times 10^{-6}$$

The iodide-ion concentration will be reduced to approximately 10^{-6} times the chloride-ion concentration. The separation is feasible if the addition of precipitant can be stopped at the stoichiometric point for the first reaction. A potentiometric titration with silver ion to the proper electrode potential will accomplish the separation, but the method naturally becomes more involved.

The fractionation of the transition metals into two groups as acid-soluble and -insoluble sulfides was described in Sec. 14.9. Calculations based on the differences in solubility products indicate the possibility of resolving these metals into at least four groups if the sulfide-ion concentration is controlled carefully. Unfortunately, even the control of sulfide-ion concentration by the homogeneous generation of hydroxyl ions does not improve the fractionation procedure appreciably because of the gross contamination of the precipitates by coprecipitation.

About the best that can be done with the fractionation of the hydrous oxides of the metals is to separate the trivalent from the divalent cations. Such a separation is achieved by precipitating the trivalent cations from a buffered solution as the basic benzoate or acetate salts. The basic salts of the trivalent cations precipitate at a lower pH than the corresponding hydrous oxides, thereby enhancing the difference in solubility between the hydrous oxides of the divalent and trivalent cations. The separation is quite useful in analysis, though, because the trivalent cations are the most serious interferences in the determination of the divalent cations. Their prior removal simplifies the subsequent analysis for the divalent cations.

Uranium can be separated from a number of other metals by the fractional hydrolysis of the uranyl ion in sulfate solution.[38] Separation from ferric, ferrous, nickelous, cobaltous, manganous, zinc, calcium, and magnesium ions can be achieved by the controlled addition of sodium or calcium hydroxide solution. The precipitation of the hydrous oxide of ferric ion is complete below pH 3.5; uranium precipitates as $U_3O_8(OH)_2$ between pH 4.0 and 6.2. The remaining ions precipitate at pH values higher than 6.2. Curves of pH versus volume of titrant for various cation solutions with alkali substantiate the above. Uranium and aluminum cannot be separated by this technique because they precipitate over the same pH range. Uranium can be separated from the same ions in phosphate solution[39] by its hydrolytic precipitation at pH 1.9 to 2.5. In each of the above cases the alkali must be added carefully with good stirring if fairly pure precipitates are desired.

When carbon dioxide and ammonium hydrogen carbonate are added at 0° to a nitrate solution of the rare earths, the carbonates are precipitated roughly in the order of increasing atomic number.[40] Clean-cut separations are not achieved, and repeated fractionations are required for purification of the metals.

It is certainly conceivable that separations by fractional precipitation can be greatly improved by generating the precipitant in a homogeneous medium. Few examples of this approach are available at this time.

14.12. Precipitate Exchange Reactions. If a difficultly soluble electrolyte AB is placed into solution with ion C which can form a more insoluble compound than AB with one of the ions of AB, reaction occurs in the following manner:

$$AB\downarrow + C \rightleftharpoons AC\downarrow + B$$

The extent of the reaction can be calculated by the law of mass action if the solubility product of both precipitates and the concentration of either B or C is known. The technique has been applied to the determination of component C for a number of systems in which the exchange or metathesis reaction is essentially quantitative. The quantity of C present can be found by determining the quantity of either AC or B that is produced. Obviously, factors that affect the solubility of either precipitate influence the determination.

Érdey and Bányai[41] used the method for the determination of chloride, sulfate, and sulfide. Chloride was determined with the use of such "exchangers" as silver chromate, oxalate, and iodate and mercurous iodate to give silver or mercurous chloride. The effect of pH on the reactions was critically examined and illustrated by the conversion quotients at various pH values. Silver and mercurous iodate are the most suitable because they give low error in strongly acid solution and increase the unknown titer sixfold. Silver chromate is the least useful and is limited to use in neutral solutions. The method is reportedly good for microestimations.

Barium iodate, oxalate, and chromate were examined as exchangers for the determination of sulfate. Barium iodate is of limited use because it permits determinations over only a narrow range of sulfate concentrations (0.004 to 0.01 M). The useful range can be extended by adding ethanol to reduce the solubility of the barium iodate. Barium oxalate and chromate are suitable only in neutral or ammoniacal solutions. The lowest sulfate concentration determinable with the oxalate and chromate is 0.06 and 0.001 M, respectively.

Sulfides were assayed by using silver and lead oxalate as exchangers. They must be used in buffered solutions but are suitable for determining concentrations of sulfide as low as 0.001 and 0.01 M, respectively.

Ballczo and Doppler[42] separated barium from calcium and strontium by an anion-exchange precipitation process. The cations are first precipitated as the oxalates, and barium is then converted into barium sulfate by an exchange reaction. This is possible because the solubility product for $BaSO_4$ is considerably smaller than the solubility product of barium oxalate. On the other hand, the strontium and calcium oxalates are left unreacted because their solubility products are appreciably smaller than the values for the corresponding sulfates. The mixed precipitate is dissolved in acid, leaving the refractory barium sulfate as an insoluble residue. Calcium and strontium can be subsequently determined by reprecipitation with carbonate and oxalate. Solubility products show that calcium is precipitated as the oxalate and strontium as the carbonate. The two elements are determined indirectly by titration of the amount of oxalate consumed by the calcium.

Precipitate exchange reactions are also possible where the product AC is more soluble than AB. Such systems are not suitable for the separation or determination of C because this component must be in excess to drive the reaction to completion. However, the reaction can be used for the metathesis of AB to AC, and the calculations of quantitativeness are very similar to the calculation mentioned above. For example, what would be the minimal concentration of sodium carbonate needed to convert 0.5 g of barium sulfate to barium carbonate in 200 ml of solution? The metathesis reaction is represented by

$$BaSO_4\downarrow + CO_3^{--} \rightleftharpoons BaCO_3\downarrow + SO_4^{--}$$

The equilibrium constant for the reaction is

$$K = \frac{[SO_4^{--}]}{[CO_3^{--}]} = \frac{K_{sp} \text{ for } BaSO_4}{K_{sp} \text{ for } BaCO_3} = 0.02$$

When the metathesis is complete, there is 0.00214 mole of SO_4^{--} in solution (0.0107 M). An equal number of moles of carbonate were consumed. The total carbonate required is that consumed plus the quantity required in solution to drive the reaction to completion. The equilibrium concentration of carbonate is

$$[CO_3^{--}] = \frac{[SO_4^{--}]}{0.02} = \frac{0.0107}{0.02} = 0.535 \ M$$

The minimal concentration of carbonate theoretically needed for the metathesis then is

$$0.535 + 0.0107 = 0.546 \ M$$

14.13. Organic Precipitants. Organic reagents have a special place in every discussion of precipitation phenomena because they are the only specific or near-specific precipitants available for inorganic ions. In a sense, the use of organic precipitants represents the pinnacle of achievement in precipitation separation processes. Of even more importance, though, is the potential that exists for the development of specific reagents for all the reactive elements. One of the most intriguing aspects of analytical chemistry is the synthesis of more sensitive and selective reagents. Practically all this interest lies in the domain of organic reagents.

In general, the precipitates obtained with organic reagents differ from the pure inorganic precipitates in that they are covalent compounds with high molecular weights. A small quantity of metal yields a large amount of precipitate. This property alone makes them a natural choice for micro- and semimicrowork. Many of the compounds are intensely colored, which makes them adaptable as spot-test reagents and useful in colorimetry. Many of them are soluble in organic solvents and can be extracted readily from an aqueous phase. Their most important characteristics, though, as far as this discussion is concerned, are their insolubility in aqueous systems and their selectivity of reaction. Organic precipitants can be conveniently classified according to the types of compounds produced, the most important of which are the chelates and the salts.

The salt-forming organic precipitants are distinct from those which form chelates inasmuch as the products are ionic and very similar to the true inorganic precipitates. Oxalic, succinic, benzoic, and phthalic acid are salt formers that produce insoluble products with many of the heavier metals. By and large these reagents are less selective than the chelate-forming precipitants and remove numerous metal ions from solution. Nevertheless, certain of these reagents are usually associated with the isolation and determination of specific elements. Calcium and magnesium can be precipitated as the oxalates, and it is becoming common practice to separate the trivalent metal ions from the divalent by the precipitation of the former as basic benzoates[43] or succinates.

Tetraphenylarsonium chloride[44]

$$[(C_6H_5)_4As]Cl$$

will quantitatively precipitate zinc, cadmium, mercury, gold, platinum, and tin as the tetraphenylarsonium salts of the appropriate complex anions, such as $PtCl_6^{--}$, $AuCl_4^-$, and $CdCl_4^{--}$. Anions such as MnO_4^-, WO_4^{--}, and ClO_4^- also precipitate. The precipitates are true salts, but occasionally the combination of large cation and anion results in the formation of a nonpolar compound that can be extracted into common organic solvents. The triphenylmethylarsonium cation, for example, forms salts with the anionic complexes of iron, antimony, cobalt, copper, and manganese, which are soluble in organic solvents.

Sodium tetraphenylboron[45]

$$Na[(C_6H_5)_4B]$$

is used for the gravimetric determination of potassium and is one of the few reagents available for this element. Ammonium, rubidium, and cesium ions interfere. A 0.6 per cent aqueous solution of sodium tetraphenylboron also forms a salt almost immediately with the cationic form of any basic amine.[46]

Benzidine

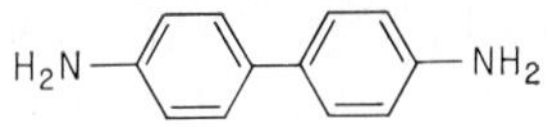

reacts with sulfate, tungstate, and a few other inorganic anions to form salts, but they are too soluble to be used for the quantitative removal of inorganic species.

Dipicrylamine[47]

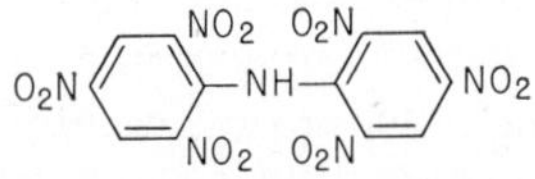

is a weak acid which is generally used as an aqueous solution of its sodium salt. It is a good reagent for the determination of potassium because of its low gravimetric factor, but it is a nonselective precipitant. The reagent precipitates most of the common metals with the exception of lithium, sodium, and the alkaline earths.

A second type of salt-forming precipitant involves a direct coordination between the metal to be precipitated and the precipitant. The ionic complex produced in turn combines with an anion or cation in solution to form the precipitate. For example, pyridine coordinates with the cupric ion to form a divalent cation

$$Cu(C_5H_5N)_2{}^{++}$$

which reacts with thiocyanate to form the insoluble

$$Cu(C_5H_5N_2)_2(CNS)_2$$

Similar insoluble products are formed between pyridine and the zinc(II), cobalt(II), nickel(II), manganese(II), and cadmium(II) ions except that 4 moles of pyridine is coordinated with the cobalt, nickel, and manganese. Other amines such as quinoline, isoquinoline, and o-phenylenediamine can be used in place of pyridine.

The remaining organic precipitants to be discussed in this section all form neutral chelate compounds with the metal ions to be precipitated. For an organic molecule to be a chelate former it must be an acid with a displaceable hydrogen atom and it must have a pair of unshared electrons available for coordination. The acid and the electron-donor group must be so situated with respect to each other that, once the reagent has coordinated with the metal, a five- or six-member ring is formed. Chelate rings with fewer than five members are strained and not easily prepared. Not only must the acidic and basic groups of the reagent be so spaced to give a strain-free five- or six-membered ring, but the metal atom must have the correct size, oxidation state, and coordination number to fit into the organic structure.

A typical chelating precipitant is 8-hydroxyquinoline or oxine

This reagent is very nonselective and precipitates almost every simple metal ion with the exception of the alkali metals. A five-member chelate ring is produced when the acidic hydrogen atom is replaced with a metal ion which has orbitals available for the acceptance of the pair of unshared electrons on the nitrogen atom. The number of molecules of oxine that coordinate with the metal is determined by the coordination number of the metal and steric factors. The divalent metal hydroxyquinolates usually contain 2 moles of water of crystallization to complete the orbital requirements of the metal atom and maintain electrical neutrality. As a result, the drying conditions are variable for the different precipitates and must be controlled. The trivalent metal oxinates contain 3 moles of the reagent and no water of hydration. Some measure of selectivity can be achieved with the reagent if the pH of the medium is controlled. It is evident that the oxinate-ion concentration and the solubility of the chelate depend on the acidity of the solution. Copper and iron require a pH of approximately 3, aluminum requires a pH greater than 4, and calcium and magnesium require a pH greater than 8 for quantitative precipitation to occur.[48] Oxine is used most frequently for the precipitation of aluminum and magnesium. Magnesium can be precipitated in the presence of calcium with little or no contamination. 2-Methyl-8-hydroxyquinoline on the other hand does not precipitate aluminum, but it does precipitate copper, ferric iron, gallium, and a few other metals.

α-Nitroso-β-naphthol

and its isomer β-nitroso-α-naphthol are used for the precipitation of cobalt. The cobalt is oxidized to the $3+$ oxidation state by the reagent and combines with it to form the cobaltic complex $Co(C_{10}H_6NO_2)_3$. The precipitate cannot be dried and weighed as such and must be ignited to Co_3O_4. Precipitation is effected from a hot 0.2 N hydrochloric acid solution. Under these same conditions iron(III), chromium(III), tungsten(VI), uranium(VI), vanadium(V), tin(IV), titanium, silver, and bismuth will precipitate and must be removed prior to the precipitation of the cobalt. Separation from nickel is complete.

α-Benzoin oxime

precipitates cupric ion, tungstate, and molybdate. Copper is precipitated from ammoniacal solution as a chelate which is very pure and easily dried. Molybdenum and tungsten precipitate from 4 N sulfuric acid and must be ignited to the oxide WO_3 or MoO_3 for weighing. Aside from columbium and tantalum, there are few interferences.

The β-diketones enolize readily:

and the acid form reacts with metal ions to form chelates in the following manner:

The products are molecular, very stable, frequently intensely colored, quantitatively insoluble in water, and soluble in the common organic solvents like alcohol, benzene, ethyl acetate, and methyl isopropyl ketone. The chelates are easily produced in most instances by reacting the sodium salt of the chelate in a neutral or slightly alkaline medium with the metal ion. Although the products are insoluble and have low chemical factors for metal content, the reagent suffers from being very nonspecific in its reactions. The alkaline-earth metals, aluminum, and the transition metals that form simple ions react under the same conditions. There appears to be little that can be done to increase the specificity of this reagent. The substitution of aliphatic, aromatic, heterocyclic, and perfluoro groups on the carbonyl carbon atom usually increases the stability and insolubility of the products but does not affect the specificity of the reagent.

Dimethylglyoxime

$$CH_3—C\!=\!NOH$$
$$CH_3—C\!=\!NOH$$

comes the closest of all to being a specific organic precipitant. Nickel is precipitated quantitatively from weakly acidic (pH 5) or ammoniacal solutions as a scarlet neutral chelate

The precipitate can be dried at 110° to a definite compound containing 20.32 per cent nickel. There are essentially no interferences in this method. Cobalt(II), iron(II), copper(II), zinc, and bismuth form soluble complexes with the reagent and thus do not interfere. Serious contamination can occur by the simultaneous precipitation of the hydrous oxides of iron and other metals at the high pH unless held in solution as soluble complexes, such as the tartrates.

Palladium(II) is quantitatively precipitated as a bright yellow dimethylglyoximate from dilute mineral acid solution with no serious interferences. The precipitate is stable and can be dried at 110° to a compound with a definite composition.

The greatest handicap encountered in the use of dimethylglyoxime is its own insolubility in water. The reagent is slightly soluble in alcohol and is generally added to aqueous solutions as an alcoholic solution. A large excess of the reagent must be avoided because dimethylglyoxime may crystallize out of solution along with the precipitate. Cyclohexanonedioxime,[49] α-furildioxime, and cycloheptanonedioxime show the same specificity for nickel and palladium as dimethylglyoxime and have the added advantage of being much more soluble in water and having a more favorable gravimetric factor.

Evidently the glyoxime grouping is the essential feature for a selective precipitant of nickel. The only limitation seems to be that the two carbon atoms cannot be part of the same aromatic ring. For example, o-benzoquinone dioxime does not precipitate nickel but numerous other dioximes do. X-ray studies show the nickel and palladium precipitate with dimethylglyoxime to be planar. For such a structure, the central metal atom must have an oxidation number of $2+$, a coordination number of 4, and a planar distribution of valence bonds. Only nickel, palladium, platinum, and copper of the common metals possess these characteristics. It is probable that the radius of the platinum and copper ions is such as not to fit into the crystalline lattice of an insoluble solid. Here then is a reagent which precipitates of all the metals only nickel and palladium and these in distinctly different pH ranges.

It would be possible to continue listing various organic precipitants, but the point has been made that herein lies the chemist's greatest hope for achieving selective or specific reagents for the metals. But specific reagents will be provided for the elements only after the chemist has discovered the proper molecular structural features to provide specificity. Excellent discussions of organic reagents are available in the works of Feigl,[50] Flagg,[51] Welcher,[52] and Martell and Calvin[53] and in the reviews of West[54] and Beamish.[55]

14.14. Selected Bibliography

Gordon, L., M. L. Salutsky, and H. H. Willard: "Precipitation from Homogeneous Solution," John Wiley & Sons, Inc., New York, 1959.

Hildebrand, J. H., and R. L. Scott: "Solubility of Nonelectrolytes," 3d ed., Reinhold Publishing Corporation, New York, 1950.

Kolthoff, I. M., and E. B. Sandell: "Textbook of Quantitative Inorganic Analysis," 3d ed., The Macmillan Company, New York, 1952.

Tipson, R. S.: Crystallization and Recrystallization, in "Technique of Organic Chemistry," vol. III, A. Weissberger (ed.), Interscience Publishers, Inc., New York, 1950.

Welcher, F.: "Organic Analytical Reagents," D. Van Nostrand Company, Princeton, N.J., 1947.

REFERENCES

1. Hildebrand, J. H., and R. L. Scott: "Solubility of Nonelectrolytes," 3d ed., Reinhold Publishing Corporation, New York, 1950.

2. McBain, M. E. L., and E. Hutchinson: "Solubilization and Related Phenomena," Academic Press, Inc., New York, 1955.
3. Schlapfer, P., and R. Flacks, *Helv. Chim. Acta*, **10**, 381 (1927).
4. Ward, H. L.: *J. Phys. Chem.*, **30**, 1316 (1926).
5. Gibson, R. E.: *J. Am. Chem. Soc.*, **56**, 4, 865 (1934).
6. "International Critical Tables of Numerical Data, Physics, Chemistry and Technology," vol. IV, p. 265, National Research Council, McGraw-Hill Book Company, Inc., New York, 1928.
7. Hulett, G. A.: *Z. physik. Chem.*, **37**, 385 (1901); **47**, 357 (1904).
8. Dundon, M. L., and E. Mack: *J. Am. Chem. Soc.*, **45**, 2479 (1923); Dundon, *J. Am. Chem. Soc.*, **45**, 2658 (1923).
9. Balarew, D.: *Z. anorg. allgem. Chem.*, **145**, 122 (1925); **151**, 68 (1926); **154**, 170 (1926); *Kolloid-Z.*, **96**, 19 (1941).
10. Cohen, E., and J. J. A. Blakkingh, Jr.: *Z. physik. Chem.*, **A186**, 257 (1940).
11. May, D. R., and I. M. Kolthoff: *J. Phys. & Colloid Chem.*, **52**, 836 (1948).
12. Knapp, L. F.: *Trans. Faraday Soc.*, **17**, 457 (1922).
13. von Weimarn, P. P.: *Chem. Revs.*, **2**, 217 (1926); "Die Allgemeinheit des Kolloiden Zustandes," Theodor Steinkopff Verlagsbuchhandlung, Dresden, 1925.
14. Kolthoff, I. M., and E. B. Sandell: "Textbook of Quantitative Inorganic Analysis," 3d ed., p. 112, The Macmillan Company, New York, 1952.
15. Davies, C. W., and A. L. Jones: *Discussions Faraday Soc.*, **5**, 103 (1949).
16. LaMer, V. K., and R. H. Dinegar: *J. Am. Chem. Soc.*, **73**, 380 (1951).
17. Klein, D. H., and L. Gordon: *Talanta*, **1**, 334 (1958).
18. Doremus, R. H.: *J. Phys. Chem.*, **62**, 1068 (1958).
19. Fischer, R. B.: *Anal. Chem.*, **23**, 1667 (1951).
20. Willard, H. H., and G. F. Smith: *J. Am. Chem. Soc.*, **45**, 286 (1923).
21. Jentoft, R. E., and R. J. Robinson: *Anal. Chem.*, **26**, 1156 (1954).
22. Pinkus, A., and A. M. Timmermans: *Bull. soc. chim. Belges*, **46**, 46 (1937).
23. Neuman, E. W.: *J. Am. Chem. Soc.*, **55**, 879 (1933).
24. Beck, G., and A. Gasser: *Anal. Chim. Acta*, **3**, 41 (1949).
25. Gordon, L.: *Anal. Chem.*, **24**, 459 (1952).
26. Moser, L., and J. Singer: *Monatsh.*, **48**, 673 (1927).
27. Stock, A.: *Ber. deut. chem. Ges.*, **33**, 548 (1900).
28. Willard, H. H., and N. K. Tang: *J. Am. Chem. Soc.*, **59**, 1190 (1937); *Ind. Eng. Chem., Anal. Ed.*, **9**, 357 (1937).
29. Elving, P. J., and R. E. Van Atta: *Anal. Chem.*, **22**, 1375 (1950).
30. Willard, H. H., and H. Freund: *Ind. Eng. Chem., Anal. Ed.*, **18**, 195 (1946).
31. Hoffman, W. A., and W. W. Brandt: *Anal. Chem.*, **28**, 1487 (1956).
32. Quill, L. L., and M. L. Salutsky: *J. Am. Chem. Soc.*, **72**, 3306 (1950).
33. Gordon, L., J. I. Peterson, and B. P. Burtt: *Anal. Chem.*, **27**, 1770 (1955).
34. Butler, E. A., D. G. Peters, and E. H. Swift: *Anal. Chem.*, **30**, 1379 (1958); E. H. Swift and E. A. Butler, *Anal. Chem.*, **28**, 146 (1956).
35. Flaschka, H.: *Chemist Analyst*, **44**, 2 (1955).
36. Willard, H. H.: *Anal. Chem.*, **22**, 1372 (1950).
37. Gordon, L., M. L. Salutsky, and H. H. Willard: "Precipitation from Homogeneous Solution," John Wiley & Sons, Inc., New York, 1959.
38. Arden, T. V., and J. Harbutt: *J. Appl. Chem.*, **8**, 141 (1958).
39. Arden, T. V., R. Humphries, and J. A. Lewis: *J. Appl. Chem.*, **8**, 151 (1958).
40. Müller, J., and K. E. Niemann: *Z. anorg. Chem.*, **282**, 63 (1956).
41. Bányai, E., and L. Érdey: *Acta Chim. Acad. Sci. Hung.*, **8**, 383, 395, 409 (1956).
42. Ballczo, H., and G. Doppler: *Z. anal. Chem.*, **151**, 16 (1956).

43. West, P. W., and M. M. Vick: "Qualitative Analysis and Analytical Chemical Separations," 2d ed., The Macmillan Company, New York, 1959.
44. Willard, H. H., and G. M. Smith: *Ind. Eng. Chem., Anal. Ed.,* **11,** 186, 269 (1939).
45. Raff, P., and W. Z. Brotz: *Z. anal. Chem.,* **133,** 241 (1951).
46. Crane, F. E., Jr.: *Anal. Chem.,* **28,** 1794 (1956).
47. Kolthoff, I. M., and G. H. Bendix: *Ind. Eng. Chem., Anal. Ed.,* **11,** 94 (1939).
48. Kolthoff, I. M., and E. B. Sandell: "Textbook of Quantitative Inorganic Analysis," 3d ed., p. 88, The Macmillan Company, New York, 1952.
49. Voter, R. C., and C. V. Banks: *Anal. Chem.,* **21,** 1320 (1949).
50. Feigl, F.: "Chemistry of Specific, Selective and Sensitive Reactions," translated by R. E. Oesper, Academic Press, Inc., New York, 1949; *Anal. Chem.,* **21,** 1298 (1949).
51. Flagg, J. F.: "Organic Reagents Used in Gravimetric and Volumetric Analysis," Interscience Publishers, Inc., New York, 1948.
52. Welcher, F. J.: "Organic Analytical Reagents," D. Van Nostrand Company, Inc., Princeton, N.J., 1947.
53. Martell, A., and M. Calvin: "Chemistry of the Metal Chelate Compounds," Prentice-Hall, Inc., Englewood Cliffs, N.J., 1952.
54. West, P. W.: *Anal. Chem.,* **30,** 748 (1958).
55. Beamish, F. E., et al.: *Anal. Chem.,* **30,** 805 (1958).

CHAPTER 15

COPRECIPITATION, ADSORPTION, AND POSTPRECIPITATION

15.1. Coprecipitation. Coprecipitation has been defined as the contamination of a precipitate by substances that are normally soluble under the conditions of the precipitation. In a much broader sense, though, the term signifies the precipitation of one substance in conjunction with one or more other substances. The more restricted definition recognized by most analytical chemists will be adopted for the basis of discussion first.

Coprecipitation is generally attributable to adsorption, solid-solution formation, compound formation, or mechanical inclusion and occlusion. But regardless of the mechanism involved, the end result is the contamination of the precipitate by substances that would normally be expected to remain in the solution phase.

Solid solutions are formed only when the foreign ion is of the appropriate size and charge to combine with or replace an ion of the precipitate and form a compound that has the same crystal structure as the precipitate. True solid solutions are single phased and not just mixtures of composite groups of ions. The miscibility can be complete or only partial, depending on the perfection of the isomorphism and the relative proportions of the components. The nearer the contaminate concentration approaches its equilibrium solubility concentration, the greater likelihood of a second phase forming. The question of whether solid solutions or mixed compounds are formed is difficult to answer unless the precipitate is studied with x rays or by microscopy. Even then the evidence is not incontrovertible. Lead ion is isomorphous with barium and will contaminate a precipitate of barium sulfate by solid-solution formation even if the lead concentration is well below the level required for the precipitation of $PbSO_4$. Similarly, barium chromate and barium sulfate are isomorphous and form solid solutions. Chromate is coprecipitated by barium sulfate in solutions which have a chromate-ion concentration insufficient to form independently a precipitate of barium chromate. Bromide and chloride ions are interchangeable in the silver halide crystal lattice and therefore form solid solutions when one of the halides is precipitated with silver in the presence of the other. Fortunately, though, this type of coprecipitation is rare. Since solid-solution formation and compound formation are of considerable lesser practical significance than adsorption and occlusion, they will not be discussed further.

Surface absorption is by far the most common mechanism by which coprecipitation occurs. Impurities are held to the surface of the precipitate more or less firmly by electrostatic forces. Consequently, as the precipitate crystal matures, the deposition of successive layers of solute on the crystal surface entraps or occludes the impurity.

15.2. Mechanism and Extent of Adsorption.   The forces responsible for adsorption are primarily electrical in nature. Ions in the surface of a crystal do not have their complete charge neutralized in the same manner as an ion in the interior of the crystal. In a body-centered cubic crystal, for example, each positive ion is surrounded by six negative ions placed in an exact geometrical pattern. In effect, each of these negative ions neutralizes only one-sixth of the charge of the cation. In a like manner, each anion is surrounded by six neutralizing cations. The geometric pattern of neutralizing ions is broken for any ion located in the surface of the crystal, and there is a partial ionic charge radiated from the surface at the ion site. Nevertheless, the entire particle is neutral because there is an equal distribution of positive and negative charges in the surface. An ion in solution would see not a neutral particle but a surface studded with both positive and negative sites. Positive solution ions are attracted to the negative centers in the surface, and the negative solution ions are attracted to the positive centers in the crystal surface. Under the proper circumstances some of these solution ions will adhere to the surface and be considered "adsorbed." It is inconceivable that such a process could populate the surface of the crystal with more than a unimolecular layer of adsorbate. In point of fact, less than a unimolecular layer is adsorbed on the surface because the adsorption mechanism is selective and withdraws only positive or only negative ions from solution. Once ions are adsorbed on the surface, the crystal carries an excess of either positive or negative charges and the surface attracts ions of opposite charge to it to maintain a sphere of electrical neutrality. When $BaCrO_4$ is placed into a solution of sodium chromate, the lattice tries to extend itself by adsorbing chromate ions. In the absence of barium ions the extension of the lattice is at most unimolecular. Creation of a negative charge on the surface now attracts the sodium ions in solution and establishes an electrical double layer as shown in Fig. 15.1. Foreign ions that adhere to the surface of the solid are said to be *primarily* adsorbed and are extremely difficult to displace from the surface. Ions attracted in close to the surface to counteract the charge of the primarily adsorbed ions are referred to as *counterions* and are still free and mobile in the solution phase. Both primary and counter adsorption play significant roles in the contamination of a precipitate.

The extent to which adsorption occurs is a function of the surface area of the precipitate, the nature of the impurity, the solubility of the impurity, and the physical nature of the precipitate. Adsorption, being what it is, establishes unequivocally the proportionality between surface area and the amount of adsorption. The only question that need arise is this: Can there be a sufficient amount of surface adsorption in the normal gravimetric procedure to alter the results significantly? There can be only if the surface area provided by the precipitate is unusually

Ba^{++}	CrO_4^{--}	Ba^{++}	CrO_4^{--}	Na^+
CrO_4^{--}	Ba^{++}	CrO_4^{--}		Na^+
Ba^{++}	CrO_4^{--}	Ba^{++}	CrO_4^{--}	Na^+
CrO_4^{--}	Ba^{++}	CrO_4^{--}		Na^+
Ba^{++}	CrO_4^{--}	Ba^{++}	CrO_4^{--}	
CrO_4^{--}	Ba^{++}	CrO_4^{--}		Na^+
	solid			solution

Fig. 15.1. Formation of electrical double layer by adsorption of sodium chromate on barium chromate precipitate.

great. Simple calculations show that the area of 1 g of any common precipitate dispersed as a colloid (10 to 1000 A particle diameter) provides a large enough surface that a unimolecular layer of adsorbate affects the total mass appreciably. Conventional precipitation techniques produce a great number of crystal nuclei instantaneously and thus present large surface areas on which adsorption can occur. Only a process that produces few crystal nuclei and a slow crystallization mechanism can avoid the creation of large surface areas for gram quantities of precipitates. But even under the most favorable adsorption conditions the weight of the adsorbate is considerably less than 10 per cent of the weight of the primary precipitate.

Solubility of the impurity is an important factor, although only unsaturated solutions (with respect to the impurity) are considered. The ion most likely to be primarily adsorbed is an ion common to the crystal lattice of the precipitate. For example, if barium sulfate is precipitated from hydrochloric acid solution with an excess of sodium sulfate, sulfate ions will be primarily adsorbed and sodium and hydrogen ions will be the counterions. In the precipitation of silver chloride by the gradual addition of silver nitrate solution to a sodium chloride solution, a colloidal precipitate is formed possessing a negative charge owing to the primary adsorption of chloride ions. Near the equivalence point of the reaction, the colloid flocculates because the electrical double layer is essentially neutralized by the presence of equal amounts of silver and chloride ions competing for primary adsorption. Beyond the equivalence point of the reaction, silver ions will be primarily adsorbed and impart a positive charge to the surface of the aggregate.

In the absence of any ion common to the precipitate, the Paneth-Fajans-Hahn rule predicts that the ion most strongly adsorbed will be the one which forms the least soluble compound with an ion of the precipitate. For example, calcium ion should be more strongly adsorbed than magnesium ion by barium sulfate because calcium sulfate is more insoluble than magnesium sulfate. There is no quantitative relationship, however.

Other factors, such as ionic size, polarizability, and concentration, also are quite important in determining the amount of adsorption. Solution ions with a high charge, high polarizability, low hydration energy, or high concentration are favored for primary adsorption. A high charge increases the electrostatic attraction between solution and surface ions and produces a stronger bond. High polarizability promotes covalent bond formation and stronger adsorption affinity. Particles with low hydration energy compete favorably for adsorption sites because of their lower attraction for the solution phase. A high concentration of solution impurity increases the probability of surface-solute interaction and favors adsorption. These terms are used in a comparative sense because it is still impossible to draw any quantitative relationships among adsorbate charge, polarizability, and hydration energy.

Finally, one must consider the effect of the nature of the precipitate on adsorption. In fresh precipitates the crystalline form is often very imperfect and foreign ions enter the lattice rather easily. Generally, large, well-formed single crystals have a much greater purity than small, imperfect crystals. Gelatinous precipitates, such as the hydrous oxides of the metals, provide unusually large surface areas for adsorption and also entrap impurities in the coagulated mass. From an analytical standpoint, these impurities are very difficult to remove.

The nature of the precipitate is frequently determined by the ease with which a colloidal precipitate is flocculated. Flocculation occurs near the stoichiometric point of some reactions because the electrical double layer is effectively neutralized by the very low and equal concentration of lattice ions in solution available for primary adsorption. Since the colloidal particles no longer repel one another, under such conditions their normal kinetic energy brings them close enough together that certain attractive forces take over. Thus, as colloidal and amorphous precipitates flocculate, the adsorbed impurities are trapped within the aggregate and appear in the final precipitate.

Ions not common to the precipitate can also effectively destroy the zeta potential at the colloid surface and produce flocculation.   If ammonium ions, hydrogen ions, or other noninterfering cations are added, they will concentrate in the region of the electrical double layer and decrease the zeta potential to the point that the colloid stability is destroyed.   A negative colloid is flocculated by the increased concentration of positive ions, and flocculation efficiency increases with ionic charge.   Likewise, the higher charged anions are most effective in flocculating positive colloids.   Exceptions to these generalities are the hydrogen and hydroxyl ions, which are the most effective flocculating agents for their respective signs.

The following example will serve to coordinate the degree of adsorption or coprecipitation observed with certain system variables.   Consider the precipitation of the hydrous oxide of iron in the presence of other metals whose solubility-product constants are not exceeded.[1]   As might be expected from their structure, the adsorption affinity of the hydrous oxides is very pH dependent.   Hydrous ferric oxide, for example, is positively charged below its isoelectric point (approximately pH 8.5 to 8.9) and negatively charged at higher pH values.   Hydrous ferric oxide adsorbs anions (but not cations) strongly from weakly acidic solutions and adsorbs cations preferentially from alkaline solutions above pH 10.   This is why it is preferable in mineral analysis to precipitate the hydrous oxides of iron and aluminum from an acid rather than an alkaline medium.   The coprecipitation of calcium, magnesium, and other cations is minimized in an acid medium.

In the usual procedure for the precipitation of hydrous ferric oxide the pH of the solution is controlled by an ammonium chloride–ammonium hydroxide buffer.   From Fig. 15.2 it is seen that the adsorption of various cations on hydrous ferric oxide decreases with an increase in ammonium chloride concentration.   The adsorption is due to the primary adsorption of hydroxide ions and the secondary adsorption of the cations.   The primary adsorption of hydroxyl ions decreases with decreasing hydroxyl-ion concentration, and so does the adsorption of cations.   The replacement effect of the ammonium ion is not solely responsible for the observed decrease in adsorption because at equal concentrations other cations such as sodium are less effective in reducing the adsorption of the heavy-metal cations.   The ammonium ions are effective in replacing the other adsorbed cations certainly, but they are more effective in reducing the hydroxide-ion concentration of the solution.

The adsorption of zinc, nickel, and cobalt decreases with increasing ammonia concentrations (Fig. 15.3), while that of calcium and magnesium increases.   The increased adsorption of calcium and magnesium at higher hydroxide concentrations is expected.   Zinc, nickel, and cobalt should also be more strongly adsorbed from more alkaline media and

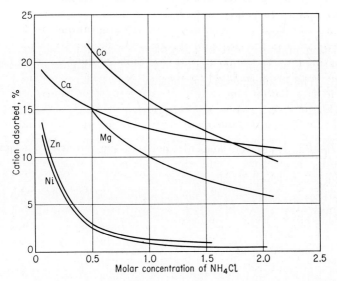

FIG. 15.2. Variation in adsorption of various cations on hydrous ferric oxide as the concentration of ammonium chloride is increased. [*After I. M. Kolthoff and L. G. Overholzer, J. Phys. Chem.*, **43,** 767 (1939).]

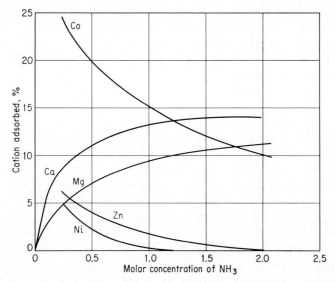

FIG. 15.3. Variation in adsorption of various cations on hydrous ferric oxide as the concentration of ammonia is increased. [*After I. M. Kolthoff and L. G. Overholzer, J. Phys. Chem.*, **43,** 767 (1939).]

no doubt would be, except for the formation of the very soluble ammonio complexes.

Prediction of the extent of adsorption (coprecipitation) on a more quantitative basis than that indicated in the preceding example is rather difficult. The homogeneous distribution law

$$\left(\frac{B}{A}\right)_{entire\ crystal} = D\left(\frac{B}{A}\right)_{solution} \tag{15.1}$$

where B and A are the concentrations of the impurity and primary precipitate, respectively, and the empirical adsorption isotherms of Freundlich (see Chap. 4), Langmuir, and others predict the distribution of impurities between the solid phase and the solution only if the precipitate is formed by conventional means, has been digested long enough to remove all concentration gradients, and is homogeneous. Such conditions are rarely encountered in analytical work because in most precipitation reactions the rate of crystal growth is too rapid for the adsorbed material to establish and maintain an equilibrium with the dissolved impurity. Impurities trapped in the interior of a crystal are only very slowly equilibrated with the solution phase unless the solid is quite porous.

On the other hand, a logarithmic distribution of solute is postulated if each crystal layer as it forms is in equilibrium with the solution at that time. Such a condition is approximated if the precipitate is formed slowly in a homogeneous medium. Since the precipitant is generated gradually and uniformly throughout the solution, the number of crystal nuclei formed is relatively small and large well-formed crystals are obtained. Foreign ions incorporated in the surface layers of the precipitate are more or less in equilibrium with the solution, whereas the ions entrapped by the deposition of successive layers of solute are not in equilibrium with the solution, since recrystallization and diffusion are slight in large crystals. The logarithmic distribution law as stated by Doerner and Hoskins[2] is

$$\log \frac{B_0}{B_f} = \lambda \log \frac{A_0}{A_f} \tag{15.2}$$

where B_0 and A_0 represent initial concentrations of foreign ions and ions to be precipitated, respectively, and B_f and A_f represent the final quantities in solution. λ is the distribution coefficient. This equation has been particularly effective in predicting the enrichment or derichment of precipitates by coprecipitation processes. An example of its use is given in the following section.

15.3. Separations Achieved with Coprecipitation Processes. Coprecipitation is not always a deleterious factor in precipitations because it can be used to concentrate microconstituents of solutions to useful levels.

Concentration is accomplished both by the formation of a primary precipitate in the solution and by the direct addition of adsorbents. The primary precipitate acts as a carrier or collector for the entrainment of the microcomponent. The carriers that have proved most effective for general scavenging action are the hydrous oxides of the metals, particularly of aluminum, iron, and other transition metals. This is undoubtedly due to their large surface area, gelatinous character, and ability to coagulate.

It is not unusual for a single precipitation to remove 90 per cent or more of the trace constituent at dilutions of $1:10^9$ by coprecipitation. For example, Chuĭko[3] has shown that over 90 per cent of the Ni, Cd, and Co in a solution containing 5 μg of Ni or Cd or 0.01 μg of Co is coprecipitated readily with the hydroxides of magnesium, iron, cadmium, and bismuth. Numerous other studies attest to the efficient scavenging ability of the hydrous oxides.

One of the most interesting applications of coprecipitation has been derived from observations made on the variation of coprecipitation with completeness of precipitation by homogeneous techniques. Willard and Sheldon[4] observed that, in the separation of basic iron formate from homogeneous solution with urea, negligible coprecipitation occurred at pH values low enough to precipitate only 95 to 99 per cent of the basic salt. Beyond this point, coprecipitation increased very rapidly. A two-stage method then was suggested for obtaining high-purity precipitates. Terminate the precipitation process near completion, and filter. Continue the internal generation of precipitant in the filtrate until precipitation is complete. The small amount of precipitate formed in the second stage does not have a high capacity for coprecipitation even if at the higher pH the coprecipitation per unit weight of precipitate is higher. The combined precipitates thus minimize contamination greatly.

Gordon and Ginsburg[5] studied the coprecipitation of aluminum, yttrium, and zinc on ferric periodate precipitated from homogeneous solution by hydrolysis of acetamide. Aluminum and yttrium were only slightly coprecipitated until 99.9 per cent of the iron was precipitated. The percentage of yttrium coprecipitated remained less than 3 per cent until 99 per cent of the iron was precipitated. As the percentage of iron precipitated increased to 99.96 per cent, the amount of yttrium coprecipitated sharply increased to 61 per cent. This is graphically represented in Fig. 15.4. Similar results were obtained for the coprecipitation of aluminum. Zinc showed considerable coprecipitation prior to the end of the iron precipitation. Occlusion was apparently a negligible part of the overall coprecipitation process.

Ginsburg, Millar, and Gordon[6] were able to separate 85 mg of iron from 10 mg of aluminum by a single precipitation of iron from a homogeneous medium with acetamide, but a two-stage precipitation was required to separate the iron from 100 mg of aluminum.

At its best, coprecipitation can be used for the concentration and fractionation of trace constituents. Salutsky, Stites, and Martin[7] found a fractional separation by coprecipitation to be a more rapid method for the concentration of radium in barium-radium mixtures than the conventional fractional recrystallization of the bromides or chlorides. Just

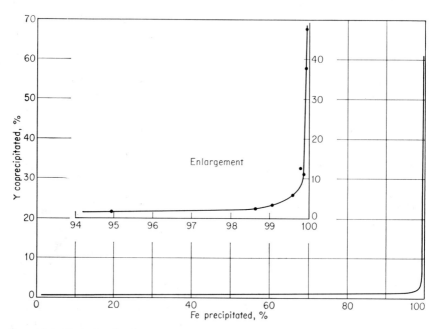

FIG. 15.4. Variation in the percentage of yttrium coprecipitated on ferric periodate precipitated from homogeneous solution. [*After L. Gordon and L. Ginsburg, Anal. Chem.,* **29**, 38 (1957).]

as in recrystallization, the method depends on the fact that a greater percentage of radium than barium appears in the precipitate in each fractionation step. When a radium salt is coprecipitated with a barium salt, the radium can be distributed in the crystals in one of two ways, either in a homogeneous distribution [Eq. (15.1)] in which the radium-barium ratio in the crystals is proportional to the radium-barium ratio in the solution or by a logarithmic distribution [Eq. (15.2)]. The efficiency of the fractional-precipitation scheme is greater, however, if the precipitation follows the logarithmic distribution law rather than the homogeneous distribution law. For example, if the distribution coefficient were 10, precipitation of half the barium would remove 99.8 per cent of the radium if it were coprecipitated logarithmically versus only 90.9 per cent if it were incorporated homogeneously.

Salutsky and coworkers found that the coprecipitation of radium by barium chromate approached closely a logarithmic distribution if the radium-barium mixtures were precipitated by the homogeneous genera-tion of chromate.   Their procedure is based upon the decrease in the solu-bility of the chromates with decreasing solution acidity.   The initial acid solution of the salts is slowly neutralized by the internal generation

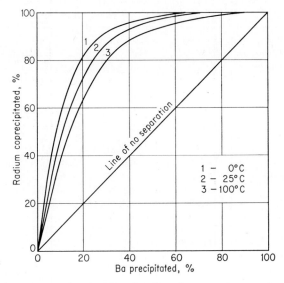

FIG. 15.5. Variation in the distribution of radium between the two phases for precipi-tations carried out at different temperatures.   [*After M. L. Salutsky, J. G. Stites, Jr., and A. W. Martin, Anal. Chem.*, **25**, 1677 (1953).]

of ammonia by the spontaneous hydrolysis of urea or potassium cyanate. Figure 15.5 indicates the variation in the distribution of radium between the two phases for precipitations at different temperatures.   At 0° approximately 99 per cent of the radium is coprecipitated with just 50 per cent of the barium.

If in each fractionation step approximately half of the barium remain-ing from the previous step is precipitated, filtered, and dissolved, the radium will rapidly be concentrated in the precipitate.   The concentra-tion of radium by fractional chromate precipitation is shown in Table 15.1.   In 19 fractionation steps the composition of the sample changed from an initial barium-radium ratio of 96,930:1 to a final ratio of 0.18:1. A great majority (84.8 per cent) of the original radium ended up in the final concentrate.   Note how uniform the distribution coefficient remained during the course of the fractionation. This is indicative at least of how close homogeneous precipitation conditions approximate the conditions specified in the derivation of the logarithmic distribution law.

The procedure is considerably more rapid than recrystallization processes, just as efficient as the recrystallization of bromides, and more efficient than the recrystallization of either chlorides or nitrates.

TABLE 15.1. CONCENTRATION OF RADIUM BY
FRACTIONAL CHROMATE PRECIPITATION*

Fraction	Barium, g	Radium, mg	λ	Ba:Ra ratio
Original	67.92	0.7007	....	96,930
1	35.62	0.6715	4.28	53,050
2	17.07	0.6356	4.49	26,860
3	8.72	0.6088	4.43	14,320
4	4.72	0.5898	4.45	8,003
5	2.28	0.5590	4.59	4,079
6	1.19	0.5309	4.05	2,241
7	0.71	0.5136	3.77	1,382
First concentrate	3.467	1.680	....	2,064
8	1.478	1.502	4.04	984
9	0.924	1.388	2.63	666
10	0.252	1.097	4.91	230
11	1.395	0.928	2.32	150
12	0.0863	0.882	3.12	98
Second concentrate	0.2418	2.135	....	113
13	0.1538	2.035	3.03	75.5
14	0.0512	1.735	4.73	29.5
15	0.0215	1.669	6.00	12.9
16	0.0066	1.522	6.62	4.3
17	0.0017	1.209	5.31	1.4
18	0.0003	1.176	....	0.26
Final concentrate	0.00021	1.172	4.73	0.18

* From M. L. Salutsky, J. G. Stites, Jr., and A. W. Martin, *Anal. Chem.*, **25**, 1677 (1953).

Gordon and Rowley[8] have shown that the coprecipitation of radium with barium sulfate precipitated from a homogeneous medium also follows a logarithmic distribution between the aqueous and solid phases. Several additional precipitate enrichment processes are considered in the review on precipitation from homogeneous media by Gordon, Salutsky, and Willard.[9]

15.4. Postprecipitation. Postprecipitation is the slow precipitation of a second insoluble substance after the formation of the primary precipitate. It differs from coprecipitation in that the solubility-product constant of the contaminant has been exceeded and a new solid phase formed. Postprecipitation occurs only if the contaminant can exist in a metastable supersaturated state which slowly releases the solute for crystallization. There are several possible explanations for retardation of the precipitation process: Soluble complexes may be produced that are not so thermodynamically stable as the final precipitate but are favored by the kinetics of the competing reactions, or the induction period required for the formation of nuclei large enough to lower the solubility of the solute below the saturation level is unusually long. Contamination of precipitates by postprecipitation increases with the time precipitate and supernatant liquid are digested together and ultimately involves all the impurity. It is worthwhile to note that the same amount of material is postprecipitated regardless of whether the impurity is added before or after the primary precipitate is formed. In some instances, though, there is evidence that the primary precipitate catalyzes the postprecipitation phenomenon.

Kolthoff and coworkers have done extensive work in evaluating the postprecipitation of zinc sulfide on cupric,[10] mercuric,[11] and antimony sulfides.[12] In each case the experimental conditions are such that a precipitate of the mercury, copper, or antimony sulfide forms immediately but zinc sulfide alone does not precipitate for many hours, although its solubility-product constant is exceeded. When acid mixtures of mercuric and zinc ions or cupric and zinc ions are treated with hydrogen sulfide, the primary precipitate of HgS or CuS is free of zinc, but upon standing, more and more zinc sulfide appears in the precipitate. The results (in Fig. 15.6) for the postprecipitation of zinc sulfide on mercuric sulfide are typical of these studies. In general, it was found that the amount of zinc sulfide postprecipitated by the other metal sulfides in a given time was inversely proportional to the acidity of the solution.

The enhanced rate of precipitation of zinc sulfide in the presence of mercuric sulfide can be explained in the following manner: Sulfide ions are strongly adsorbed on the surface of the primary precipitate (CuS or HgS), and zinc is induced to precipitate on the surface of the primary precipitate because of the high sulfide-ion concentration. The effect of surface-active agents on the rate of postprecipitation substantiates this theory. When organic substances containing polar sulfur groups are present in solution, they replace the adsorbed sulfide or hydrosulfide ions on the primary precipitate and seriously inhibit the postprecipitation of zinc sulfide. Cysteine, thiourea, and thiophenol also are active inhibitors. Postprecipitation is also inhibited by the competition between hydrogen ions and sulfide ions and among hydrogen ions, zinc ions, and other solution cations for adsorption as counterions on the precipitate. Strychnine acts as an inhibitor to the postprecipitation of zinc sulfide by competing for the same exchange sites in the electrical double layer as the zinc. Strychnine ion is preferentially adsorbed, and the amount of zinc sulfide produced is decreased. It is probable that other large deformable cations would also be effective inhibitors.

One of the most striking results of this study is the postprecipitation of zinc sulfide on mercuric sulfide from 2 N acid solutions. This is an apparent contradiction of the mass-action law because pure zinc sulfide will dissolve under these conditions. Postprecipitation might be due

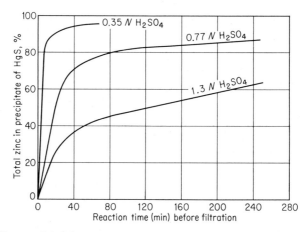

Fig. 15.6. Postprecipitation of zinc sulfide on mercuric sulfide at various acidities. [*After I. M. Kolthoff and R. Moltzau, J. Phys. Chem.*, **40**, 779 (1936).]

to the fact that mercuric and zinc sulfide are isomorphous. The secondary adsorption of zinc ions on the precipitate of HgS would extend the crystalline lattice without defect. A combination of isomorphism with low recrystallization rates and high sulfide-ion concentration at the solid solution interface could explain the formation of zinc sulfide. For comparison, the promoting effect of cupric sulfide on the postprecipitation of zinc sulfide is much less than that of mercuric sulfide. Here it is known that the cupric and zinc sulfides are not isomorphous.

The best known example of postprecipitation is the formation of magnesium oxalate. Magnesium oxalate is only moderately soluble in water ($K_{sp} = 8.6 \times 10^{-5}$) but forms stable supersaturated solutions because of the formation of a soluble oxalato complex $Mg(C_2O_4)_2^{--}$. Calcium and magnesium can be separated by precipitation of their respective oxalates because of this characteristic. A solution containing calcium, magnesium, and oxalate ions involves several equilibria, represented by

$$Mg^{++} \overset{C_2O_4^{--}}{\rightleftharpoons} Mg(C_2O_4)_2^{--}$$
$$+$$
$$HC_2O_4^- \rightleftharpoons H^+ + C_2O_4^{--}$$
$$+$$
$$Ca^{++} \rightleftharpoons CaC_2O_4\downarrow$$

In practice calcium oxalate is precipitated from hot ammoniacal (pH 7 to 8) solutions by adding ammonium oxalate. The suspension is digested for less than 1 hr and filtered. Longer digestion in hot solution results in contamination of the calcium precipitate with magnesium. The precipitation is quantitative for calcium and leaves magnesium in solution as the soluble complex. If more oxalate is added to the filtrate and the solution is left standing several hours, magnesium can be quantitatively recovered also as the normal oxalate.

Postprecipitation is known to occur with other compounds, but it is not common and does not warrant further discussion. The review of postprecipitation by Kolthoff and Moltzau[13] is excellent.

15.5. Selected Bibliography

Gordon, L., M. L. Salutsky, and H. H. Willard: "Precipitation from Homogeneous Solution," John Wiley & Sons, Inc., New York, 1959.

Kolthoff, I. M., and E. B. Sandell: "Textbook of Quantitative Inorganic Analysis," 3d ed., The Macmillan Company, New York, 1952.

West, T. S.: *Anal. Chim. Acta*, **25**, 405 (1961).

REFERENCES

1. Kolthoff, I. M., and L. G. Overholzer: *J. Phys. Chem.*, **43**, 767 (1939).
2. Doerner, H. A., and W. M. Hoskins: *J. Am. Chem. Soc.*, **47**, 662 (1925).
3. Chulko, V. T.: *Zhur. Neorg. Khim.*, **2**, 685 (1957).
4. Willard, H. H., and J. L. Sheldon: *Anal. Chem.*, **22**, 1162 (1950).
5. Gordon, L., and L. Ginsburg: *Anal. Chem.*, **29**, 38 (1957).
6. Ginsburg, L., K. Millar, and L. Gordon: *Anal. Chem.*, **29**, 46 (1957).
7. Salutsky, M. L., J. G. Stites, Jr., and A. W. Martin: *Anal. Chem.*, **25**, 1677 (1953).
8. Gordon, L., and K. Rowley: *Anal. Chem.*, **29**, 34 (1957).
9. Gordon, L., M. L. Salutsky, and H. H. Willard: "Precipitation from Homogeneous Solution," John Wiley & Sons, Inc., New York, 1959.
10. Kolthoff, I. M., and E. A. Pearson: *J. Phys. Chem.*, **36**, 549 (1932).
11. Kolthoff, I. M., and R. Moltzau: *J. Phys. Chem.*, **40**, 779 (1936).
12. Kolthoff, I. M., and F. S. Griffith: *J. Phys. Chem.*, **42**, 541 (1938); *J. Am. Chem. Soc.*, **60**, 2036 (1938).
13. Kolthoff, I. M., and R. Moltzau: *Chem. Revs.*, **17**, 293 (1935).

CHAPTER 16

FLOTATION

16.1. Introduction. Flotation is the process by which finely divided solids are suspended in a solution and floated to the surface of the liquid. Even a solid with a density greater than that of the solution can be floated. Buoyancy is the result of a small bubble of gas (20 to 200 times as large as the particle) adhering to the particle, thus reducing the effective density of the particle sufficiently to allow flotation. The natural differences in the floatability of various substances make it possible to resolve mixtures of solids by flotation techniques. Inherently associated with the phenomenon are the displacement of a liquid from a solid surface by a gas and the stabilization of the solid surface in a gas-liquid interface. Surface or interfacial forces are responsible for a particle being stabilized in a gas-liquid interface. Therefore, for better understanding of the process, one must consider the properties of solid and liquid surfaces and the various interfaces produced among solids, liquids, and gases.

16.2. Topochemical Reactions. The term *adsorption* signifies the accumulation of material on the surface of a second material. Adsorption occurs to a varying extent on all surfaces or at all interfaces and is one of the most selective processes known. Minute differences in the molecular structure of two substances can result in one being strongly adsorbed at an interface and the other being almost totally excluded. Adsorption mechanisms are not completely defined, and it is not known if adsorption proceeds by a purely physical or chemical process. There still is little known relating the adsorption affinity of a substance to its molecular structure.

If the adsorption occurs by a chemical process, then it can be defined as a topochemical reaction. Topochemical reactions are simply reactions that are localized on the surface of a solid. Exemplifying such reactions are corrosion, chemical reactions of solids, galvanizing, activation of bleaching earths, gas-solid reactions, and certain adsorption processes. Such reactions proceed by direct combinations involving the ions or molecules of the solid or, as some have proposed, by reaction with dissolved portions of the solids in the immediate vicinity of the surface.

310

It would seem that the latter mechanism might be ruled out by the definition of topochemical.

The complete insolubility of the heavy metals in water indicates that the dissolving of metals by acids or bases must be topochemical; the reaction must proceed on the surface. The same is true for the dissolution of the difficultly soluble sulfides of mercury(II) and arsenic(III).

Reactions of solid particles with solutions to form colored products have been observed closely with a microscope. Pietsch et al.[1] studied the reaction of hydrogen sulfide with solid copper(II) sulfate, dimethylglyoxime with solid nickel(II) sulfate, and iron(III) chloride with acetate ions. In each instance the reaction began at the edge of the crystal and appeared to spread over the entire surface.

The conclusion can be drawn from these interfacial reactions that the surface atoms of at least some solids are reactive and that adsorption could conceivably proceed by chemical bonding. There will continue to be some element of doubt about specific adsorption mechanisms until more is known concerning all types of surface phenomena.

The general properties of solids are well known, but the characteristics of the two-dimensional solid surfaces are not so well established. Since it is to be expected that surface characteristics will be determined, at least partially, by the underlying material in the interior, it will be worthwhile to review the general properties of solids.

16.3. General Properties of the Solid State. The term *solid* is used to describe a form of matter that is rigid and retains its physical shape and volume in spite of gravitational forces. Solids are classified according to the internal arrangement of the molecules, atoms, or ions of which the substance is constituted. *Crystalline* solids are distinguished by the definite geometrical pattern created by the constituent particles. Even the external form of a crystalline substance is unique. The regularity of the internal arrangement is reflected in the geometrical pattern of the external form. Crystalline solids have plane faces that meet to form straight-line edges. The angles between faces are characteristic of the substance. If a crystal is crushed or broken, the breaks tend to occur along planes parallel to the surface in such a way as to produce smaller pieces with the same general characteristics. The sizes and shapes of the smaller crystals may vary, but the interfacial angles are always the same.

Amorphous solids are distinguished by the absence of a completely regular arrangement of constituents. The basic particles are distributed throughout the material in a random fashion with only a slight or transient regularity noticed. Amorphous solids are usually produced by the rapid condensation of a vapor or by chemical reaction. Many precipitates that have been considered amorphous are now known to be crystalline, although their gross appearance suggests amorphism. There are two amorphous states recognized in metals. One is a relatively dense structure obtained by polishing or cold-working a metal. The second is a very loose structure created by the rapid evaporation or condensation of a metal.

Vitreous, or *glassy*, solids are sometimes recognized as a third form of the solid state. Vitreous solids have properties that are intermediate between those of the crystalline state and amorphous state. In other words, these solids are neither completely crystalline nor completely amorphous. For most purposes, though, they can be treated as non-crystalline solids.

16.4. Heterogeneity of Solid Surfaces. The heterogeneity of solid surfaces is indicated by a number of different physical and chemical processes. Microscopic examinations, etching patterns, catalytic properties, differential heats of adsorption, and topochemical reactions all indicate the heterogeneity of solid surfaces.

Even with the regular arrangement of particles in the crystalline state there is a variation of physical properties along different crystalline axes. Anisotropy is indicated in measurements of heat conductivity, optical rotatory power, and light refractivity made along different axes of the crystal. Except for the cubic system, all crystalline lattices exhibit anisotropy to a certain extent. The cubic system and the amorphous state are isotropic because they have the same structure regardless of the direction in which the physical property is measured. The heterogeneous character of solid surfaces is of the greatest importance to surface chemistry. Many surface phenomena are explained on the basis that surface particles are energetically different from identical particles found in the interior. Microscopic observations made on solid surfaces, even "smooth" ones, show that the surface is very irregular. There are pits, elevations, aggregates of different material, projections, and crevices of different sizes and irregular shapes. Even in the relatively simple structure of a single crystal there are different types of surfaces on it. The linkage among surface atoms is different in different faces and corners and along the edges. Even interatomic spacing varies from face to face. These differences are due to the geometrical arrangement of atoms in the crystal. As a surface is exposed, the continuity of the pattern is broken.

Most surfaces are not single crystals and thus are even more complex. These surfaces may consist of aggregates and pieces of smaller crystals in all possible orientations. The variation of surface structure in non-crystalline substances is even greater. Charcoal, which is produced from a variety of complicated organic compounds, must exhibit an unusually large number of irregularities in the surface.

Perhaps the best evidence for the heterogeneous character of solid surfaces comes from studies on catalysis. There are different levels of catalytic activity exhibited by the same substance, and it is fairly well established that the catalytic power of a solid lies in active patches on the surface. Leidheiser and Gwathmey[2] investigated the selective deposition of solid reaction products on single large metal crystals. When iron and nickel crystals were heated in carbon monoxide or in carbon monoxide–hydrogen mixtures, carbon was formed rapidly on some faces while the rate of deposition was very slow or negligible on other faces.

Cunningham and Gwathmey[3] investigated the reaction of hydrogen and ethylene on several faces of a single crystal of nickel. There was evidence of the deposition of carbon on all faces, but the amount varied from face to face with the least amount deposited on the (111) areas.

Smith and Polley[4] compared the rate of attack of oxygen on parent carbon black and the homogeneous graphitized carbon blacks obtained at temperatures up to 2700°C. Using comparable surface areas per gram of carbon, experimentation revealed that the homogeneous surface oxidized at a rate comparable to the heterogeneous surface only in a temperature range some 200 to 300° higher. A porous surface was created on the heterogeneous material, but the homogeneous material was left planar by the slow oxidation of surface particles. The view was expressed that the oxygen attack on the heterogeneous surface occurred preferentially at specific high-energy sites, such as edge atoms in the surface lattice.

Heterogeneous catalysis is now generally conceded to be due to the presence of active patches on the surface of the catalyst. This must be the case, since quantities of poison incapable of completely covering the surface of the catalyst are sufficient to reduce catalytic activity to zero. There also are different levels of activity after successive poisoning steps which indicate the heterogeneous character of the surface.

The rate of dissolution of crystals along different axes has been known for a long time. If the surface of a crystalline substance is highly polished and then treated with an appropriate solvent, a faint pattern will be etched on the surface owing to the different rates of attack on different faces.

Heterogeneity of solid surfaces is indicated by heats of adsorption data. The heat evolved by the adsorption of the first small quantities of a gas is often much higher than that evolved as the surface becomes more nearly saturated.

The heterogeneous character of solid surfaces is also illustrated by the "memory" of some solid surfaces. When β-naphthyl salicylate is repeatedly melted and recrystallized, there is a strong tendency for crystallization to begin at the same point on the surface of the container.

This memory may be due to the orientation of particles in the surface. In any case, the memory is destroyed by mild treatment with hydrofluoric acid. As a result, a uniformly active surface for crystallization is obtained. The hydrofluoric acid treatment may destroy the old active points or simply may expose a multitude of new active points.

The inevitable conclusion that must be drawn from these data and others is that no two adjacent surface atoms or molecules have exactly the same properties. Solid surfaces are heterogeneous.

16.5. Partial Mobility of Solid Surfaces. There is a pronounced tendency for surface particles to migrate in the solid state, even though we consider the gross structure of solids as being rigid. It is common knowledge that metals will diffuse in metals. Gold has been shown on numerous occasions to migrate readily into a block of lead. When crystalline solids are polished, the surface layers become amorphous owing to the rearrangement of the surface particles. Below the melting point many solids begin to flow when subjected to stress and the corners of crystals become smooth and rounded. Contrary then to the general property of rigidity associated with solids is this limited mobility. There are cohesive forces always pulling inward on a solid just as with a liquid and it is justifiable to consider that solids have an inherent surface tension.

16.6. Adhesion between Solids and Liquids. One of the general properties of solids is their affinity for liquids. Some liquids will spontaneously spread over the surface of a solid and "wet" the surface, whereas other liquids will contract and exhibit little or no affinity for the solid surface. The phenomenon of flotation is so closely allied to the forces that produce adhesion between solids and liquids that solid-liquid affinities must be discussed.

First, consider the surface of the liquid that will be interrupted or displaced when solid-liquid contact is made. The surface of the liquid is not too well defined because of the violent agitation of surface particles. This perturbation of the surface particles is the result of their thermal energies. The gas-liquid interface is approximately 10 A thick, and the density of the medium may vary by 1000-fold from one extreme to the other. Nevertheless, there must be an appreciable amount of attraction between the liquid molecules or the bulk of the liquid would rapidly disappear by volatilization. For water, the complete escape of a molecule from the surface requires sufficient energy to overcome the bonds of association which account for the high latent heat of vaporization. It is not difficult to visualize the existence of such an attractive force between molecules of liquids. In fact, it is fairly easy to obtain a relative measure of the attractive forces existing between particles in the liquid state.

Although the bulk of a liquid is isotropic, the surface is not necessarily isotropic. Polar solutions containing heteropolar molecules have an unusually high concentration of hydrocarbon groups in the surface layer. When small amounts of alcohol are added to water, the effect on the surface tension of the solution is completely out of proportion to the quantity of alcohol added. The reason is that the solute molecule is expelled from the bulk of the solution and concentrated in the surface because of its hydrophobic hydrocarbon portion. The result is that the surface molecules are at least partially oriented because of the absence of bonding in the direction of the surface. The missing bond energy in the direction away from the surface is replaced by the total surface free energy of the liquid, which is numerically equal to the surface tension γ. Just as the potential energy of a system tends to a minimum, so does the surface free energy of a liquid. The surface energy is minimized by the spontaneous contraction of the surface or gas-liquid interface to a minimum. This then is the fundamental explanation of why a liquid tends to draw itself into a sphere with a minimum surface exposed for the maximum quantity of substance contained. There is undoubtedly a direct relationship between the total surface free energy of a liquid and the bonding between liquid molecules.

The attraction that two liquids have for each other requires that work be done in separating the two liquids. The work required is equal to the sum of the surface tensions of the individual liquids, $\gamma_A + \gamma_B$, minus the interfacial tension of the liquid-liquid interface γ_{AB}. The work required to effect the separation of a unit cross-sectional area of the liquids is the work of adhesion W_{AB}.

$$W_{AB} = \gamma_A + \gamma_B - \gamma_{AB}$$

The criterion for complete miscibility of two liquids is that the interfacial tension γ_{AB} is zero. Therefore, the work required to break apart a column of pure liquid and create two new surfaces of unit area must be the sum of the surface energies involved. That is, the work of adhesion W must equal two times the surface tension of the pure liquid.

In a similar fashion, when the interface between a solid and a liquid is broken to expose a unit area of each phase, the work of adhesion W_{SL} must be the difference between the solid-liquid interfacial tension γ_{SL} and the total energy of the free solid surface γ_S and the liquid surface γ_L.

$$W_{SL} = (\gamma_S + \gamma_L) - \gamma_{SL} \tag{16.1}$$

This expression is not particularly useful because it involves the difference between two unknown solid surface tensions. Although the evidence is very strong for the existence of a solid surface tension, there is no means of evaluating such at the present time (see Sec. 14.4).

Nevertheless, the surface tensions can be treated mathematically as forces pulling parallel to the surface and resolved parallel to the surface. It has been observed that when a liquid rests on a solid, the angle of contact θ measured within the liquid is a definite angle. Under equilibrium conditions then, when a liquid rests on a solid, the surface tension of the solid can be expressed by the equation

$$\gamma_S = \gamma_{SL} + \gamma_L \cos \theta \tag{16.2}$$

Combining this equation with the equation for the work of adhesion between a solid and a liquid results in

$$\begin{aligned} W_{SL} &= (\gamma_{SL} + \gamma_L \cos \theta) + \gamma_L - \gamma_{SL} \\ &= \gamma_L (1 + \cos \theta) \end{aligned} \tag{16.3}$$

Equation (16.3) shows that the contact angle between a liquid and a solid is determined by the relative strengths of adhesion that exist between the solid and liquid and the liquid and itself. For a contact angle of zero, the work of adhesion must equal twice the surface tension of the pure liquid. That is, there is at least as much attraction of the liquid for the solid as for itself. A contact angle of 90° indicates that the attraction of the liquid for the solid is only one-half the attraction for itself. An angle of 180° indicates no adhesion between the solid and liquid. Herein rests the significance of contact angles; they furnish a relative measure of the interaction between molecules or particles of different phases.

Actually there is some practical significance associated with the value of contact angles. They offer a way of defining the wetting power of a liquid for a given solid. Liquids that spread out over a plane solid surface to form a thin lens invariably have a small contact angle and are said to wet the solid. Examples would be water on glass or clean metal surfaces and mercury on silver. Liquids do not spread spontaneously on all solid surfaces; some liquids tend to contract and pull back into themselves. These liquids have large contact angles and are said not to wet the surface. Various types of contact angles are depicted in Fig. 16.1. Many organic liquids and water form zero contact angles with clean glass, silica, and metal surfaces, but no solids are known to have an air-water contact angle greater than 110°.

More refined information can be obtained concerning the orientation of molecules in the surfaces of solids by measuring the contact angle between the solid and water. This procedure has been effective in elucidating the structure of the surface of heteropolar solids. For example, long-chain alcohols and acids that are solidified in air may have their particles oriented in one of several possible ways. The particles may be arranged in a completely random fashion, but this is unlikely. The principal bonding between molecules will be between the polar groups, resulting in a solid crystallized in double layers. The hydrocarbon tails (Fig. 16.2) may be normal to the plane of the layer or may be inclined. This leaves unanswered, though, the question of the molecular orientation in the surface. If the polar groups are located in the surface, then

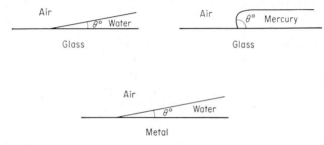

FIG. 16.1. Gross appearance of some typical contact angles created with different three-phase systems.

the contact angle with water should be low and water should tend to spread over the surface. If the hydrocarbon tails are oriented outward and make up the surface, then the surface should be hydrophobic and exhibit a large contact angle. This is what is actually observed. A contact angle of approximately 100° is obtained, which is essentially the same value obtained for a paraffin wax. Apparently the polar group has little or no effect on the contact angle, since it lies beneath the surface.

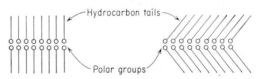

FIG. 16.2. Relative position of hydrocarbon tails and polar groups in solid heteropolar compounds.

The polar group is separated from outer space by 12 to 27 A, depending upon the length and inclination of the hydrocarbon structure. The distance between terminal carbon atoms in the surface is approximately 4 A, and the chain length increases by 1.25 A per CH_2 group added.

16.7. Measurement of Contact Angles. Several ingenious methods have been devised for the measurement of contact angles, but a brief description of the plate method of Adam and Jessop[5] and the captive-bubble method will suffice here. If a clean plate of the solid is immersed in water (Fig. 16.3), it can be observed that the surface of the water is deformed at the point of contact. The liquid tends to contact the plate

with an angle characteristic of the system. This characteristic angle
can be determined by slowly rotating the plate about the one-dimensional
line of contact between the solid-liquid-gas interface. When the plate is
at an angle to the liquid surface equal to the contact angle, there is no
deformity in the plane of the liquid surface. At this point the inclination of the plate and the contact angle must be identical.

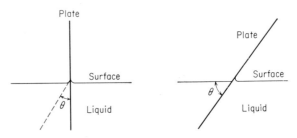

FIG. 16.3. Rotating-plate method of Adam and Jessop used for the measurement of
contact angles.

The captive-bubble method[6] of Taggart, Taylor, and Ince used for
measuring contact angles gives excellent results. A clean, polished
surface of the mineral is submerged in water and brought in contact
with a bubble held to the tip of a capillary. If the bubble adheres to
the mineral, then the contact angle can be observed with a microscope
and measured. Figure 16.4 illustrates a nonadhering and an adhering
bubble.

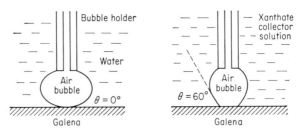

FIG. 16.4. Captive-bubble method of observing contact angles between solids and
bubbles.

The measurement of contact angles between powders and liquids is
difficult, but the depth to which the particle floats on the liquid is a
measure of the contact angle. If the particle floats high, it may have a
large contact angle. If it floats low, the contact angle may be small.
If the particle cannot be floated, it is a good indication that the contact
angle is very small or zero. For the larger particles, microscopic examination reveals the contact angle reasonably accurately.

16.8. Stabilization of a Solid in a Gas-Liquid Interface. It is possible to evaluate qualitatively the relationship between the contact angle and the adherence of a gas bubble to a solid particle. For a contact angle of zero degrees the liquid will completely wet or envelop the solid surface and expel the gas from the solid surface. On the other hand a contact angle of 180° would represent the complete envelopment of the solid by a gas and the exclusion of the liquid. In practice, no solids are known to have an air-water contact angle greater than 110°. Even so, it is known that air bubbles will spontaneously adhere to solids even when contact angles are less than 90°. A contact angle of 90° represents

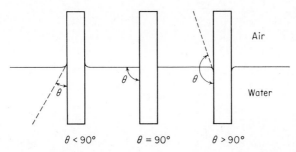

Fig. 16.5. Relative affinity of solids for different fluids is indicated by the contact angle. For $\theta < 90°$, the solid has a greater affinity for water; for $\theta > 90°$, the solid has a greater affinity for the gaseous phase; and for $\theta = 90°$, the solid has an equal affinity for both fluids.

a complete indifference of the solid to the two fluid phases in contact with it.

Gaudin[7] has graphically represented these three cases by considering the amount of work (other than gravitational) required to immerse or emerse a given area of material with different contact angles (Fig. 16.5). Aside from gravitational energy, the emergence of a given area of the solid requires work when θ is less than 90°, supplies work when θ is greater than 90°, and is workless when θ is 90°. Thus, we can reason qualitatively that for small particles the gravitational effects may be so small that immersion or emersion of a particle can be determined predominantly by the contact angle.

It is possible to show through basic energy requirements that a gas bubble will spontaneously adhere to a solid if its contact angle is finite. Consider, for example, a gas bubble and a solid suspended separately in a liquid medium. If the gas bubble spontaneously adheres to the solid, then there must be a loss in energy accompanying the process. The two-dimensional interfaces that previously existed between the gas-liquid and liquid-solid phases have been replaced by a one-dimensional line of contact where the three phases coalesce. The energy change can be evaluated from the change in interfacial surface area and the three interfacial energies. If the measured contact angle is introduced, the unknown solid-liquid and solid-gas interfacial energies are removed. The energy change then can be evaluated in terms of the contact angle, the surface energy or tension of the liquid, and the area of interface involved. For the special case where the bubble is small and the solid

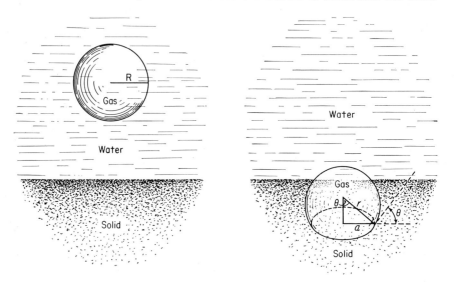

FIG. 16.6. New interfaces are created and old ones destroyed as a gas bubble coalesces with a solid suspended in solution.

particle is large, the surface of the bubble can be considered planar, since the interface is confined to a surface of the particle.

The decrease in free energy which occurred when the bubble and the particle coalesced is the sum of the two interfacial energies less the sum of the terminal surface energies. The adherence of the bubble with radius R to the solid surface is depicted in Fig. 16.6. Let a be the radius of the one-dimensional three-phase interface inscribed on the surface of the solid and r equal the radius of the adhering bubble. The height and area of the spherical portion remaining in contact with the liquid phase are $r(1 + \cos \theta)$ and $4\pi r^2 (1 + \cos \theta)/2$, respectively. The change in free energy or work of adhesion will be equal to

$$W = (A\gamma_{SL} + 4\pi R^2 \gamma_L) - \left[(A - \pi a^2)\gamma_{SL} + \pi a^2 \gamma_S + 4\pi r^2 \frac{1 + \cos \theta}{2} \gamma_L \right] \quad (16.4)$$

where A is the total area of the solid surface and γ_{SL}, γ_L, and γ_S are the surface energies (tensions) of the solid-liquid, liquid-gas, and solid-gas interfaces, respectively.

The terms in A cancel, and the equation can be reduced to

$$W = 4\pi R^2 \gamma_L + (\pi a^2 \gamma_{SL} - \pi a^2 \gamma_S) - 4\pi r^2 \frac{1 + \cos\theta}{2} \gamma_L$$

$$= \pi a^2 (\gamma_{SL} - \gamma_S) + \left(4\pi R^2 - 4\pi r^2 \frac{1 + \cos\theta}{2}\right) \gamma_L \qquad (16.5)$$

By substituting in $\gamma_{SL} - \gamma_S = -\gamma_L \cos\theta$ from Eq. (16.2) and $a = r\sin\theta$, the work of adhesion becomes

$$W = -\pi r^2 \sin^2\theta \cos\theta\, \gamma_L + \left(4\pi R^2 - 4\pi r^2 \frac{1 + \cos\theta}{2}\right) \gamma_L \qquad (16.6)$$

Equation (16.6) can be simplified by letting $r = fR$.   Then

$$W = -\pi f^2 R^2 (1 - \cos^2\theta) \cos\theta\, \gamma_L + \left[4\pi R^2 \gamma_L - 4\pi f^2 R^2 \frac{(1 + \cos\theta)}{2} \gamma_L\right]$$

$$= 4\pi R^2 \gamma_L \left[\frac{-f^2(1 - \cos^2\theta)\cos\theta}{4} + 1 - \frac{f^2(1 + \cos\theta)}{2}\right]$$

$$= 4\pi R^2 \gamma_L \left[\frac{f^2(-\cos\theta + \cos^3\theta - 2 - 2\cos\theta)}{4} + 1\right]$$

$$= 4\pi R^2 \gamma_L \left(1 - f^2 \frac{2 + 3\cos\theta - \cos^3\theta}{4}\right) \qquad (16.7)$$

If it is assumed that there is no volume change in the gas bubble when it adheres to the solid, then the parameter f can be evaluated.   The volume of a spherical segment with height $h = r(1 + \cos\theta)$ and radius r is $\frac{1}{3}\pi h^2(3r - h)$.   From this it follows that the volume of the independent bubble is equal to

$$\tfrac{4}{3}\pi R^3 = \tfrac{1}{3}\pi r^2 (1 + \cos\theta)^2 [3r - r(1 + \cos\theta)] \qquad (16.8)$$

The parameter f is evaluated by substituting fR for r in Eq. (16.8) and solving for f.

$$\tfrac{4}{3}\pi R^3 = \tfrac{1}{3}\pi f^2 R^2 (1 + \cos\theta)^2 [3fR - fR(1 + \cos\theta)]$$

$$= (\pi f^3 R^3 - \tfrac{1}{3}\pi f^3 R^3 - \tfrac{1}{3}\pi f^3 R^3 \cos\theta)(1 + 2\cos\theta + \cos^2\theta)$$

$$= \pi f^3 R^3 (1 - \tfrac{1}{3} - \tfrac{1}{3}\cos\theta)(1 + 2\cos\theta + \cos^2\theta)$$

$$f^3 = \frac{4\pi R^3}{3\pi R^3 (\tfrac{2}{3} - \tfrac{1}{3}\cos\theta)(1 + 2\cos\theta + \cos^2\theta)}$$

$$f^3 = \frac{4}{2 + 3\cos\theta - \cos^3\theta}$$

$$f = \left(\frac{4}{2 + 3\cos\theta - \cos^3\theta}\right)^{1/3} \qquad (16.9)$$

Substitute f into Eq. (16.7), and let $F = 1/f$.

$$W = 4\pi R^2 \gamma_L \left(1 - f^2 \frac{1}{f^3}\right)$$
$$= 4\pi R^2 \gamma_L (1 - F) \tag{16.10}$$

The work of adhesion thus can be shown to be equal to the product of the surface of the original bubble, the specific surface energy of the liquid, and the parameter $(1 - F)$, which is a function of the contact angle θ only. The parameter F is positive and less than unity for all values of θ between 0 and 180°, so the energy change is in a direction favoring the spontaneous adhesion of the bubble to the particle. In other words, a particle can be stabilized in a gas-liquid interface if the contact angle is finite. In actual practice, adherence of bubble and particle is favored by angles not too near to zero and by sharp particle edges.

For a large bubble and a small particle the surface of the bubble can be considered planar. It can then be shown that the work of adhesion equals

$$W = S\gamma_L(1 - \cos\theta)$$

when S equals the area of the interface involved and γ_L is the surface free energy of the liquid. Again, one can see how dependent the stabilization of a particle in a gas-liquid interface is on the contact angle. The work of adhesion is real for all finite values of the contact angle but is dependent also on the size of the particle.

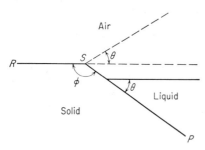

Fig. 16.7. In order for the liquid to spread over face RS, enough energy must be supplied to swing the liquid front through an angle of $180° - \phi$.

When a solid particle is stabilized in an air-liquid interface, there is a decrease in the potential energy of the system as the two independent interfaces are replaced by the single interface. Therefore, a large bubble will tend to extend spontaneously and cover the entire plane solid surface that is available. It will extend to a point of sharp change in the orientation of the solid-liquid interface. Perhaps this can be more easily seen if we consider the displacement of a gas by a liquid on a solid surface. In Fig. 16.7 the liquid is spreading over the solid surface PS with its characteristic contact angle θ. When the liquid front reaches the edge of the solid, then it will not proceed down the surface RS until its characteristic contact angle has been established. This requires that the liquid front be rotated through an angle of $180° - \phi$. Obviously energy

is required to swing the liquid front through this angle.   As a result, the
interface has a tendency to become stable or static at the edge or sharp
corner of the solid surface.   This is precisely why a tumbler can be filled
above its rim without overflowing.   Overflow does not occur until the
hydrostatic head builds up sufficiently to overcome the interfacial energy
at the edge.   This edge effect is also a contributing factor in floating a
steel needle or razor blade or dense particles with small contact angles.

16.9. Flotation.   Many substances have been observed to float that
have a greater density than the fluid in which they are suspended.   If
submerged, the particle may not spontaneously rise again to the surface.
If it is brought back to the surface, however, it may float again.   Gravitational forces are relentlessly pulling the particle downward, whereas
surface forces tend to resist the wetting of the particle by the liquid and
counteract the effect of gravity.   This flotation phenomenon is determined by the character of the solid surface rather than by the character
of the bulk solid.

Several steps are generally involved in the flotation process.   The
solid is dispersed as a fine powder (0.01 to 0.001 cm in diameter) in water.
Air is then forced into the system to produce a froth with gas bubbles 20
to 200 times as large as the solid particles.   Soaps and saponins are
generally unsuitable as frothing agents because they lower the surface
tension of the air-liquid interface.   Any lowering of surface tension will
decrease the work required to separate a given area of solid surface from
the interface.   The most stable flotation is observed when the work of
adhesion is large and/or the contact angle is large.   A decrease in surface
tension also causes a lowering of the contact angle.   Some of the dispersed solids, namely, those having a large contact angle, adhere to the
bubbles and are selectively floated to the surface, where they can be
skimmed off and recovered.   The photomicrograph of particle-bubble
attachment shown in Fig. 16.8 illustrates the flotation process far better
than a word description.   We are indeed indebted to H. R. Spedden of
Union Carbide Ore Company for permission to reproduce such a graphical
illustration of the flotation process.

The floated material is usually referred to as the *concentrate*.   Substances with small or zero contact angles are left in the liquid phase.
The nonfloated material is referred to as the *tailings* or *gangue*.

The principal quality of the mineral surface required for flotation is that
it should be sufficiently hydrophobic to produce a large contact angle.
Actually, for stability of a particle in an interface, the contact angle only
needs to be finite.   Greater stability is achieved, however, if the angle is
not too near zero and the edges of the particle are sharp.   The most
stable flotations will be obtained with large values of W, work of adhesion,
or large contact angles.   The material differences in contact angles

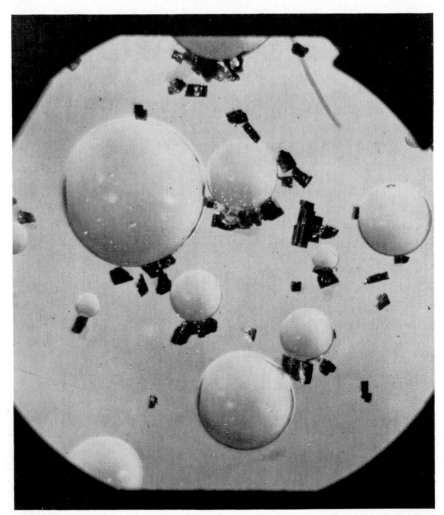

FIG. 16.8. Photomicrograph of particle-bubble attachment in flotation. Particles of zanthate-conditioned 65/100-mesh galena are clinging to air bubbles and are being rafted to the surface. The view is horizontal through the side of a glass flotation cell. (*Reproduced by permission of H. Rush Spedden.*)

exhibited by various solids are sometimes too small to effect a separation by flotation. Substances with a given contact angle can be selectively floated by controlling either particle size or bubble size. This became evident when considering the work of adhesion between solids and gases. There appears also a vast range of possibilities for increasing the selectivity of flotation by the addition of reagents to the system that are selectively adsorbed and will modify the surface of the particles.

16.10. Collectors.   Particles of minerals present variations in floatability because of the chemical composition of the surface and size.   Floatability is less affected by shape, angularity of particles, and specific gravity. Native floatability is encountered only in solids with a nonionic surface character.   Solids with ions in the surface are naturally nonfloating in character.   Gaudin compiled a list of solids (Table 16.1) and compared the crystal type with native floatability.   In general, minerals lack native floatability because their surfaces can be considered as giant polyfunctional ions that are hydrophilic.   Air does not even partially replace

TABLE 16.1. NATIVE FLOATABILITY COMPARED WITH CRYSTAL TYPE*

Solid	Crystal type	Native floatability
Iodine, sulfur.............	Molecular	Some
Naphthalene, paraffin......	....	High
Graphite.................	Filament and sheet	Considerable
Diamond................	Diamontine	Probably nil
Salt, fluorite.............	Simple ionic	Nil
Calcite, olivine..........	Complex ionic	Nil
Pyroxenes................	Fiber ionic	Nil
Micas...................	Layer ionic	Nil
Talc....................	....	Considerable
Fatty acids...............	....	High
Boric acid................	....	High
Feldspars, quartz.........	Framework	Nil
Copper..................	Metallic	Nil
Galena, pyrite............	Semimetallic	Nil

* From A. M. Gaudin, "Flotation," 2d ed., p. 92, McGraw-Hill Book Company, Inc., New York, 1957.

water from clean surfaces of common sulfides.   The flotation of minerals and other nonfloating solids is effected by the addition of collectors. *Collectors* are reagents that attach themselves to normally nonfloating species and endow them with hydrophobic surfaces.   All the common collectors are organic substances that will attach themselves to the mineral surface and form a hydrocarbonlike surface.   In general, hydrocarbons are not satisfactory collectors because they will not displace water from the surface.   An exception is the hydrocarbon oil Nujol, which will spread over the surface of a mineral and form a hydrophobic surface.   The mechanism for its spreading is unknown.   What is needed is an organic molecule that will be reactive enough to attach itself to the particle and still impart a hydrophobic character to the surface.   Any organic molecule that possesses a reactive functional group attached to a hydrocarbonlike structure is a potential collector.   Thus, all monofunctional organic acids, bases, and salts are potential collectors.   Table 16.2 lists some of the common types of collector.   The mercaptans,

TABLE 16.2. TYPES OF ORGANIC COMPOUNDS COMMONLY USED AS
COLLECTORS IN FLOTATION

Anionic Collectors

Mercaptans   R—S · · · H

Thiocarbonates (xanthates) $R—O—C—S · · · H$
                                                            $\parallel$
                                                            S

Carboxylates
                                                            O
                                                            $\parallel$
                                                 $R—C—O · · · H$

Thioureas
                                                            H
                                                            $\mid$
                                          $R—N—C=N—R'$
                                                            $\overset{..}{S}$
                                                            $\vdots$
                                                            H

Thiophosphates
                                                            R
                                                            $\mid$
                                                            O
                                                            $\mid$
                                          $R'—O—P—S · · · H$
                                                            $\parallel$
                                                            S

Thiocarbamates
                                                            R'
                                                            $\mid$
                                          $R—N—C—S · · · H$
                                                            $\parallel$
                                                            S

Sulfonates
                                                            O
                                                            $\parallel$
                                          $R—S—O · · · H$
                                                            $\parallel$
                                                            O

Acid alkyl sulfates
                                                            O
                                                            $\parallel$
                                          $R—O—S · · · H$
                                                            $\parallel$
                                                            O

Cationic Collectors

Primary amines $R—NH_2$

Secondary amines
                                          $R—NH$
                                                $\mid$
                                                R'

Tertiary amines
                                                R'
                                                $\mid$
                                          $R—N—R''$

Quaternary amines
                                  $\left[\begin{matrix} R' & & R'' \\ & N & \\ R & & R''' \end{matrix} \right]^+$

xanthates, thioureas, thiocarbamates, and thiophosphates apparently attach themselves to minerals by bonding through the sulfur atom. The hydrocarbon group is in the anionic portion of the collector and is left oriented outward after the collector attaches itself to the mineral. The carboxylates, sulfates, and sulfonates apparently attach themselves to the mineral through the oxygen.

The amines are called cationic collectors because the hydrocarbon portion of the molecule is part of the cation in amine salts, the reactive species.

Each of the above types of collector is somewhat selective in its attachment to minerals and will enhance the separation of minerals by flotation. *Modifiers* can be used to modulate the action of collectors and make them more specific in their affinity for different substances. Examples of modifier action can be found in Sec. 16.12.

16.11. Mechanism by Which Collectors Function. The mechanism by which collectors enhance the floatability of diverse solids is the central problem in the development of flotation theory. The theory has evolved from the original hypothesis that collector and mineral are attracted and held to each other by static electricity. Molecular adsorption processes supplanted this theory. Now, the most widely accepted mechanism by which collector and mineral combine is by ion-exchange adsorption. Still, there is no completely acceptable systematic presentation of collector action.

The flotation of galena with potassium ethyl xanthate collector has been studied more than any other system. The results of these studies give an excellent indication of the collection mechanism for at least certain types of minerals. Clean polished surfaces of galena exhibit a contact angle of 0° in pure water, but the same surface will form a contact angle of approximately 60° in a dilute solution (exceeding 20 ppm) of potassium ethyl xanthate. Lower concentrations of collector result in intermediate values for the contact angle (see Fig. 16.9). Apparently the collector forms a surface film over the mineral with the alkyl group of the collector oriented outward, thus producing a hydrophobic surface with a lower electrolytic potential and a larger contact angle. Wark[8] substantiates this concept by showing that the contact angle produced with collectors is independent of the underlying mineral. When potassium ethyl xanthate is used as the collector, essentially the same contact angle, 59 to 60°, is obtained for a number of different minerals (see Table 16.3). Similar results are observed when other collectors are used. The contact angle seems to be independent of the polar group in the collector, for the contact angle increases with an increase in the length of the alkyl portion of the collector. This is in line with expected results, because the surface should become more hydrophobic with increasing hydrocarbon character.

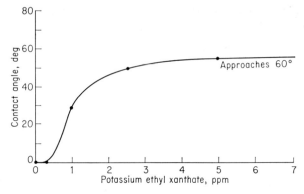

Fɪɢ. 16.9. Contact angle of galena in dilute potassium ethyl zanthate collector solution after 40-min to 1-hr contact. [*After I. W. Wark and A. B. Cox, Principles of Flotation, Trans. AIMME*, **112**, 209 (1934).]

Galena that is freshly cleaved or ground in an inert atmosphere[9] has a zero contact angle with pure water and will not float. The electrolytic potential of the clean surface does not change when treated with xanthate because xanthate does not adsorb on the clean surface. Apparently a certain amount of air oxidation of the mineral surface is necessary before the xanthate will adhere to it. If the freshly cleaved galena is first exposed to oxygen, then the material can be floated.

TABLE 16.3. INDEPENDENCE OF CONTACT ANGLE FROM UNDERLYING MINERAL WITH VARIOUS COLLECTORS*

Mineral	Contact angle with various collectors, deg			
	Na diethyl dithio-carbamate	Benzyl mercaptan	K methyl xanthate	K cetyl xanthate
Galena....................	59	71	50	100
Sphalerite...............	59	71	51	97
Pyrite....................	58	69	49	95
Chalcopyrite.............	59	72	52	94
Bornite..................	62	72	51	95

* From I. W. Wark, "Principles of Flotation," Australasian Institute of Mining and Metallurgy, Inc., Melbourne, Australia, 1938.

This air oxidation of the galena surface is analogous to the hydroxylation of fractured surfaces of quartz. Figure 16.10 is a simple projected two-dimensional diagram of the quartz crystalline lattice showing a central silicon atom surrounded by only three of the four combined oxygens. If the crystal is fractured, some oxygen-silicon bonds are broken.

The unsatisfied charges on the fractured surface then compete with ions of the same sign in solution for ions of opposite charge. Adsorption of ions takes place with the creation of the electrical double layer. The adsorbed hydrogen and hydroxyl ions then can exchange with other ions in solution. This may be why pH plays such a major part in modulating the collection process.

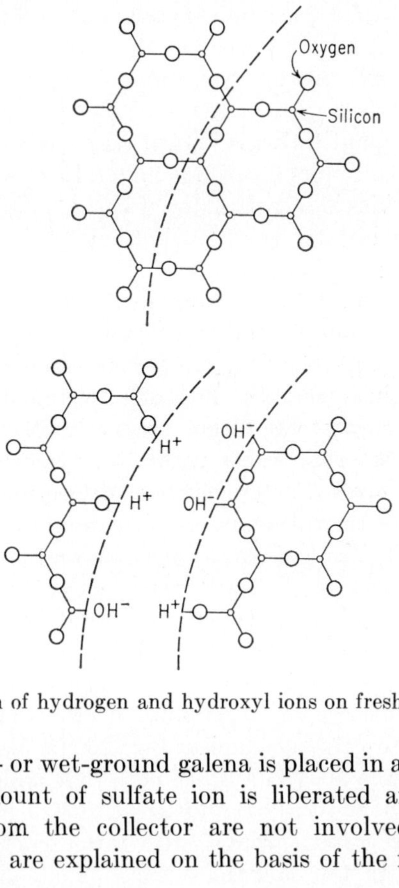

FIG. 16.10. Adsorption of hydrogen and hydroxyl ions on freshly cleaved quartz.

When either dry- or wet-ground galena is placed in a xanthate solution' an appreciable amount of sulfate ion is liberated and the pH rises.[10] Potassium ions from the collector are not involved in the reaction. These observations are explained on the basis of the following exchange reactions.

$$Pb(OH)_2 + 2KS \cdot CS \cdot OC_2H_5 \rightleftharpoons Pb(S \cdot CS \cdot OC_2H_5)_2 + 2KOH$$
$$PbSO_4 + 2KS \cdot CS \cdot OC_2H_5 \rightleftharpoons Pb(S \cdot CS \cdot OC_2H_5)_2 + K_2SO_4$$

The heavy metal xanthate is formed in a layer over the surface of the mineral. Simultaneously, hydroxyl, sulfate, and sulfite ions are liberated.

The quantity of anion participating in the exchange reaction is directly proportional to the concentration of the collector and the length of time the galena has been oxidized. The solution is not enriched with lead, and there is no evidence to suggest the replacement of sulfide by xanthate. In fact, solutions of lead xanthate are destroyed by sulfide owing to the formation of the more stable PbS. One can conclude that galena is covered with lead sulfite, sulfate, hydroxide, or other oxidized products prior to collection and by lead xanthate after collection. Further evidence to support the topochemical exchange mechanism is the amount of collector required to float a mineral effectively. The quantity of collector used is insufficient to form a monolayer over the surface of the mineral.

Almost nothing quantitative is known concerning the actions of fatty acids and soaps as collectors for sulfide minerals. Oxidized minerals and ores, such as the oxides and carbonates of basic metals, are floated by the addition of long-chain fatty acids. The soap of the heavy metal forms with the hydrocarbon tail oriented away from the surface.

The action of amine collectors is unknown. In alkaline solutions there is an adsorption of amine without the desorption of metal ions. Metal ions apparently are desorbed only under acid conditions.

Some authors believe that the rate of attachment of particles to the bubble is as important to flotation as the contact angle. Since the bubbles spend only a short time within the suspension and since the collector action involves a heterogeneous surface reaction, it is believed that the diffusion of the collector across the fluid-film barrier is the rate-determining step.[11] This, of course, is based on the broader assumption that flotation systems are dynamic and not in an equilibrium state. Measured rates of contact between solids and liquids indicate a wide variation for different systems. In general, collectors tend to hasten the rate of contact between solids and gases suspended in a liquid. Such evidence only emphasizes one's inability to propound a theory that will explain unequivocally the mechanism by which collectors operate.

In summarizing the above data, we note that minerals lacking native floatability can be made to float by the takeup of hydrocarbon-bearing groups. The hydrocarbon groups, with few exceptions, are ionic and attach themselves to the mineral surface by an ion-exchange surface reaction. In any event, partitioning of the collector between the mineral surface and the solution favors the mineral surface. The collector need not saturate the solution to form an incomplete monolayer on the mineral surface.

16.12. Modulation of Collector Action. Certain sulfide ores are not floated by xanthate collectors unless the mineral surface is first activated. For example, sphalerite ZnS cannot be floated normally. If, however, the zinc sulfide is treated with a dilute solution of copper sulfate, xanthates will effect flotation. Copper sulfide is deposited on the mineral surface and activates the surface in so far as collector attachment is concerned. In general, activation of a sulfide ore involves treatment with a metal that will form a more insoluble sulfide than the ore itself. Silver, copper, mercury, cadmium, and lead salts will activate zinc sulfide.

The pH of the system has a large effect on the floatability of different species. There is usually only a narrow pH range within which flotation is possible. Excessive hydrogen-ion concentrations will destroy some collectors, and excessive hydroxyl-ion concentrations may provide too much competition for the anion-exchange sites.

Some reagents act as depressants and prevent flotation by deactivating the surface. The sulfides of zinc, iron, and lead can be separated by treating the mixture with cyanide. The cyanide prevents the flotation of the iron and zinc sulfides but does not interfere with the flotation of the lead sulfide. After the lead has been removed, the iron and zinc sulfides can be activated with copper salts and floated. Thus, through a combination of activators, depressants, and collectors, a fair degree of specificity can be obtained with flotation. The selection of reagents for modulating the action of collectors is still an empirical procedure.

16.13. Applications. Flotation has been applied to the concentration of metallic ores, separation of solids and liquids, separation of minerals and nonminerals, concentration of trace quantities of solid material in interfaces, etc. The principal application has been the concentration of valuable minerals. Complex mixtures of sulfide ores have been successfully resolved into the individual components with the proper selection of collectors and modifiers. Only limited success has been achieved in the separation of silicates and other nonsulfide oxidized ores. There is a distinct possibility that flotation can be used successfully for concentrating low-grade iron ores and sundry other solids. For a comprehensive coverage of mineral recovery consult the chemical literature, particularly the patents, and the monographs and reviews found in Sec. 16.14.

Although clean fractured diamond surfaces are probably hydrophilic, diamonds can be floated and separated from other materials.[12] With only a fraction of a pound of collector to a ton, diamonds up to 16- or 20-mesh size are floated in 5 to 10 min at a pH of 7 to 9.

Oil-field brines and petroleum-refinery wastes can be treated by flotation procedures for the recovery of oil.[13] The waste water containing a coagulant, such as alum, is saturated with air under high pressure. The solution is reduced to atmospheric pressure while a flocculating agent is added. The dissolved air is released at the reduced pressure and trapped by the colloidal floc, which floats to the surface carrying with it the oil and solids.

Various flotation procedures have been set up for cleaning peas,[14] sorting seeds,[15] and removing the oil-rich fractions of milled seeds.[16]

Analytical applications of flotation are limited but noteworthy. Newly formed precipitates that are insoluble in water and a water-immiscible solvent often can be collected in the interface between the two liquids if the suspension is shaken vigorously and the phases then allowed to separate. A particle collecting at the interface of two liquids is effecting an extraction and concentration of the material. This is a type of flotation with the particle stabilized in the interface of two liquids rather than in an air-liquid interface. The fundamental treatment of particle stabilization in the liquid-liquid interface is very similar to the treatment for an air-water interface. The solid must have some aversion for both phases; otherwise it will be enveloped by the fluid with a very small contact angle.

Young[17] concentrated traces of nickel dimethylglyoximate by shaking aqueous suspensions of the complex with kerosene. A perceptible pink color was imparted to the water-kerosene interface even when the nickel complex was invisible in the aqueous ammoniacal layer. Johnson and Newman[18] concentrated traces of nickel in copper salts by making the aqueous solution ammoniacal and by adding nioxime. The mixture was then shaken vigorously with benzene. After 35 to 40 min the nickel complex settled into the interface and was separated from the copper salts by discarding most of the aqueous layer. After washing the benzene layer successively with aqueous ammonia and water without losing the interfacial deposit, the nickel complex was extracted into hydrochloric acid solution.

Ziegler and Glemser[19] developed a method for detecting as little as 0.3 μg of palladium in a concentration of 0.3 ppm palladium. One milliliter of the acid solution was mixed with several drops of lauryl mercaptan (n-dodecanethiol) and extracted with five drops of amyl alcohol. The palladium complex concentrated at the interface.

Mixtures of arsenic, antimony, and tin sulfides are frequently contaminated with elemental sulfur in qualitative analysis when the alkaline polysulfide solution is acidified. The sulfur and sulfides can be separated by shaking the aqueous suspension with amyl alcohol and chloroform; the sulfur remains in the aqueous phase, but the sulfides collect at the interface.

When acid solutions of selenium are treated with stannous chloride the selenate is reduced to elemental selenium. If the mixture is shaken with ether, the metal collects in the water-ether interface.[20]

Other analytical flotation systems can be found in the works of Feigl,[21] Hofmann,[22] Reinders,[23] Kerschner,[24] and others.[25]

A variation of the flotation technique has recently been reported which concentrates inorganic ions from aqueous solutions. A surfactant ion of charge opposite to that of the ion to be concentrated is used as the collector.   When air is bubbled through the solution, the surfactant produces a froth and eventually a scum of insoluble soap with the ions to be collected. The scum can be easily removed from the surface.   Quaternary ammonium salts can be used as cationic surfactants to collect anions, while sodium laurate or palmitate or sodium salts of sulfated fatty alcohols can be used to collect cations.   Sebba[26] reports that ferrocyanide, ferricyanide, cobalticyanide, chloroplatinate, fluoberylate, uranyl sulfate, chromate, vanadate, molybdate, silicate, polythionate, copper, nickel, cobalt, aluminum, zinc, manganese, calcium, barium, strontium, vanadyl, uranyl, and thorium ions can be concentrated by the technique.   The method appears applicable to very dilute solutions and has possibilities in the fields of by-product recovery, treatment of wastes, and analytical chemistry.   Finding the best surfactant for a given separation is mostly a matter of screening numerous compounds, however.

Flotation has a great potential application to analytical chemistry, both for the qualitative detection of trace quantities and in quantitative measurements.   Flotation has always involved aqueous phases, probably because water is available, cheap, and almost a universal solvent in wet analyses and commercial operations, but there is no reason why other solvents should not be suitable.   Nothing seems to have been done with nonaqueous solvents.

16.14. Selected Bibliography

Adam, N. K.: "The Physics and Chemistry of Surfaces," 3d ed., Oxford University Press, London, 1941.

Berkman, S., and G. Egloff: "Emulsions and Foams," Reinhold Publishing Corporation, New York, 1941.

Bikerman, J. J.: "Foams: Theory and Industrial Applications," Reinhold Publishing Corporation, New York, 1953.

Booth, R. B.: *Ind. Eng. Chem., Chem. Eng. Revs.*, **47**, 551 (1955).

Chem. Eng. Progr. Symposium Ser., **50**, 1–96 (1954).

Cooke, S. R. B.: Flotation, in "Advances in Colloid Science," vol. III, H. Mark and E. J. W. Verwey (eds.), Interscience Publishers, Inc., New York, 1950.

Gaudin, A. M.: "Flotation," 2d ed., McGraw-Hill Book Company, Inc., New York, 1957.

Moeller, A.: *Z. Elektrochem.*, **59**, 296 (1955).

The Physical Chemistry of Flotation.   I. The Significance of Contact Angle in Flotation, I. W. Wark, *J. Phys. Chem.*, **37**, 623–644 (1933); II. The Nature of the Adsorption of the Soluble Collectors, A. B. Cox and I. W. Wark, *ibid.*, pp. 797–803; III. The Relationship between Contact Angle and the Constitution of the Collector, E. E. Wark and I. W. Wark, *ibid.*, pp. 805–814; IV. A Criticism of Ostwald's Theory of Flotation, I. W. Wark and A. B. Cox, *ibid.*, pp. 815–819.

Spedden, H. R.: Flotation, in "Encyclopedia of Chemical Technology," vol. 6, R. E. Kirk and D. F. Othmer (eds.), Interscience Encyclopedia, New York, 1951.

Taggart, A. F.: "Handbook of Mineral Dressing," sec. 12, John Wiley & Sons, Inc., New York, 1945.

Wadsworth, M. E., R. C. Conrady, and M. A. Cook: Contact Angle and Surface

Coverage for Potassium Ethyl Xanthate on Galena According to Free Acid Collector Theory, *J. Phys. & Colloid Chem.*, **55**, 1219 (1951).

Wark, I. W.: "Principles of Flotation," Australasian Institute of Mining and Metallurgy, Melbourne, Australia, 1938.

REFERENCES

1. Pietsch, E., A. Kotowski, and G. Behrend: *Z. physik. Chem.*, **B5**, 1 (1929).
2. Leidheiser, H., Jr., and A. T. Gwathmey: *J. Am. Chem. Soc.*, **70**, 1206 (1948).
3. Cunningham, R. E., and A. T. Gwathmey: "Proceedings of the International Congress on Catalysis, Philadelphia, 1956," pp. 25–36, Academic Press, Inc., New York, 1957.
4. Smith, W. R., and M. H. Polley: *J. Phys. Chem.*, **60**, 689 (1956).
5. Adam, N. K., and G. Jessop: *J. Chem. Soc.*, **127**, 1865 (1925).
6. Taggart, A. F., T. C. Taylor, and C. R. Ince: *Trans. AIMME*, **87**, 285 (1930).
7. Gaudin, A. M.: "Flotation," 2d ed., p. 149, McGraw-Hill Book Company, Inc., New York, 1957.
8. Wark, I. W.: "Principles of Flotation," Australasian Institute of Mining and Metallurgy, Melbourne, Australia, 1938.
9. Herd, H. H., and W. Ure: *J. Phys. Chem.*, **45**, 93 (1941).
10. Taylor, T. C., and A. F. Knoll: *Trans. AIMME*, **112**, 382 (1934).
11. Tuwiner, S. B., and S. Korman: *Trans. AIMME*, **187**, 217 (1950).
12. Weavind, R. G., I. Wolf, and R. S. Young: *Mining Eng.*, **3**, 596 (1951).
13. D'Arcy, Jr., N. A.: *Oil Gas J.*, **50**, 319 (1951); *Proc. Am. Petrol. Inst.*, **31M**, 34 (1951).
14. Neubert, A. M.: *Food Inds.*, **19**, 769, 890, 892 (1947).
15. Earle, T.: U.S. Pat. 2,115,219, 1939.
16. Grace, N. H., and J. B. Palmer: *Can. J. Research*, **24F**, 338 (1946).
17. Young, R. S.: *Chemist-Analyst*, **34**, 88 (1945).
18. Johnson, E. A., and E. J. Newman: *Analyst*, **81**, 318 (1956).
19. Ziegler, M., and O. Glemser: *Z. anal. Chem.*, **146**, 101 (1956).
20. Yoshida, Yukito: *J. Chem. Soc. Japan, Pure Chem. Sect.*, **76**, 856 (1955).
21. Feigl, F.: "Chemistry of Specific, Selective and Sensitive Reactions," Academic Press, Inc., New York, 1949.
22. Hofmann, F. B.: *Z. physik. Chem.*, **83**, 385 (1913).
23. Reinders, W.: *Kolloid-Z.*, **13**, 235 (1913).
24. Kerschner, K., and R. D. Duff: *J. Chem. Educ.*, **9**, 1271 (1932).
25. Maxim, I., T. Braun, and I. Gălăteanu: *J. Inorg. & Nuclear Chem.*, **10**, 166 (1959).
26. Sebba, F.: *Nature*, **184**, Suppl. 14, 1062 (1959).

CHAPTER 17

BIOLOGICAL METHODS

17.1. Introduction. The living cell is a separation tool which has been grossly neglected by the chemist until very recent years. There are sound reasons for the rejection in the past, but it seems inevitable that chemists must now become familiar with the selective properties of living cells and apply them to difficult separation problems. The early literature contains many reports on the essentiality of nutrients other than energy and nitrogen sources for the growth of plants, animals, and microorganisms, but only in relatively recent years have the nutritional needs been more fully recognized. Of particular importance here is the recognized dependency of life processes on the availability of just traces of certain inorganic constituents in the environment of the biological system.

Nearly every element has been found to occur in living tissues by one method or another, but it appears that certain elements are required to greatly different extents by biological systems. Carbon, hydrogen, oxygen, nitrogen, sulfur, phosphorus, calcium, potassium, sodium, chlorine, and magnesium normally occur in relatively high concentrations in all living tissues and are referred to as the *major elements*. Fe, Cu, Mn, Zn, I, Co, Mo, Al, Cr, Sn, Ti, Si, Pb, Rb, Li, As, F, Br, Se, Ba, Sr, Ni, and B are constantly present in tissue, but their concentration is usually low and quite variable. These are generally designated as the *trace elements*. V, Ag, Au, and Ce are also occasionally or frequently encountered in tissues and should be classified with the trace elements. There is considerable reason to believe that other elements will be added to the list of trace elements in the future.

Of the above group of trace elements only six, Fe, Cu, Mn, Zn, I, and Co, have been unequivocally established as being nutritionally essential to higher forms of animal life, although there is some justification for including Mo, F, Ba, and Sr. Only seven of the trace elements, Fe, Cu, Mn, Zn, B, Si, and Mo, have been definitely established as essential for the life of higher plants. Vanadium must be added as essential to the life processes of some lower forms of animal and plant life.

Some of the trace elements to which no definite biological functions can be ascribed do occur in the fluids and tissues in concentrations significantly higher than those of the essential trace elements. Plants apparently do not require I or Co, although these elements are invariably present in plant tissues, and animals have not been shown to require B and Si, although these elements are also normally present in animal tissues.

The small number of trace elements constantly present in tissues and known to be essential should not be interpreted to mean that the other trace elements are merely accidental contaminants. The ability of some biological systems to concentrate other trace elements need not imply that these elements serve an essential biological function. It may mean only that the organism has developed a tolerance for these elements.

Studies conducted on the mode of action of trace elements in animal and plant nutrition leave little doubt that the trace elements function as activators or catalysts within the living cell and that they lie at the root of living processes. This perhaps accounts for the remarkable specificity living cells exhibit for certain minerals. Neither similar physical nor chemical properties imply similar physiological properties. Even cobalt and nickel, which are very similar in terms of atomic weight, ionic radii, and many other physical and chemical characteristics, are completely differentiated by living cells. Nickel can neither replace cobalt in ruminant metabolism nor effectively economize in its utilization. Nor can one element take over the functional activity of another element even when they are as alike as bromine and iodine. Even so, no form of life has a completely unique metabolic or functional requirement. All plants and animals require certain elements in widely varying amounts to exist.

Equally important to the chemist is the fact that living cells tend to produce or metabolize only one of a pair of enantiomorphs or optical isomers. It has been noted that each of the natural amino acids, except glycine, has at least one asymmetric carbon atom and is, therefore, capable of existing as optical isomers. It is a striking fact, though, that careful hydrolysis of proteins invariably yields optically active amino acids, never racemic mixtures, and that the α-carbon atoms of all these forms have the same absolute configuration. Another curious fact is that some essential amino acids can be metabolized in either form (d or l configuration of α-carbon atom) while others must be supplied in the natural (l) configuration. This indicates that, in some cases at least, the organism can convert one optical isomer into its enantiomorph.

The pronounced physiological effects of many other metabolically active substances, such as vitamins, hormones, and antibiotics, are also traceable to a single enantiomorph.

A great incentive to study further the ability of plants and animals to concentrate certain elements is thrust upon us by the knowledge that radioactive isotopes of strontium, cesium, barium, and iodine from fallout are finding their way into the human body via food plants and animals. The danger involved in ingesting highly radioactive materials is great and must be avoided. We must learn what elements are concentrated by foodstuffs and avoid an unnecessary risk.

The analytical significance, as far as separations are concerned, of the rather specific function of cells is mainly academic at this time, but there is much to suggest that living cells can be used as highly selective and specific reagents in separations work. The following examples will serve to point up the ability of plants, animals, and microorganisms to concentrate substances and resolve mixtures.

17.2. Metabolic Selectivity of Plants. The concentration of trace elements in plants is primarily dependent on the species and the nature of the soil on which they are grown, although climatic conditions, season, and stage of growth are significant on occasion.

Iodine is greatly concentrated in various forms of marine life, especially seaweeds, although sea water is not particularly rich in this element. Ordinarily sea water contains only 17 to 18 μg of iodine per liter, whereas figures as high as 0.2 per cent iodine on a fresh basis have been recorded for seaweeds. The iodine content of kelp is great enough that kelp has served as a commercial source of iodine. Marine plankton, sea fish, and shellfish also have a high iodine content, indicating their ability to concentrate iodine from their environment.

The great differences that exist in the ability of plants to take up selenium from the soil assume special significance in the case of a few species which are known as *indicator* plants. These plants are very rare or do not occur in nonseleniferous areas. Such plants not only absorb and accumulate very large amounts of selenium but do so on soils that contain low concentrations of selenium. No satisfactory explanation of this special ability of indicator plants to absorb selenium is available.

Selenium concentrations typical of indicator plants grown on seleniferous soils range from 1000 to 3000 ppm (dry basis) and occasionally as high as 9000 ppm. It is significant that these concentrations are attained on soils containing less than 5 ppm (dry basis) of selenium, and this frequently in a relatively insoluble form. The plant genus or species is a very important factor in determining the ability of a plant to concentrate selenium from a particular soil. Some of the more common indicator plants[1] are of the orders Leguminosae, Cruciferae, and Compositae and in particular the species *Stanleya pinnata, Oonopsis condensata, Astragalus racemosis, A. bisulcatus,* and *A. pectinatus.* It is worth noting here that most other plants including crop plants do not have this ability to concentrate selenium.

Most plants contain only about 15 to 20 ppm of aluminum, but there are a few species of trees and ferns which habitually accumulate vastly greater quantities of aluminum.   Values of 3000 to 4000 ppm are quite common with these *accumulator* species.[2,3]

Barium is concentrated as high as 3000 to 4000 ppm in brazil nuts[4,5] and the ephiphyte Spanish moss (*Tillandsia usneoides L.*), which derives all its nutrients from the atmosphere, is known to accumulate as much as 285 ppm (dry-weight basis) of manganese, 1400 ppm of iron, and 11,200 ppm of Si.[6]

There are plants known to accumulate copper and other elements.   It is reasonable to expect that there are also plants that concentrate or accumulate in their tissues some of the rarer elements, such as gold, and that these plants can be used for the concentration and ultimate isolation of such elements from very dilute soils and solutions.

17.3. Metabolic Selectivity of Animals.   Much less is known about the mineral-accumulating powers of animals, but there are a few specific cases which warrant mention because of their rather obvious analytical potential.

It has been known for some time that the oyster can concentrate copper in its body to a point 1000 times higher than in the sea around it, but there are some other examples which are more intriguing.

Professor Ciereszko at the University of Oklahoma has been studying the manner in which marine animals concentrate radioactive isotopes from their environment.   An interesting observation is the mineral-concentrating power of the sea squirt, a small marine animal ranging in length from about $\frac{1}{8}$ in. to several inches.   Sea squirts are able to concentrate vanadium to levels as great as $\frac{4}{1000}$ their body weight (dry-weight basis) in 18 hr from sea water containing only 1 part of vanadium in every 10 billion to 100 billion parts of water.   This is an amazing accomplishment.

No less interesting is the concentrating power of the "killer" clam (*Tridacna gigas*) reported on by Weiss and Shipman.[7]   The clams have been shown to contain as much as $\frac{1}{3}$ microcurie of cobalt 60 even though the environment of the clam may never contain more than a trace of cobalt 60.   Other clams have been observed to concentrate cobalt from waters with exceedingly low cobalt concentrations.   The work is revealing in that an unsuspected biological mechanism has been found that acts selectively on a single radioactive isotope.   Biologists cannot be certain that other organisms do not also concentrate radioactive isotopes to levels which might be considered harmful.

17.4. Metabolic Selectivity of Microorganisms.   Microorganisms are regularly used to assay vitamins, amino acids, antibiotics, inorganic ions, and other metabolically active substances[8-10] because of their great specificity in carrying out certain reactions with a minimum of side reactions and ease of handling.   The increased use in recent years of microorganisms for the identification and quantitative determination of a variety of nutritional and growth-inhibitory substances has been an important factor in the development of biochemical and nutritional knowledge, but it does not represent the full potential of the microorganism as an analytical tool. All too frequently their possible use in separations is overlooked.

Pasteur discovered in 1858 to 1860 that the microorganism *Penicillium glaucum*, the green mold found on aging cheese and rotted fruits, preferentially assimilates the *d* form of tartaric acid. When the mold is grown in a dilute aqueous solution of nutrient salts (phosphates, ammonium salts) containing racemic tartaric acid, the originally optically inactive solution slowly acquires a levorotatory character. If the process is interrupted at the appropriate point, the unnatural *l*-tartaric acid can be isolated. However, if the process is continued, the *l* form is eventually consumed. Separation of the *l* form is dependent on the microorganism attacking the natural *d*-tartaric acid much more rapidly than the unnatural *l* form.

Aspergillus niger destroys the *l* form of cystine, and yeast (*Saccharomyces cerevisiae*) destroys the *d* form of tyrosine and *l*-leucine.

Many other instances are known of the preferential destruction of one of two enantiomorphs by molds or bacteria or higher organisms, but the preceding examples illustrate the point. The method is seldom useful for preparative purposes, however. The method usually destroys the more interesting of the enantiomorphs and is applicable only in dilute solutions containing nutrient salts which favor the growth of the organism. All too often, the separation of the unmetabolized form from the culture medium is difficult and inefficient. Nor is it easy to find the appropriate biological agent.

The microorganism does not, however, have to metabolize a given sample component selectively to be useful in separative or preparative work. The organism may simply provide the catalyst (enzyme) for a specific reaction. The microorganism, actually the enzyme, is used thus as an analytical reagent to catalyze a specific reaction of the substance in question. Oxidation, reduction, hydrolysis, decarboxylation, amination, deamination, phosphorylation, methylation, dehydration, and esterification reactions are among the more important types effected with microorganisms.

The most important advantage of enzymatic catalyzed reactions is the specificity. Frequently only one member of a homologous series is active in the catalyzed reaction. As an example, glucose oxidase will catalyze the oxidation of glucose but not some 36 other sugars, including some substituted glucoses. Some 13 other sugars are activated by the enzyme but to less than 2 per cent that of glucose.

Stodola[11] has catalogued some 15 examples of microorganisms being used to introduce single hydroxyl groups into most of the assailable positions of the steroid molecule. The microbes are quite specific in their action; even the chemically difficult introduction of the necessary 11-hydroxyl group in the preparation of cortisone can be accomplished with microorganisms. But as might be expected, all enzymes are not so specific as glucose oxidase or the ones involved in the hydroxylation of steroids.

Most enzymes are also specific for only one optical isomer of a racemic mixture, thus permitting a differentiation of enantiomorphs.

It is not unlikely that stocks of well-described microbes which are capable of performing a given function singularly well or can be used for the concentration and isolation of a desired constituent will soon be as commonplace as conventional reagents in the chemist's laboratory.

Methods need not be limited, however, to the customarily used bacteria, yeasts, and molds, since enzymatic activity in cell-free preparations can frequently achieve the same end result.[12] Enzymes alone have not been extensively applied, though, because of the difficulties of preparing and storing pure enzymes. However, in the past several years a number of pure enzymes have become commercially available, and it is expected that pure enzymes will become very important analytical reagents.

17.5. Suggested Exploitation of Living Cells for Isolating and Concentrating Substances. The foregoing examples of the specific affinities that various plants, animals, and microorganisms exhibit toward certain organic and inorganic substances serve to suggest the possible application of living cells to concentration (separation) problems. It seems reasonable to conclude that various plants or animals or microorganisms can be used to concentrate greatly specific substances from the environment of the organism in a relatively short period of time and that such biological systems can be used to glean minerals from the sea or from soils where their concentration is below the level of economical recovery by more conventional means. Minerals might be harvested much as food crops are presently harvested.

More exacting inorganic assays might be possible if living organisms could be used to concentrate selectively the desired components to levels which could then be determined by conventional chemical means.

Levin[13] of Resources Research, Inc., has outlined a novel and in some ways startling process for the desalinization of salt water with algae. The heart of the proposed system is the use of salt-accumulating algae which can develop and maintain an internal concentration of sodium chloride many times greater than the salt concentration in their environment. Supply the necessary metabolic energy, such as sunlight, to a salt solution containing nutrients, and the algae pick up salt; cut off the energy, and the algae eliminate the salt. Levin proposes growing the algae in a basin of saline water under conditions for the optimum pickup of sodium chloride and feeding the sodium chloride-laden algae into another basin where conditions are such that the algae cannot maintain the concentration gradient. The algae dump the salt in the second basin and are ready for recycling back to the first basin. The proposal envisions a multistage continuous operation with the salt content being continually reduced in successive basins by different algae. In addition to the desalinization of the brine, there is a bonus in the process. Since the algae are reproducing while working, the excess algae can be bled off the recycle stream and used as a source of protein.

There are, of course, many problems associated with the use of biological systems for concentrating specific substances. Applications must wait for the discovery of organisms that exhibit an unusual specificity for the substance to be concentrated. Even then, the rate at which the substance is concentrated by the organism may be so slow as to rule out practical methods. These problems appear, however, to be more than counterbalanced by the advantages offered by biological methods. The organisms can be quite specific in their action, easily distinguishing elements as similar as cobalt and nickel or bromine and iodine, and can concentrate elements, under certain circumstances at least, rapidly enough to compare favorably with existing methods. Considering the likelihood of simple techniques being evolved, it appears that biological methods offer some distinct advantages to the chemist in the realm of separations work.

17.6. Selected Bibliography

Chaberek, S., and A. E. Martell: Organic Sequestering Agents, chap. 8, in "Metal Chelates in Biological Systems," John Wiley & Sons, Inc., New York, 1959.

Stodola, F. H.: "Chemical Transformations by Microorganisms," John Wiley & Sons, Inc., New York, 1958.

Underwood, E. J.: "Trace Elements in Human and Animal Nutrition," Academic Press, Inc., New York, 1956.

REFERENCES

1. Underwood, E. J.: "Trace Elements in Human and Animal Nutrition," p. 351, Academic Press, Inc., New York, 1956.
2. Hutchinson, G. E.: *Quart. Rev. Biol.*, **18,** 1, 128, 242, 331 (1943).
3. Webb, L. J.: *Australian J. Botany*, **2,** 176 (1954).
4. Robinson, W. O., and G. Edginton: *Soil Sci.*, **60,** 15 (1945).
5. Seaber, W.: *Analyst*, **58,** 575 (1930).
6. McIntyre, R. T., and E. W. Berg: *Ecology*, **37,** 605 (1956).
7. Weiss, H. W., and W. H. Shipman: *Science*, **125,** 695 (1957).

8. Hunter, S. H., A. Cury, and H. Baker: *Anal. Chem.*, **30,** 849 (1958).
9. Hendlin, D.: *Anal. Chem.*, **31,** 970 (1959).
10. Loy, H. W., and W. W. Wright: *Anal. Chem.*, **31,** 971 (1959).
11. Stodola, F. H.: "Chemical Transformations by Micro-organisms," p. 53, John Wiley & Sons, Inc., New York, 1958.
12. Devlin, T. M.: *Anal. Chem.*, **31,** 977 (1959).
13. *Chem. Eng. News,* Dec. 9, 1957, p. 142.

CHAPTER 18

ELIMINATION OF UNDESIRED REACTIONS
THROUGH USE OF SEQUESTERING (MASKING) AGENTS

PHILIP W. WEST

Boyd Professor of Chemistry, Louisiana State University, Baton Rouge, La.

18.1. Introduction. Rather than resort to the separation of an undesirable species or the isolation of a prime reactant, it is often expeditious to employ sequestering (masking) agents for the elimination of spurious reactions. Through the simple expedient of adding a complexing ligand, for example, it is possible so to reduce the concentration of a given metal ion that it no longer is subject to its usual reactions. Although such an approach is not strictly a method of separation, since there is no isolation of phases, the method may serve the same purpose as an actual separation. Therefore, although masking does not belong philosophically in a treatise dealing with methods of separation, the practical aspects of the elegant technique dictate that at least some discussion be included.

The term *masking* was introduced many years ago by Prof. Fritz Feigl, who utilized this technique in making specific or highly selective spot tests when the available reagents were general or, at best, only partially selective. The German word *maskieren* was first used to describe the process, but in translation to English, the term *masking* was evolved. In some ways, this was unfortunate, because the English word does not have the exact meaning of its German counterpart and does not accurately describe the process involved. Because there is no physical hiding produced, it would be more accurate to describe the process as *sequestering* rather than masking. However, because the term is so firmly established in the literature, the term masking is used synonymously with sequestering, and where applicable, the more restrictive term *complexation* can also be employed.

The advantages of masking as a means of eliminating interferences derive from the elegance of the technique. By the simple expedient of introducing excess addendum, it is often possible to minimize or completely eliminate interfering effects of diverse metals. There is no tedious expenditure of time, nor is there any demand for special equipment or special manipulative techniques. A typical example will serve to illustrate the advantages of masking. Dithiooxamide (rubeanic acid) was introduced by Rây in 1926 as an extremely sensitive reagent for copper, as well as for nickel, cobalt, and iron. Obviously, a reagent for copper should not react with such closely allied metals as the other three mentioned, so the lack of selectivity in this case restricted the use of the reagent to special applications where the copper could be isolated from possible interferences. Because the reagent had such fantastic sensitivity that it could be used to detect the copper left by a copper coin caught in one's hand, a study was undertaken to develop a simple yet selective test procedure. It was found through this investigation that masking provided the ideal answer. When a drop of unknown was treated on filter paper with a drop of malonic acid solution, stable, unreactive complexes were formed with the interfering metals, leaving the copper free to react with the reagent with essentially no loss in sensitivity.[1] Thus by a single drop of masking agent and an operation involving less than 10 sec, a relatively valueless reagent was established for use in a simple, rapid, and extremely reliable spot test.

About the only deterrent to the use of masking is the fact that it is essentially an art. Although, in most cases, masking agents are complexing ligands, it is not possible to calculate from available instability constants a sufficient number of effective concentrations to enable practical application of such data. Surprising as it may be, it is not even possible to find in the literature any single collection of recommended masking agents that may be of possible use in sequestering the individual common metal ions. For a number of years, the author of this chapter has called attention to various masking agents as part of the reviews of inorganic microchemistry.[2] A wealth of information on masking can be found in Feigl's "Spot Tests in Inorganic Analysis" (see Selected Bibliography). In some cases, individual tests mention the various masking agents that can be used to eliminate certain interferences, and in other cases, the use of masking agents is inherent in the test procedure, and the function of such agents can be deduced only from a thorough knowledge of the reaction characteristics of the reagents employed in the tests. A brilliant discussion of the chemistry of masking and demasking has been presented by Feigl in his monumental treatise "Chemistry of Specific, Selective and Sensitive Reactions."

18.2. Methods and Scope. As mentioned in the preceding paragraphs, the technique of masking is so simple that a detailed discussion is not necessary or even possible. Almost all metal ions are sequestered through the formation of stable complexes, and therefore, it is only necessary to add excess amounts of the complexing ligand. Unlike precipitation reactions, where excess precipitant may sometimes introduce difficulties (through the formation of soluble complexes which may cause partial or even complete dissolution of the precipitate originally formed), substantial excesses of masking agents tend to ensure the utmost stability in the complexes produced owing to mass-action effects. In those cases where the sequestering action is due to the formation of pseudosalts, mass-action effects may not be so significant but excess reagent does help. It might be pointed out in connection with the latter type of reaction that the salts formed are seldom as stable as the complexes mentioned earlier. For example, many reactions of lead ion can be masked by the formation of the pseudosalt lead acetate. That this salt is not particularly stable is evidenced by the fact that it is advisable to use a soluble acetate, rather than acetic acid, as the masking agent, because formation of lead acetate is not sufficiently dominant to ensure overcoming the equilibrium of acetic acid with its ions. The solutions should, of course, be neutral or basic. A third type of sequestering action results from the synthesis of stable species other than complexes or pseudosalts. For example, nitrite ion can be sequestered through diazotization with sulfanilic acid. Likewise, ammonia can be masked using formaldehyde or chloral to produce hexamethylenetetramine or chloral

ammonia. In such cases, it is obviously important to have sufficient reagent to carry out the reaction involved, and it is equally apparent that little harm should result from the presence of excess amounts of reagents.

Most applications of masking are in the prevention of undesired precipitation or color-formation reactions. Likewise, the preponderance of applications is in the masking of cations, because most of them can be complexed while the anions are not readily handled in this way and must be sequestered as pseudosalts or other compounds of unique stability. In this connection it is interesting to note that, although the anions are usually the complexing ligands employed when metals are masked, the reverse situation is not generally applicable because in practical application, the central atom of the complex would have to be the reagent, and if an excess of the metal were added, the complex first formed would be broken down owing to the shifting of the equilibrium to form a precipitate. For example, if cyanide were to be masked by the addition of silver to form the silver cyanide complex,

$$Ag^+ + 2CN^- \rightarrow [Ag(CN)_2]^-$$

with the addition of an optimum amount of silver ion, the complex formed would be so slightly dissociated that only a minute amount of free cyanide would be left in solution. It would be very difficult to attain the ideal ratio of central atom to addendum, however, and any excess of silver ion would lead to destruction of the complex,

$$[Ag(CN)_2]^- + Ag^+ \rightarrow 2AgCN$$

One of the few exceptions to the above example is found in the case of fluoride, which can be sequestered as the fluoroborate, BF_4^-, which is the species formed with the addition of either stoichiometric or excess amounts of borate.

In addition to the applications in gravimetry and spectrophotometry, it should be noted that masking can be used in redox reactions to stabilize a given oxidation state. For example, the oxidation of titanium(III) by iodine can be prevented if fluoride is added to the system.[3] The stabilization undoubtedly results through the formation of $[TiF_6]^{3-}$.

The importance of the oxidation state of the metal to be masked should not be overlooked. Iron(III) is readily masked by a wide variety of ligands, and in fact, most such agents enhance the oxidation of iron(II) as summarized below, where L represents an equivalent of appropriate

$$Fe^{++} \rightleftharpoons Fe^{3+} + e$$
$$\xrightarrow{6L^-} [FeL_6]^{3-}$$

ligand.   The reverse system is rarely encountered except for the case of 2,2'-dipyridyl, which forms particularly stable complexes with iron(II) and can, therefore, be used to stabilize this form or to enhance its formation at the expense of the higher valence state.

The masking of metals at desired oxidation states provides a very convenient way for conditioning systems for polarographic analysis.   Because the redox potentials for different metal ions vary when different ligands are present, it is possible to shift half-wave potentials for metals that are reducible at the dropping-mercury electrode and so establish a desired order of polarographic waves.   By use of different supporting electrolytes, the polarographic wave for a given metal can be shifted or even eliminated owing to differing stabilities of the complexes produced.

In appraising the significance of masking, it should be recognized that, although the sequestered species usually is left in solution as part of a homogeneous system, it may be possible to isolate the complexes on ion-exchange columns.   Usually the complex anions are involved in such separations, but occasionally cation complexes are exchanged on the columns.   Pseudosalts and association complexes are commonly separated in solvent-extraction processes, and therefore, masked species can also be collected in selective solvents as part of true separation processes.

18.3. Masking of Individual Ions.   The following section is presented as a practical guide for the selection of possible masking agents for use in sequestering the individual ions listed.   There is no way to predict accurately which addenda may prove satisfactory for any given application.   Where cobalt interferes with a given reaction for copper, a number of ligands are known that will form stable complexes with the cobalt and conceivably prevent it from reacting with the reagent being used. Unfortunately, many of the masking agents for cobalt will also sequester copper, and therefore, the final choice will have to be made on the basis of trial and error in the hope that at least one agent will be found that will give sufficiently stable forms of cobalt, still leaving the copper free to react.   It should be remembered that, at least in the case of color reactions, the primary reagent is itself probably reacting to form inner-complex chelates or other complex salts, and therefore, the final system will consist of a number of equilibria.   Such complicated systems defy easy mathematical study, even where data are available for the necessary calculations, and the best attack must be the practical approach of trial and error.

In listing the common masking agents, many are mentioned without reference to the literature because they have become classic in use and complete reference to the pertinent literature would be unnecessarily cumbersome.   A few chosen references will be given for purposes of illustration or where unique systems justify special emphasis.

Aluminum.   Classic complexing agents such as fluoride, oxalate, citrate, and tartrate have found innumerable applications in the sequestering of aluminum.   More recently, EDTA* has been established as an extremely valuable complexant.   Sulfosalicylate, acetylacetonate, and gluconate have also been used to complex aluminum, and some reactions of aluminum can be prevented by the addition of formate, sulfate, and acetate, which presumably form pseudosalts.

Ammonia.   Ammonia or, more properly, an aqueous solution of

---

* Although references to EDTA are recognized as referring to the disodium salt of ethylenediaminetetraacetic acid, it can be assumed generally that other aminopolycarboxylic acids will apply equally well and often provide operational flexibility owing to differences in the stabilities of the respective complexes formed.

ammonium ion can be masked by the addition of formaldehyde, which reacts to form hexamethylenetetramine.

Antimony. Antimony(III) can be sequestered by the addition of iodide, fluoride, polysulfide, citrate, and tartrate. 2,3-Dimercapto-propanol also forms a stable chelate useful in masking.

Arsenic. The classic masking agent for arsenic is the homo-atomic sulfide ion commonly designated as polysulfide. This agent has been used for decades in effecting subgroup separations of metal sulfides. In addition to the polysulfide ion, the use of British anti-lewisite (BAL) should be mentioned. BAL, which is 2,3-dimercaptopropanol, was developed as a detoxifying agent for military use but also finds application in the analytical inactivation of arsenic. Thiosulfate is also effective in masking arsenic(III).

Barium. There are relatively few masking agents for barium. The principal one is EDTA, and occasionally polyphosphates, such as the hexametaphosphate, prove to be of value.

Beryllium. Fluoride, citrate, and tartrate are the common seques-terants for beryllium, although salicylate is occasionally used. It is generally overlooked that the carbonato complex of beryllium is rela-tively stable and can be used in various ways for masking or isolating this metal.

Bismuth. Citrate and tartrate are well-established masking agents for bismuth. EDTA is finding increased use, and thiosulfate and iodide are of considerable value. 2,3-Dimercaptopropanol (BAL) forms stable complexes with bismuth and can be used to inhibit most of its reactions. Thiosulfate, iodide, chloride, bromide, and thiourea have been used, although the last lacks appeal because of the color of the complex formed.

Boron. It is well known that fluoride forms stable tetrafluoroborate, which proves of value in many analytical methods. Likewise, the complexes formed with hydroxy acids and polyhydroxy alcohols are used to sequester boron as well as to enhance the acidity of boric acid prior to its titrimetric determination.

Bromine. Free bromine, which may be added to a system as an oxidant or may be produced through the action of oxidizing agents on bromides present in solution, can be inactivated by the addition of sulfosalicylic acid.

Cadmium. The classic ligands ammonia, ethylenediamine, tri-ethylenetetramine, thiocyanate, cyanide, citrate, and tartrate have now been supplemented with EDTA. Iodide, pyrophosphate, and thiosulfate are also useful agents in complexing cadmium.

Calcium. Calcium, like other alkaline-earth metals, is not readily complexed and, therefore, is difficult to mask. Moderately strong com-plexes are formed with various polyphosphates, such as hexametaphosphate and tripolyphosphate.   EDTA has proved to be very effective as a sequesterant and is now widely used for such purposes.

Cerium.   Cerium(IV) tends to form complex fluorides with excess alkali fluorides.   Tartrate, likewise, may inhibit reactions of tetravalent cerium.   Cerium(III) can often be complexed with EDTA.

Chromium.   Chromium(III) can be masked by the addition of EDTA, sulfate, thiosulfate, formate, and acetate.   The last is particularly effective and probably functions mainly through the formation of the pseudosalt.   Sulfates tend to inhibit and sometimes prevent reactions of chromium, but little general use has been made of this effect.   It should be noted that the aquo complexes of chromium are relatively stable, and this reduces the likelihood of complexation by many of the common ligands.   Also, reactions of various ligands with chromium are so slow that even heating the solutions may not speed up reactions sufficiently to permit practical masking of this metal.   The effect of acetate, however, is quite dramatic, particularly when it is realized that acetate is a rather unusual ligand.   Alkali or ammonium acetate will so stabilize chromium (III) that chromium hydroxide is not precipitated at ordinary pH levels, in spite of the great insolubility of this precipitate ($K_{sp} = 1 \times 10^{-30}$). Formate seems to be a stronger masking agent than even acetate. Citrate, tartrate, and 2,2′,2″-nitriloethanol are effective agents.

Cobalt.   Ordinarily, cobalt(II) is the only species to be sequestered, and citrate, tartrate, fluoride, thiocyanate, cyanide, and thiosulfate have all been used successfully.   EDTA forms stable complexes with cobalt, and the nitrite ion has also been used.   In the case of nitrite, it is generally known that the cobalt(II), which must be the species present in simple aqueous solution, is readily oxidized upon the addition of nitrite, and the complex finally obtained is that of the hexanitritocobaltate(III).

Copper.   A wide variety of masking agents has been proposed for sequestering copper.   Cyanide complexes both copper(I) and copper(II) as $[Cu(CN)_3]^{--}$.   Ethylenediamine, tetramine, 2,2′,2″-nitrilotriethanol, thiourea, and EDTA form ammine-type complexes which are relatively stable.   Thiosulfate is an excellent agent, as is the thioglycolate ion. Citrate, tartrate, and ammonia are classic masking agents for this metal.

Cyanide.   This ion presents special problems because it is an anion and because it forms many stable complexes with metals and, therefore, constitutes a general interference in analytical reactions involving the various metals forming such complexes.   Fortunately, it is often possible to mask cyanide by the addition of formaldehyde, which, of course, leads to the formation of the glycolic nitrile.[7]   A clever innovation dealing with cyanide has been introduced recently by Platt and Marcy.[4]   These authors describe a method for the determination of zinc employing Zincon.   Various interfering metal ions were masked by the addition of cyanide. Unfortunately, the reaction with zinc was also inhibited in the presence of cyanide, but it was found that the zinc could be liberated from its complex by the addition of chloral hydrate, which combined with the cyanide in the case of the zinc complex but not in the case of other metal cyanide complexes. This illustration serves as an excellent example of the use of relative stabilities in setting up masking and demasking systems.

Fluoride. Fluoride is one of the few anions that can be sequestered easily. Excess amounts of boric acid readily convert fluoride to the tetrafluoroborate complex, which is so stable that it eliminates fluoride interferences from most reactions.

Germanium. Germanium forms stable complexes with both oxalate and fluoride, and these have proved to be very effective masking agents. Like boric acid, germanic acid forms very stable complexes with polyhydric alcohols such as glycerol, mannitol, and glucose, and these are, therefore, excellent sequestering agents for this metal.

Gold. The most common sequesterant for gold is cyanide. Bromide and iodide form relatively stable complexes, as does thiosulfate, which has the further advantage that it tends to diminish the color of most gold solutions. Pyrophosphate and thiourea can also be used.

Halides. Chloride, iodide, and bromide all form pseudosalts with mercury(II), and this fact can be used to mask a number of reactions of these ions.

Indium. Both fluoride and oxalate sequester indium.

Iron. Iron(II) is not readily masked, although cyanide can be added to form the ferrocyanide complex or 2,2'-dipyridyl (or 1,10-phenanthroline) can be used to form stable nonreactive complexes. In the case of the latter reagents, effective masking may be obtained but the reaction products are so intensely colored that this in itself interferes with most analytical operations. Iron(III), on the other hand, is readily amenable to masking. EDTA is an excellent agent, and classic ligands, such as fluoride, oxalate, cyanide, citrate, tartrate, thiosulfate, orthophosphate, and pyrophosphate, are well known and widely used. Polyphosphates are often effective, and salicylate and sulfosalicylate are often used.

Lead. Lead is not generally susceptible to complexation, although EDTA salts are moderately stable. Acetate, which forms a pseudosalt, is a valuable masking agent, and thiosulfate complexes are sufficiently stable that they can be used to prevent many of the interfering reactions of lead. Citrate, tartrate, and 2,3-dimercaptopropanol have also been used to form stable chelates of value in masking lead reactions.

Magnesium. Masking in this case is difficult, being limited to EDTA, pyrophosphate, and the polyphosphates.

Manganese. Manganese(II) can be complexed upon the addition of fluoride, oxalate, cyanide, EDTA, o-phosphate, pyrophosphate, tartrate, or citrate. Because of the relative stability of complexed manganese(III), there is a distinct tendency for oxidation to take place, so that manganese(III) complexes are finally formed.

Mercury. Mercury is ordinarily masked in the form of mercury(II) complexes with iodide, chloride, or cyanide. It is interesting that sulfite forms disulfitomercurate(II) or dichlorosulfitomercurate(II) complexes that are remarkably stable[5] and can be used to prevent many of the ordinary reactions of this metal. Thiosulfate, thiourea, thiocyanate, EDTA, 2,2',2''-nitrilotriethanol, and BAL are valuable sequestering agents.

Molybdenum. Molybdenum(VI) forms relatively stable complexes with fluorides, probably of the type $[MoO_2F_4]^{--}$. Molybdenum(VI) may also be masked by the addition of hydrogen peroxide, presumably because of the formation of permolybdic acid.[8]

$$MoO_4^{--} + H_2O_2 \rightarrow MoO_5^{--} + H_2O$$

Oxalate is effective in masking reactions of molybdenum(VI), apparently because of the formation of a molybdenooxalic acid of the type $MoO_3 \cdot H_2C_2O_4$ or $2MoO_3 \cdot H_2C_2O_4$. An unusual method of sequestering molybdenum is to add thiocyanate to a solution containing molybdenum(VI), followed by the addition of a reducing agent such as tin(II). The red complex which is formed, $[MoO(NCS)_4]^-$, is remarkably stable. Molybdenum(III) can be complexed with EDTA, citrate, and tartrate.

Nickel. Cyanide, thiocyanate, fluoride, citrate, tartrate, and malonate have all been used to sequester nickel. Ammonia, triethylenetetramine, and EDTA form complexes useful in restricting the reactions of nickel.

Niobium. Niobium forms complexes with EDTA, lactates, citrates, tartrates, and hydrogen peroxide.

Nitrite. This anion can sometimes be masked by the addition of cobalt(II), resulting in the formation of the hexanitritocobaltate(III). The unusual but effective use of sulfanilic acid to form a diazo compound has been introduced by Westland and Langford.[6]

Oxalate. Oxalate can, of course, be destroyed by oxidizing it to carbon dioxide in an acidic solution using permanganate. An interesting and somewhat more elegant approach is to add excess molybdate. In fact, large excesses of molybdate will stabilize oxalic acid so that even permanganate fails to oxidize it. The reaction in this case serves to emphasize the general value of adding excess addendum because a stoichiometric ratio of molybdenum or molybdic acid to oxalic acid in accordance with the equilibrium

$$MoO_3 \cdot H_2C_2O_4 \rightleftharpoons MoO_3 + H_2C_2O_4$$

gives enough free oxalic acid in solution that there is some reaction upon the addition of potassium permanganate. Excess molybdic acid shifts the equilibrium to the left sufficiently to inhibit completely such evidence of oxidation. It can be added that the molybdenooxalic salt is sufficiently stable to prevent the reaction of calcium with oxalate.

Platinum Metals. The various members of this family of metals are well known for their similarity of reactions. A number of ligands have been introduced for masking individual platinum metals, and the following summary presents the more important agents introduced to date. Iridium has been masked using thiourea, ammonia, thiocyanate, citrate, and tartrate. Osmium can be masked using thiourea or cyanide. Palladium can be sequestered with ammonia, cyanide, nitrite, thiocyanate, pyrophosphate, iodide, sulfite, and thiosulfate. Platinum can be masked through the use of ammonia, ethylenediamine, EDTA, cyanide, iodide, nitrite, thiocyanate, and thiosulfate. For rhodium, thiourea, citrate, and tartrate have been used. Thiourea has been reported as a masking agent for ruthenium.

Silver. The masking of silver(I) by cyanide, ammonia, and thiosulfate is so well known that even undergraduate chemistry students are aware of these complexing agents and their use in qualitative analysis, in electrochemical separations, and, of course, in such commercial operations as the use of thiosulfate in photographic processing. Along with these very common sequesterants should be listed other ammine ligands such as ethylenediamine, tetramine, EDTA (ethylenediaminetetraacetate), and thiourea. Acetylacetonate and bromide have also been used to mask silver. Although no examples can be cited where silver (II) has been masked, it is conceivable that there may be times when an oxidizing system is to be encountered, and silver could then be oxidized and tied up with a ligand such as 1,10-phenanthroline.

Strontium. Strontium, like other members of the alkaline-earth group, is not generally subject to complexation. The most effective means of masking is to add EDTA or possibly a polyphosphate.

Sulfur Family. Although the various sulfur-containing ions react quite differently, and although selenium and tellurium have some distinctive differences, it is expeditious to group the family and their respective ions for comparative purposes. The elements themselves can be masked. For example, sulfur is complexed by cyanide to form thiocyanate, by sulfide to form the homo-atomic complex, and by sulfite to form thiosulfate. Likewise, selenium[9] reacts with sulfide to form the selenosulfide complex $[S \cdots Se]^{--}$ and with sulfite to form the selenosulfate ion $[SSeO_3]^{--}$. Tellurium is distinctive in that it dissolves in the presence of iodide to give the complex $[TeI_6]^{--}$. Sulfide can be masked partially by the addition of sulfur to form the homo-atomic complex $[S_2]^{--}$. Sulfite (or sulfur dioxide) can be masked by the addition of tetrachloromercurate(II), whereby the exceedingly stable dichlorosulfitomercurate(II) complex is formed.[5] Sulfite also can be masked by the addition of formaldehyde to produce the familiar addition product.[10] Sulfate is not generally susceptible to masking, but many of its reactions can be eliminated if chromium(III) is added, which leads to the formation of a pseudosalt or, more probably, the formation of a complex such as $[Cr(SO_4)_2(H_2O)_2]^-$. The substitution of sulfato for aqua groups is sluggish and must be expedited by heat. Once the complex is formed, however, the sulfate is not precipitable by either lead or barium.

Tantalum. Tantalum is masked quite effectively upon the addition of hydrogen peroxide. Citrate, tartrate, and fluoride can also be used.

Thallium. Thallium forms stable fluoride complexes which can be used for the purposes of masking. Cyanide, oxalate, thiocyanate, citrate, tartrate, and EDTA are also useful sequestering agents.

Thorium. The most common masking agent used for sequestering thorium is fluoride, although acetate, tartrate, citrate, and EDTA can also be used.

Tin. Tin(IV) is complexed by fluoride, oxalate, and BAL and, to some extent, by tartrate and citrate. Tin is also complexed by thioglycolate ion. The behavior of the tin fluoride complex is of interest because the reaction between tin and sulfide is completely prevented in the presence of excess fluoride.[11] However, the addition of boric acid as a demasking agent to remove the fluoride enables the tin to precipitate as SnS_2.

Titanium. Titanium(IV) can be masked by the addition of hydrogen peroxide, sulfate, sulfosalicylate, citrate, malonate, tartrate, or fluoride.

Tungsten. Hydrogen peroxide, fluoride, phosphate, citrate, and tartrate are of value in sequestering tungsten.

Uranium. Uranium forms numerous complexes, most of which have applications in masking. Hydrogen peroxide effectively sequesters uranium. Fluoride, oxalate, tartrate, citrate, malonate, sulfite, and sulfosalicylate have also been used. Quite unique is the sequestering action of nitrate and carbonate, both of which inhibit many of the reactions of uranium.

Vanadium. Vanadium can be masked by the addition of cyanide, fluoride, EDTA, or hydrogen peroxide.

Zinc. The reactions of zinc can be inhibited or prevented by the addition of fluoride, cyanide, thiocyanate, citrate, tartrate, EDTA, BAL, glycerol, ammonia, and triethylenetetramine.

Zirconium. Zirconium can be masked by malonate, citrate, tartrate, sulfate, fluoride, EDTA, and hydrogen peroxide.

Thus far the discussion of masking has been limited to the conventional sequestering of ions through the formation of stable complexes, pseudo-salts, or undissociated compounds obtained by the direct synthesis of organic compounds.   In certain fields, such as spot-test analysis, masking can also be accomplished by precipitation of the unwanted species in the pores of filter paper, and the interferences are thus eliminated in a single simple operation.   Although such a process corresponds closely to conventional masking, the principle involved does differ, and the reactions employed are so conventional that further discussion at this point does not seem justified.

Another process sometimes employed in eliminating interferences is oxidation-reduction.   Although redox agents do not sequester the ion in question, they do so alter its identity that it is very often possible to eliminate complicating reactions that interfere with the analytical method.   Oxidants that may interfere can be eliminated by reduction of the offending species, although care must be taken that the agent used does not introduce new complications through the reduction of metal ions to the respective metals or through the formation of interfering residues.   Some of the oxidants, together with recommended "masking" agents for their destruction, are as follows: bromate: this ion can be reduced with hydrazine, sulfite, thiosulfate, or arsenite; chlorate: reduced with thiosulfate; dichromate: ascorbic acid, hydroxylamine, and hydrazine are excellent, but sulfite, thiosulfate, and arsenite are also effective agents; ferricyanide: ascorbic acid, hydroxylamine, sulfite, and thiosulfate can be used; iodate: sulfite, thiosulfate, and hydrazine; perchlorate: sulfite and hydroxylamine; periodate: ascorbic acid, hydrazine, sulfite, thiosulfate, and arsenite; permanganate: sodium azide, ascorbic acid, hydrazine, hydroxylamine, sulfite, thiosulfate, and arsenite are all effective, and oxalic acid can also be used in most instances; persulfate: hydoxylamine, thiosulfate, and ascorbic acid are all effective.

Reducing agents can be "masked" by the addition of appropriate oxidizing agents, although in many instances true masking through complexation can also be employed.   One of the most satisfactory oxidizing agents for general application in eliminating interferences is iodine. In this case, the reduction product iodide is generally harmless, and excess oxidant can be removed from the system by extraction with carbon tetrachloride.

18.4. Demasking.   If masking is considered from the standpoint of chemical equilibrium, a reduction in the concentration of the sequestered species becomes the result of an application of the law of mass action. Furthermore, it is apparent that a shifting of the equilibria involved may proceed in either direction, so that masking efficiency increases with any shift favoring the formation of the complexes or pseudosalts involved. Likewise, the complexes or pseudosalts can be broken down by shifting the equilibria involved in the reverse direction. Such breaking down of masked species is known as *demasking,* and the process may be of great importance for the release of sequestered species for subsequent analytical study. The processes of masking and demasking can be summarized by the equation

$$C + L \underset{\text{masking}}{\overset{\text{demasking}}{\rightleftharpoons}} CL$$

In this expression, C represents the central atom which is to be sequestered by the addition of a ligand L, which forms either a complex or pseudosalt CL. Masking efficiency is obtained by shifting the equilibrium to the right, while demasking the system is accomplished by removal of one of the reactants so as to shift the equilibrium to the left.

Demasking has long been used in analytical chemistry, and even beginning students of chemistry learn the process, although not necessarily with complete understanding, in the course in qualitative analysis. In the conventional qualitative-analysis chloride group, silver is complexed as diammine silver(I). The demasking of the silver from its complex is simply accomplished upon the addition of a strong mineral acid. A more general example of demasking, and certainly one that is more sophisticated, is the breaking down of cyanide complexes. It is well known that most of the heavy metals form relatively stable complexes in the presence of excess cyanide, and these complexes mask the normal reactions of the metals concerned. If formaldehyde is added to a cyanide complex, the cyanide can be removed with consequent release of the metal ion as shown by the following equation:

$$[Ni(CN)_4]^{--} + 4HCHO \rightarrow 4CH_2\begin{smallmatrix}O^- \\ \diagup \\ \diagdown \\ CN\end{smallmatrix} + Ni^{++}$$

The breaking up of the cyanide complex affords a ready means for liberating the metal ion from its sequestered state.

The methods used in demasking fall into two main categories. The first and most common approach is to change drastically the hydrogen-ion concentration of the solution. In most such cases a strong mineral acid is added, and the ligand is removed from the coordination sphere of the complex through the formation of a weak acid. For example, certain of the cyanide complexes can be demasked by the formation of volatile HCN. Complexes in this category include $[Ag(CN)_2]^-$, $[Cu_2(CN)_4]^{--}$, and $[Pd(CN)_4]^{--}$, which are precipitated in the form of the corresponding acid-stable salts. Other cyanide complexes such as $[Zn(CN)_4]^{--}$ and $[Cd(CN)_4]^{--}$ are demasked with the liberation of the respective metal ions.   Other ligands derived from weak acids can likewise be attacked for demasking, as, for example, the carbonato group, which can be removed from copper and beryllium complexes, and the thiosulfato group, which can be removed from the silver complex.

Although not so common, there are a number of instances where complexes can be demasked by lowering the hydrogen-ion concentration. For example, $[Al(C_2O_4)_3]^{3-}$, $[Fe(CNS)_6]^{3-}$, and $[ZrF_6]^{--}$ are all broken down upon the addition of a strong base.   The corresponding hydroxides are precipitated, but once the precipitates have been isolated, they can be put back into solution free from the masking effect of the complexing ligand originally present.

The second type of demasking commonly encountered involves the formation of new complexes or other nonionized compounds that are more stable than the masked species.   An example of this is the formation of the glycolic nitrile referred to earlier in the discussion of masking agents for cyanide ion.   Fluoride complexes are often employed in masking undesirable reactions.   In order to liberate the masked metal for subsequent study, the demasking action of the borate ion can be employed. A classic example of this type of application is given by the work of Furman, who has shown that tin is masked by fluorides and so prevented from precipitation by sulfide.[11]   If boric acid is added to such a masked system, the tin is demasked through the formation of very stable tetrafluoroborate ion.   The reaction involved can be summarized as follows:

$$[SnF_6]^{--} \rightleftharpoons Sn^{4+} + 6F^-$$
$$4F^- + BO_3{}^{3-} + 6H^+ \rightarrow [BF_4]^- + 3H_2O$$

Similar application of boric acid can be made in the demasking of most fluoro complexes.

It is interesting to note that some complexes can be demasked even through the formation of pseudosalts.   For example, prussian blue can be destroyed by the addition of mercury(II) ions, which results in the formation of water-soluble but not dissociated $Hg(CN)_2$.

A final and somewhat different example of demasking is the breaking down of complex aluminum tartrate ions by the catalytic oxidation of the ligand by hydrogen peroxide and copper salts.[12]   The actual destruction of the ligand in this case provides a good example of how metals can be released from complexes involving oxidizable, organic ligands.

18.5. Selected Bibliography

Feigl, F.: "Chemistry of Specific, Selective and Sensitive Reactions," Academic Press, Inc., New York, 1949.

Feigl, F.: "Spot Tests in Inorganic Analysis," 5th ed., Elsevier Publishing Company, Amsterdam, 1958.

REFERENCES

1. West, P. W.: *Ind. Eng. Chem., Anal. Ed.*, **17**, 740 (1945).
2. West, P. W.: *Anal. Chem.*, **21**, 121–131 (1949); **22**, 79–89 (1950); **23**, 51–59 (1951); **24**, 76–85 (1952); **26**, 121–128 (1954); **28**, 757–766 (1956); **30**, 748–759 (1958); **32**, 71R–79R (1960).
3. Glen, K.: *Ber. deut. chem. Ges.*, **61**, 707 (1928).
4. Platt, J. A., and V. M. Marcy: *Anal. Chem.*, **31**, 1226 (1959).
5. West, P. W., and G. C. Gaeke: *Anal. Chem.*, **28**, 1816 (1956).
6. Westland, A. D., and R. R. Langford: *Anal. Chem.*, **28**, 1996 (1956).
7. Feigl, F., and H. J. Kapulitzas: *Mikrochemie*, 1930, p. 128.
8. Feigl, F., and I. D. Raacke: *Anal. Chim. Acta*, **1**, 317 (1947).
9. Feigl, F., and P. W. West: *Anal. Chem.*, **19**, 351 (1947).
10. Peniston, Q. P., V. F. Felicetta, and J. L. McCarthy: *Anal. Chem.*, **19**, 332 (1947).
11. Furman, N. H.: *Ind. Eng. Chem.*, **15**, 1071 (1923).
12. Meigen, W., and J. Schnerb: *Angew. Chem.*, **37**, 208 (1924).

Index

Accumulator species, 338
Acetamide, hydrolysis of, 281
Acetylacetone, extractions involving, 75
Activity, definition of, 267
Activity coefficient, calculation of, 271, 272
 definition of, 267
Activity product, 269
Adhesion, between solids and liquids, 314–317
 work of, 315, 317, 322
Adsorbents, chromatographic, 95
 characteristics of, 92–95
 for GLC, 120
 methods of packing, 98
 specificity of, 89
 standardization of, 93–94
Adsorption, 5, 12, 13, 296–306
 factors controlling extent of, 298–302
 heat of, 313
 on hydrous ferric oxide, 300
 primary, 297
Adsorption affinity, of common functional groups, 95
 of common solutes, 88
 of common solvents, 89
 effect on, of molecular weight, 88, 96
 of polarity, 95
 electron donor and acceptor strength related to, 91
 of members of homologous series, 88
Adsorption chromatography (see Chromatography)
Adsorption isotherm, 81–83
 Freundlich, 219
 Langmuir, 219
Adsorption mechanism, 297
Aluminum, sequestering agents for, 347
Ammonia, sequestering agents for, 347
Amorphous solids, properties of, 311

Antimony, sequestering agents for, 348
Arsenic, sequestering agents for, 348
Azeotropic distillation, 34–36

Barium, sequestering agents for, 348
Barium sulfate solubility in various solutions, 271
Benzidine, 289
α-Benzoin oxime, 291
Beryllium, sequestering agents for, 348
Binodal curve, definition of, 54
Biological assay, 141
Biological printing, 139
Biological separation techniques, 5, 14, 335–341
Bismuth, sequestering agents for, 348
Boiling-point-composition diagram, 16
Boron, sequestering agents for, 348
Breakthrough capacity, definition of, 195
 dependence, on column parameters, 196, 198
 on number of solutes, 196–198
Bromine, sequestering agents for, 348
Bromo complexes, extraction of, 77

Cadmium, sequestering agents for, 348
Calcium, sequestering agents for, 348
Capillary column, 122
Captive-bubble method for measuring contact angles, 318
Carlton pipet, 61
β-Carotene, resolution of α-carotene and, 101
Carrier gas, 118
 flow rate of, 119
 pressure differential of, 119
Cellulose, 4, 134
 ion exchange on, 136